# BASIC THEORIES

## of

# PHYSICS

## Mechanics and Electrodynamics

By

## PETER GABRIEL BERGMANN

Professor of Physics
Syracuse University

## DOVER PUBLICATIONS, INC.
## NEW YORK • NEW YORK

Manufactured in the United States of America

Dover Publications, Inc.

180 Varick Street

New York 14, N. Y.

# Preface

In teaching introductory theoretical physics, I have found it necessary time and again to define for myself the purpose and scope of my field. Generally, experimental, theoretical, and mathematical physics are considered today to be subdivisions of "pure" physics, with the remainder of physics classed as applied physics.

It is not easy to define theoretical physics, to properly distinguish it from neighboring fields; but a working concept is necessary for the instructor if he is to give the course direction of purpose and if he is to arouse and hold the interest of his students. I think that those of us who are concerned with the development of physics as a whole feel that the crucial task of the theoretical physicist is to help clarify our conceptual framework and to reforge it from time to time to keep it abreast of experimental progress.

In introducing novices to the field, we may assume that they are qualitatively aware of the basic facts of physics. They have taken mechanics, and they know it not only as an engineering subject, but as the theory of motion of particles: they have learned enough about electricity and magnetism to appreciate the existence of forces which depend on the state of motion of particles, and they have come into contact with field concepts; they may even have studied some atomic and nuclear physics on a phenomenological level. Their principal deficiency lies in an almost complete lack of awareness of physics as a living science, as a field of human culture which will never be "complete." They do not realize that new discoveries are not merely added to the ever-growing store of previous knowledge, but that almost all decisive advances are preceded by periods of crisis and conceptual chaos.

It is customary to deemphasize in our textbook presentations all controversial questions, and with good reason. To participate intelligently in the discussion of basic concepts and theories, the working physicist must be conversant with all current theories of reasonable promise, including a large proportion which by subsequent developments will be shown to have been without merit. He must have an assured knowledge of the mathematical tools, which are required not only for the analysis, but also for the presentation

iii

PREFACE

of these theories. In short, he must be a mature scientist, having assimilated at least the training commensurate with a doctor's degree in physics. But the underemphasis on unresolved questions as an educational policy has its drawbacks. Students of physics are apt to get the impression that anything they read in a book is either true (almost always) or false (almost never), and that the professor in charge, if he is competent, will be able to point out the few errors committed by the author. That crucial questions of the day may not have been resolved, that the greatest physicists of his generation may disagree, these are facts of which he becomes aware only late in his career as a graduate student. Thus, for the better part of his attendance at a university, the student of physics may not realize the nature of the quest in which he will one day participate. Worse yet, not realizing that present-day research in theoretical physics is, to a very large extent, a groping for new concepts, the student has no occasion to find out how one goes about analyzing and modifying a theory whose validity has become questionable.

What is to be done? To present to the student our present difficulties in the theory of nuclear forces or Schwinger's new approach to field quantization is out of the question, if the presentation is not to descend to the level of dilettantism. I believe that much can be learned from a critical presentation of classical physics. After all, Maxwell's theory of the electromagnetic field was not born without bitter misgivings on the part of its father; even Hertz continued attempts to put electrodynamics on a mechanical basis. For that matter, Galileo, Kepler, and Newton had to break new ground to formulate the theoretical framework which was to become *the* theory of the physical universe for three centuries. Accordingly, I have presented in this book the theoretical foundations of "classical" physics, that is Newton's mechanics and Maxwell's electrodynamics, and I have traced this development through to the special theory of relativity. A companion book will be devoted to statistical mechanics and the foundations of quantum physics.

In the organization of the material, I have attempted to concentrate attention on physical ideas and to relegate the mathematical techniques to the role of tools. Since the tools are not generally available to the student at the stage at which he begins to study theoretical physics as a separate subject, discussions of variational calculus, vector and tensor calculus, and Fourier analysis are scattered through the book. While much can be said for the method initiated by Joos, to preface the main body of the text by an introduction to these mathematical methods, I consider it preferable to get started with the physics right away and to introduce mathematical discussions only when they are needed and when it is, therefore, possible to motivate the diversion by its obvious necessity. In the selection of physical subjects, I have been guided by the importance which they have for an understanding of modern physics. I have considered it necessary to include a discussion of Hamilton-Jacobi's partial differential equation, because of its historical relationship to the Schrödinger equation, but I have, for instance, omitted a discussion of rigid body dynamics, because of its relatively minor bearing on the foundations of modern physics. A great deal of care has gone into an exposition of the differences between mechanics and a field theory and the impossibility of having a unified theoretical structure contain both. The need for an examination of the transformation properties of every physical theory has been stressed in the latter portion of the book. The number of problems has been kept small. Most are of the "thinking" kind, and few would be suitable for assignment from one meeting of the class to the next.

The final form of this book has been influenced to a great extent by the reactions of my students at Lehigh University, Polytechnic Institute of Brooklyn, and Syracuse University. While I have had the benefit of this experience, covering virtually the same ground in classes of very different composition, I am fully aware of the pitfalls besetting the author who attempts a novel approach. If the book should be found helpful by instructors in the subject and enjoyable and stimulating by its student readers, I shall have to pass much of the credit on to my teachers, to Ph. Frank, who during my student years at Prague taught me theoretical physics not as a bewildering collection of formulas and techniques, but as a logically connected, though never to be completed, structure of the human mind, and to A. Einstein, under whose guidance I learned that a systematization of experimental facts is by itself not yet a physical theory and that in many respects the theoretical physicist is a philosopher in workingman's clothes.

P. G. B.

*Syracuse, New York*

# Contents

# PART I
# CLASSICAL MECHANICS

# Chapter 1
# Mechanics of Mass Points

**Introduction.** The concepts of modern theoretical physics as well as many of its mathematical tools are far removed from those of the so-called classical period. If courses in theoretical physics nevertheless lead off with a presentation of Newtonian mechanics, the student reader may well feel the need for having this procedure justified.

Modern physics is frequently characterized as "abstract." This expression refers to the circumstance that the basic concepts of the theory are connected with the results of experiments only through a rather lengthy chain of intermediate notions. In earlier periods of our science, this connecting chain was much shorter; the basic concepts of the theory were earthy. The theoretical physicist is, or at least he should be, foremost a *physicist;* that is, he wants to understand nature, and his mathematical techniques are merely artifices fashioned for this purpose. A theory derives all of its merit from its relationship to the experimental facts and from how well and how simply it accounts for them. Naturally, the understanding of a physical theory is not made easier by the need to keep a long connecting chain constantly in mind. As a matter of fact, to do so requires considerable mental practice. Thus, to start a presentation of current physical theories with a description of quantum mechanics would make demands on the mathematical techniques and on the theoretical intuition of the student reader which he simply cannot meet.

Fortunately, it is not necessary to prepare the student for modern physics through meaningless mental exercises. Historically, modern physics is the outgrowth of its classical predecessor. Many of the modern abstract concepts are merely reinterpretations of essentially simple notions of classical mechanics and classical electrodynamics. To study classical theoretical physics means to lay a sound foundation on which our current theories can be evolved. Moreover, since we have every reason to believe that quantum physics in its present form is only the forerunner of the more perfect theories of the future, knowledge of its historical roots may well prove helpful later on when we all shall be called on to absorb still more elaborate theoretical constructions.

Broadly, physics has passed through three stages of development since its establishment as a science by Galileo and Newton. We may call these stages *mechanics, field physics,* and *quantum physics.* During the mechanical period, the elementary building stones of the universe were believed to be very small particles, the *mass points,* which affect each other's motions by means of long-range forces acting across empty space. When it was demonstrated that the phenomena of electromagnetic interaction cannot be comprehended on the basis of mechanical interaction alone, the field concept emerged. In a field theory, we encounter, along with the mass points (which continue to represent matter), space-pervading quantities, the *force fields.* In empty space, the field at one point is determined merely by the field in the immediate vicinity. Perturbations propagate through space from point to point and with a finite velocity.

Neither mechanics nor field concepts are capable of explaining the phenomena of atomic physics. Once we deal with masses of the order of $10^{-28}$ gram and distances of the order of $10^{-8}$ cm, it turns out that we cannot assign to the location or the velocity of a particle any definite physical significance without reference to specific measurements to be carried out. Since our measuring devices possess themselves atomic structure, each measurement interferes with the system under observation, so that a determination of momentum, for instance, invalidates previous knowledge concerning location. The systematic inclusion of this lack of mechanical determinacy in our concepts of the physical universe has led to quantum mechanics.

Each of these three historical stages of physical theory employs most of the concepts originated in the preceding stages, although with some modifications. We shall begin with an exposition of the classical mechanics of mass points.

## 1.1. The equations of motion

**Mass points.** Newton's mechanics was developed primarily from astronomical observations and from experiments with falling bodies. In astronomy, Kepler had been able to systematize the motions of the planets in a manner which described their motions irrespective of their shape or size. Likewise, Galileo was able to show that all bodies, when falling freely, move along simple parabolas, again irrespective of shape. Consequently, it appeared that of the various parameters which might determine the mechanical behavior of a body, its mass was by far the most important; for many purposes, the actual body might be replaced by a single geometrical point in which all its ponderable mass was concentrated. In Section 1.2, and more extensively in Chapter 3, we shall find that there are important properties connected with the spatial extension of bodies. But we shall also find that once the basic laws of nature are stated in terms of mass points and their interactions, extended bodies may be described as collections of very many mass points. For the time being, we shall treat mass points alone, discrete mass points; first of all, we shall analyze the significance of Newton's famous three laws.

**Newton's first law.** Newton's laws of mechanics set up the manner in which mass points are found to interact with each other (influence each other's motions) in the observable world. These laws use the concept of *force*, and they describe *the motion of bodies in space as functions of time.* For the present, we can define *force* only qualitatively as the action of one body on another. To observe a force, we must have a system of at least two bodies, one of which exerts a force and the other of which experiences that force. We must further assume that bodies, and mass points in particular, are able to exert forces on each other directly across empty space at considerable distances ("action at a distance"). Otherwise, we should not be able to understand how the planets in empty space can be constrained to circulate about the sun, or the moons to circulate about the planets. By the same token, it is reasonable to assume that, other things being equal, such forces are weaker if distances are larger. In excellent approximation, we can understand the behavior of all members of the solar system in terms of the forces which they exert on each other, without worrying about the forces caused by the billions of fixed stars about us. Without attempting any rigor of expression, we may express the expectation that it is possible, in principle at least (disregarding the limitations of our earthbound laboratories), to construct isolated mechanical systems of a few mass points. We should have to take these mass points into interstellar space to a location so far removed from all astronomical bodies that we could understand their behavior completely in terms of the forces they would exert on each other.

*Bodies not subject to external forces continue in a state of rest or of straight-line, uniform motion.* This first law describes the effect of forces negatively: if there are no forces, the body will not experience acceleration. Let us describe the motion of bodies by means of a Cartesian coordinate system in space and a time scale. Call the three space coordinates $x_1$, $x_2$, and $x_3$.[1] The time coordinate may be designated by $t$. The first law can be formulated mathematically by three linear equations,

$$\begin{aligned}
x_1 &= a_1 + b_1 t, \\
x_2 &= a_2 + b_2 t, \\
x_3 &= a_3 + b_3 t.
\end{aligned} \tag{1}$$

Here the $a$'s and $b$'s are constants which characterize the location and velocity of the body at the time $t = 0$. More concisely, and by using the notation of differential calculus, we may write:

$$\frac{d^2x_1}{dt^2} = \frac{d^2x_2}{dt^2} = \frac{d^2x_3}{dt^2} = 0. \tag{2}$$

For the first law to be meaningful, it is necessary to restrict to some extent the possible choice of coordinate system. If we envisage a coordinate system merely as a rigid framework of mutually perpendicular straight lines, then it is obviously possible to choose a coordinate system so that in terms of its coordinates any one designated body is at rest. We can construct such a system by choosing this body as the origin of the coordinate system $x_1 = x_2 = x_3 = 0$. However, in such a coordinate system, if our choice of primary body should be an unhappy one, the motion of all other bodies would be extremely involved. Let us, then, amplify the statement of the first law and assert that *it is possible to find a coordinate system (or a frame of reference) with respect to which the*

---

[1] It is more usual to designate the three space coordinates by $x$, $y$, and $z$. However, for our purposes it is preferable to designate them by the same letter, supplemented by an index. We shall follow this method throughout, even though some readers may experience some initial difficulty. Actually, the conversion is very simple: the components of vectors are indexed with 1, 2, and 3, respectively, instead of with $x$, $y$, and $z$, and so on.

*motions of all mass points not subject to forces are unaccelerated.* In other words, if we choose a coordinate system properly, that is, in the right state of motion, then the motions of force-free mass points obey eq. (2). Such coordinate systems are called *inertial systems*.

A direct verification of the first law is next to impossible. It should be necessary to realize a coordinate system in terms of direct physical measurements which would extend over astronomical distances, large enough so that "force-free mass points," as many as possible, could have their motions measured with respect to this one system. Negative verifications are easy to obtain. Within the limits of our present measuring accuracy, fixed stars (if single) are moving almost free of acceleration with respect to a coordinate system whose origin coincides with the center of gravity of our solar system and with respect to which extremely distant stars have negligible angular velocities. However, even today only radial velocities of fixed stars can be determined with any degree of accuracy; tangential accelerations would have to be enormous to be detected at all. As a matter of fact, there is not too much point in attempting to verify the first law by itself. After all, this law is only part of an over-all structure, Newtonian mechanics, the predictions of which are subject to extremely sensitive checks.

**Newton's second law.** *Bodies which are subject to forces undergo accelerations. The acceleration is parallel to the force, and its magnitude is the ratio of the force acting on the body and the (inertial) mass of the body.*

In order to formulate the second law mathematically, we shall use the concepts of vector algebra. A vector, it will be recalled, is defined as a set of three quantities which transform (in the case of transitions from one Cartesian coordinate system to another) according to the same law as a set of three coordinate differences. Geometrically speaking, a vector may be represented as a straight line of definite length and direction. Its three projections on the three coordinate axes are called the *components* of the vector (with respect to that particular coordinate system). In the event of a coordinate transformation, the components of the vector in the first coordinate system are related to the three components in the second system by the same transformation equations which apply in the case of coordinate differences.

A single relationship between two vector quantities is equivalent to three equations between algebraic quantities (i.e., the components of the vector). In this book, we shall use interchangeably two different notations, one adapted to the specific unity of the three equations, the other spelling out the separateness of the three component relationships. Mathematical expressions of the second law (force equals mass times acceleration) are the following three sets of equations:

$$\mathbf{f} = m \, \mathbf{a}, \tag{3}$$

$$f_1 = m \, a_1, \qquad f_2 = m \, a_2, \qquad f_3 = m \, a_3, \tag{4}$$

and
$$f_i = m \, a_i \qquad (i = 1 \cdots 3). \tag{5}$$

All these three sets of equations are, of course, equivalent. The form (4) is rather clumsy and not very useful. We shall use either form (3), in which vectors are indicated by boldface symbols, or form (5), in which subscripts denote the components. Equations (5) are understood to hold for the components with respect to any Cartesian inertial coordinate system.

The *acceleration* **a** is defined as the vector consisting of the second time derivatives of the three coordinates,

$$a_i = \frac{d^2 x_i}{dt^2}. \tag{6}$$

A change of direction as well as one of speed is considered to be an acceleration.

We shall next consider the concept of *inertial mass*. First of all, inertial mass is a *permanent* property of all matter. If the matter contained in a certain body remains the same, then its mass will not change, no matter what deformations or even chemical transformations may be performed on that body. Moreover, mass is an *additive property* of matter. If we combine two bodies into one, the first having the mass $m_1$ and the second the mass $m_2$, then the mass of the combined body will be $(m_1 + m_2)$.

We have previously described *force* as the interaction of bodies, or as the effect which one body exerts on another. Having introduced the force vector $f_i$, we can now be much more specific. If two mass points exert forces on each other, then *the magnitude of the force which mass point A exerts on mass point B depends only on their distance $\overline{AB}$, and its direction is parallel to the connecting straight* *line.* If the force experienced by $B$ points away from $A$, it is called *repulsive,* if it points toward $A$, then it is called an *attractive* force. If more than two mass points interact with each other, then the force experienced by any one mass point is the vector sum of the partial forces exerted separately by every one of the remaining mass points.

**Newton's third law.** *To each force exerted by a mass point A on another mass point B corresponds a force exerted by B on A. This second force is equal in magnitude to the first one and points in the opposite direction.*

According to the third law of Newton, a mass point cannot act on another one without, at the same time, itself experiencing a reaction. Since the two forces are of equal magnitude, it is purely arbitrary which one is to be called "action" and which "reaction." In fact, this original terminology is frequently a cause of confusion, but the intent of Newton's original formulation is equivalent to the italicized statement above.

While the forces which two mass points exert on each other are equal in magnitude, the same does not hold for their resulting accelerations. According to the second law, with equal forces the accelerations will be inversely proportional to the masses of the two mass points involved. Take, as an instance, the force which the sun and the earth exert on each other. According to the third law, the earth attracts the sun with the same force which the sun exerts on the earth. But the acceleration suffered by the sun is negligible compared to that of the earth.

We may express the forces which two mass points exert on each other as the partial derivatives of a single function of their distance, which is known as the *potential energy.* Call the coordinates of the first mass point $x_i$ and, in the same way, the coordinates of the other mass point $x_i$. Their distance $r$ is of course, given by the expression
$$r^2 = \sum_{i=1}^{3} (x_i - x_i)^2. \tag{7}$$

Because of our assumption that the force experienced by either mass point is parallel to the connecting straight line, it follows that if the magnitude of the repulsive force be designated by $f$ (or that of an attractive force by $-f$), the components of the force experienced by the second mass point are given by expressions of the form

$$f_i = f \frac{x_i - x_i}{r},$$
$$\phantom{f_i =} \, _2 \quad _1 \qquad (8)$$

whereas the components of the force acting on the first mass point are

$$f_i = f \frac{x_i - x_i}{r}.$$
$$\phantom{f_i =} \, _1 \quad _2 \qquad (9)$$

Now the potential energy is a function of $r$ which may be introduced with the help of the defining equation

$$f = - \frac{dV}{dr}. \qquad (10)$$

By means of eq. (10), eqs. (8) and (9) may be combined into one:

$$f_i = - \frac{\partial V}{\partial x_i} \qquad (a = 1, 2; \quad i = 1, 2, 3). \qquad (11)$$

Thus, the potential energy describes completely the interaction between two mass points. Let us note, in passing, that $V$ is defined by eq. (10) only up to an unspecified constant of integration. Whenever the forces between two particles decrease rapidly enough for large values of the distance $r$, this constant of integration is disposed of by the requirement that

$$\lim_{r \to \infty} \{V(r)\} = 0. \qquad (12)$$

## 1.2. The conservation laws

We call a *mechanical system* a collection of mass points which exert forces on each other and which move under the influence of these mutual forces. In general, the members of the mechanical system are also subject to *external forces*, caused by other mass points that do not belong to the mechanical system under consideration. As a special case the mass points which make up the system may be so far removed from other bodies that the only forces experienced by them are those caused by the other members of the system; then we speak of an *isolated mechanical system*.

Suppose we know both the internal and the external forces of a given mechanical system. That is, for any configuration of the system we can compute the internal forces by means of the potential energies $V_{m,n}$ (between the $m$th and the $n$th particles) of all pairs of member mass points, and, at the same time, we are given the external forces experienced by each member of our system as functions of the time $t$. Then, if we designate the external force experienced by the $n$th particle by $f_{i\,n}^{*}$, the acceleration of the $n$th particle is given by the equation

$$ m_n \, \ddot{x}_{i\,n} = -\sum_{m=1}^{N} \frac{\partial V_{m,n}}{\partial x_{i\,n}} + f_{i\,n}^{*} \qquad (i = 1, 2, 3; \quad n = 1, \cdots, N). $$

(13)

In other words, the total force acting on any one particle is the vector sum of all the forces acting simultaneously on that particle —the internal forces due to the other members of the system, and the external force.

It is possible to prove, without regard to the details of the mechanical system under consideration but just because it obeys Newton's three laws, that certain quantities change in the course of time only under the influence of the external forces; in an isolated mechanical system, they remain constant. These quantities are, respectively, the *linear momentum* of the system, its *angular momentum*, and its *energy*. These theorems are known collectively as *conservation laws*. Their importance lies in their generality. They permit certain conclusions concerning the history[1] of any isolated system which do not depend on the explicit solution of the differential equations (13).

Before launching into these proofs, we shall introduce a formal simplification of eqs. (13). In the sum on the right-hand side, there appear the individual potential energies of those pairs of particles of which one is the mass point under consideration (in this case the $n$th particle). If we now introduce the sum over all potential energies as a new variable, $V$, the potential energy of the system,

---

[1] The term "history" is used here in the sense that we are interested in processes taking place in the course of time.

$$V = \tfrac{1}{2} \sum_{m,n=1}^{N} \underset{m,n}{V} \qquad (14)$$

can be used to rewrite eq. (13) in the form

$$\underset{n}{m}\,\underset{n}{\ddot{x}_i} = -\frac{\partial V}{\partial x_i}_{n} + \underset{n}{f_i^*}, \qquad (15)$$

because when the potential energy of the system, $V$, is differentiated partially with respect to one coordinate of a particular particle (say the $n$th), only those terms in the sum (14) contribute which also appear on the right-hand side of eq. (13). The factor $\tfrac{1}{2}$ in eq. (14), incidentally, is required, because each potential energy in the sum appears twice; for instance, the term $\underset{3,7}{V}$ appears once with $m = 3, n = 7$, and once with $m = 7, n = 3$. Naturally, the potential energy of a particle with respect to itself, $\underset{n,n}{V}$, vanishes identically, since particles cannot very well exert forces on themselves.

**Linear momentum.** In accordance with the custom in elementary mechanics, we shall introduce the momentum of a single particle, $\underset{n}{\mathbf{p}}$, by means of the defining equations

$$\underset{n}{p_i} = \underset{n}{m}\,\underset{n}{\dot{x}_i}, \qquad (16)$$

and the momentum of the system as the sum of the individual moments,

$$P_i = \sum_{n=1}^{N} \underset{n}{p_i} = \sum_{n=1}^{N} \underset{n}{m}\,\underset{n}{\dot{x}_i}. \qquad (17)$$

Now the change of each momentum in time, $\underset{n}{p_i}$, is simply equal to the force exerted on the particle,

$$\underset{n}{\dot{p}_i} = \underset{n}{m}\,\underset{n}{\ddot{x}_i} = -\frac{\partial V}{\partial x_i}_{n} + \underset{n}{f_i^*}. \qquad (18)$$

The change of the momentum of the system can now be obtained by adding up the changes in momentum of the individual particles,

$$\dot{P}_i = \sum_{n=1}^{N} \underset{n}{\dot{p}_i} = -\sum_{n=1}^{N} \frac{\partial V}{\partial x_i}_{n} + \sum_{n=1}^{N} \underset{n}{f_i^*}. \qquad (19)$$

Going back to the form (13) of the equations of motion, we find that

$$\sum_{n=1}^{N} \frac{\partial V}{\partial x_i}_n = \sum_{m,n=1}^{N} \frac{\partial V_{m,n}}{\partial x_i}_n. \tag{20}$$

In this double sum, each potential energy $V_{m,n}$ appears twice, once differentiated with respect to $x_i$, and once with respect to $x_i$. The sum of these two terms vanishes [compare eqs. (8) and (9)], so that the whole double sum appearing in eq. (20) must equal zero. As a result, we find that eq. (19) simplifies and assumes the form

$$\dot{P}_i = F_i^*, \qquad F_i^* \equiv \sum_{n=1}^{N} f_i^*_n. \tag{21}$$

In other words, the change in the momentum of the system does not depend on the internal interactions but equals the sum of the external forces experienced by the system. For an isolated system, the momentum **P** does not change at all in the course of time but is a constant of the motion of the system.

The result of eq. (21) may be presented in a slightly different form. If we introduce the notion of the center of mass of a system, the coordinates of the center of mass are given, in terms of the coordinates of the individual members of the system, by the expression

$$X_i = \frac{1}{M} \sum_{n=1}^{N} m_n x_i{}_n, \qquad M = \sum_{n=1}^{N} m_n. \tag{22}$$

We find, therefore, that in terms of the mass of the system $M$ and the coordinates of the center of mass, $X_i$, the momentum of the system takes the form

$$P_i = \sum_{n=1}^{N} m_n \dot{x}_i{}_n = M \dot{x}_i. \tag{23}$$

As a result, eq. (21) may be written in the form

$$F_i^* = \dot{P}_i = M \ddot{X}_i. \tag{24}$$

In other words, the mass of the system, multiplied by the acceleration of the center of mass, equals the total external force acting on the system. We find that in this sense Newton's first law and second law hold not only for individual mass points but for mechanical systems as well.

Since, in practice, checks of the laws of mechanics can be made only on bodies which are either known to consist of many mass points or about which it cannot be definitely known whether they are elementary particles or possess an internal structure, it is of great importance that the basic assumptions about mass points reproduce themselves for complex systems.

**Angular momentum.** The angular momentum of a mass point with respect to a particular point of reference is usually defined as the vector product (cross product) of the connecting straight line by the linear momentum of the mass point. We shall define the angular momentum more directly as a set of three quantities, $I_{23}, I_{31}, I_{12}$), which equal the following expressions:

$$I_{ik} = m(x_i \dot{x}_k - x_k \dot{x}_i) = x_i p_k - x_k p_i \qquad (i, k = 1, 2, 3). \quad (25)$$

These expressions satisfy the equations

$$I_{ik} = -I_{ki}, \qquad I_{ii} = 0, \quad (26)$$

through which they are effectively reduced to three independent components. These components correspond to the angular momenta about the $x$-axis ($I_{23}$), the $y$-axis ($I_{31}$), and the $z$-axis ($I_{12}$), in accordance with the usual definition,

We shall now examine the change of the angular momentum components in the course of time. Differentiating the right-hand side of eq. (25), we find

$$\dot{I}_{ik} = m(x_i \ddot{x}_k - x_k \ddot{x}_i) = x_i \dot{p}_k - x_k \dot{p}_i, \quad (27)$$

the remaining terms canceling. If now we sum over all members of the system to obtain the change in total angular momentum and substitute eq. (15) for the accelerations, we shall discover again that the internal forces (entering by way of the potential energy $V$) contribute nothing to the change of the angular momentum of the system. It is necessary, for this purpose, to go back to eqs. (14), (8), and (10). We must replace $\partial V / \partial x_i$ in eq. (15) by
$$\frac{\partial V}{\partial x_i} = \sum_{m=1}^{N} \frac{d V}{d r} \frac{x_i - x_i}{r}. \quad (28)$$

The change in the total angular momentum of the system now becomes

$$\dot{I}_{ik} = \sum_{n=1}^{N} \left\{ x_i \left[ f_k^* - \sum_{m=1}^{N} \frac{d}{d} \frac{V}{r} \frac{x_k - x_k}{r} \right] \right.$$
$$\left. - x_k \left[ f_i^* - \sum_{m=1}^{N} \frac{d}{d} \frac{V}{r} \frac{x_i - x_i}{r} \right] \right\} \quad (29)$$

The underscored terms cancel each other outright. The remainder becomes

$$\dot{I}_{ik} = \sum_{n=1}^{N} t_{ik}^* + \sum_{n,m=1}^{N} \frac{d}{d} \frac{V}{r} \frac{x_i x_k - x_k x_i}{r} \quad (30)$$

$$(t_{ik}^* = x_i f_k^* - x_k f_i^*).$$

The first sum represents the sum of the torques due to the external forces. The second sum on the right-hand side is zero because of the double summation over all members of the system (represented by the indices $m$ and $n$), in which each combination of different indices $(m,n)$ appears twice, with opposite signs. We find, therefore, that the time rate of change of the angular momentum of the system equals the applied external torque; the angular momentum of an isolated mechanical system remains constant. This is the second conservation law.

We can derive a further interesting property of the angular momentum of a system by introducing the coordinates of the individual members of the system relative to the common center of mass. We define these relative coordinates by means of the equations

$$\xi_i = x_i - X_i. \quad (31)$$

These relative coordinates have the property that the expression $\sum_n m_n \xi_i$ vanishes, because of the basic definition of the center of mass, eq. (22). With the help of these relative coordinates, the angular momentum of the system can be shown to consist of two parts,

$$I_{ik} = M(X_i \dot{X}_k - X_k X_i) + \sum_{n=1}^{N} m(\xi_i \dot{\xi}_k - \xi_k \xi_i). \quad (32)$$

The first term has to do only with the motion of the center of mass of the system relative to the chosen origin of the coordinate system, while the second term, which depends only on the internal motions, might be called the *intrinsic angular momentum* of the system. The derivative of the right hand side of eq. (32) with respect to time must, of course, equal the sum of the external torques applied,

$$M(X_i \ddot{X}_k - X_k \ddot{X}_i) + \sum_{n=1}^{N} m_n(\xi_i \ddot{\xi}_k - \xi_k \ddot{\xi}_i) = \sum_{n=1}^{N} t_{ik}^* \equiv T_{ik}^* \quad (33)$$

The total external torque, too, decomposes into two terms,

$$T_{ik}^* = (X_i F_k^* - X_k F_i^*) + \sum_{n=1}^{N} (\xi_i f_k^* - \xi_k f_i^*). \quad (34)$$

Because of eqs. (21) and (24), the first term on the right-hand side of eq. (34) equals the first term on the left hand side of eq. (33). It follows that the second terms must equal each other by themselves. The change in the intrinsic angular momentum of a system is determined completely by the external torques with respect to the center of mass. In an isolated system, the intrinsic angular momentum and the remainder (the contribution of the motion of the center of mass to the total angular momentum) are each separately constant.

**Energy.** The conservation law of energy is probably the best known of the three great conservation laws of classical mechanics. It is obtained by multiplying the equations of motion by the corresponding components of the velocities of the mass points and then summing over all coordinate indices as well as over all members of the mechanical system. We have

$$\sum_{n=1}^{N} \sum_{i=1}^{3} m_n \ddot{x}_i \dot{x}_i = - \sum_{n=1}^{N} \sum_{i=1}^{3} \frac{\partial V}{\partial x_i} \dot{x}_i + \sum_{n=1}^{N} \sum_{i=1}^{3} f_i^* \dot{x}_i. \quad (35)$$

Concerning the terms on the left-hand side, we find that this sum equals the time derivative of the kinetic energy of the system,

$$\sum_{n=1}^{N} \sum_{i=1}^{3} m_n \ddot{x}_i \dot{x}_i = \frac{d}{dt} \left\{ \sum_{n=1}^{N} \sum_{i=1}^{3} \tfrac{1}{2} m_n \dot{x}_i^2 \right\}. \quad (36)$$

The first double sum on the right-hand side of eq. (35) is nothing but the (negative) time rate of change of the potential energy; so that the change of total energy with time is completely determined by the external forces:

$$\dot{E} = \frac{d}{dt}\left\{\sum_{n=1}^{N}\sum_{i=1}^{3}\tfrac{1}{2}\underset{n}{m}\,\dot{\underset{n}{x}}_i^2 + V\right\} = \sum_{n=1}^{N}\sum_{i=1}^{3}\underset{n}{f}_i^*\,\dot{\underset{n}{x}}_i. \tag{37}$$

The energy of the mechanical system, just like the angular momentum, can be separated into an *intrinsic energy*, which depends only on the internal configuration and the internal motions, and a remainder, which depends only on the motion of the center of mass. If we introduce again the relative coordinates $\xi_i$, then the energy of the system, $E$, assume the form

$$E = V + \sum_{n=1}^{N}\sum_{i=1}^{3}\tfrac{1}{2}\underset{n}{m}\,\dot{\underset{n}{\xi}}_i^2 + \sum_{i=1}^{3}\frac{M}{2}\dot{X}_i^2. \tag{38}$$

The first two terms together constitute the intrinsic energy of the system. The right-hand side of eq. (37) also can be split up into two portions,

$$\sum_{n=1}^{N}\sum_{i=1}^{3}\underset{n}{f}_i^*\,\dot{\underset{n}{x}}_i = \sum_{n=1}^{N}\sum_{i=1}^{3}\underset{n}{f}_i^*\,\dot{\underset{n}{\xi}}_i + \sum_{i=1}^{3}F_i^*\,\dot{X}_i. \tag{39}$$

We can easily show that

$$\sum_{i=1}^{3}F_i^*\,\dot{X}_i = \frac{d}{dt}\sum_{i=1}^{3}\frac{M}{2}\dot{X}_i^2. \tag{40}$$

This relationship follows from eqs. (21) and (24), from which $\dot{P}_i$ has been eliminated and which have then been multiplied by $\dot{X}_i$ and summed over the index $i$. As a result, the change in intrinsic energy of a mechanical system is given by

$$\dot{E}_{\text{intr}} = \sum_{n=1}^{N}\sum_{i=1}^{3}\underset{n}{f}_i^*\,\dot{\underset{n}{\xi}}_i. \tag{41}$$

In an isolated system, both the total energy $E$ and the intrinsic energy of the system remain constant.

## 1.3. Planetary motion

We shall apply the general laws discussed in the first two sections to at least one instance which possesses considerable physical and historical significance, namely, the theory of planetary motion. The problem of treating the solar system in full rigor, including the interactions of the planets and minor bodies with each other, would lead far beyond the confines of this book.   We shall restrict ourselves to the problem of solving the equations of motion for the two-body problem presented by the interaction of the sun with a single planet.   The results obtained provide at least a fair approximation to actual planetary motion in our solar system, because the effects of the planets on each other are sufficiently small, compared with the overwhelming force exerted by the sun, that they may be considered as minor perturbations.

To set up our problem completely, we need to add to the general laws of mechanics the specific dependence of the potential energy of our system on the distance between the two bodies involved.   This dependence, the *law of gravitation*, first discovered by Newton, specifies that the potential energy is given by the expression

$$V = - \frac{G M m}{r}. \tag{42}$$

Here $M$ is the mass of the sun, $m$ the mass of the planet, $G$ is Newton's constant of gravitation (the force of gravitational attraction that two mass points of one gram each exert on each other at a distance of one centimeter), and $r$ is the distance between the two celestial bodies.   In addition to this law, we have available not only the equations of motion in the form of eq. (15) but also the conservation laws.   As a matter of fact, it is advisable to introduce immediately the coordinates of the center of mass, $X$, $Y$, $Z$, and the relative coordinates $\xi_s$, $\eta_s$, $\zeta_s$ of the sun and $\xi$, $\eta$, $\zeta$ of the planet, respectively.   Equations (21) reduce to the three equations

$$\ddot{X} = 0, \qquad \ddot{Y} = 0, \qquad \ddot{Z} = 0 \tag{43}$$

for the motion of the center of mass of our system.   In the absence of external forces (which in the case of our solar system are certainly very small), the center of mass will follow a straight-line path with constant velocity.   As for the relative coordinates, they satisfy the three algebraic relationships

$$m\,\xi + M\,\xi_s = 0, \qquad m\,\eta + M\,\eta_s = 0, \qquad m\,\zeta + M\,\zeta_s = 0, \tag{44}$$

by means of which the relative coordinates of the sun can at all times be expressed in terms of the relative coordinates of the planet.

Before going any further we shall further restrict the choice of coordinate system in which we describe the motion of our system. Transition to the relative coordinates has already disposed of the choice of origin of the coordinate system. The origin is at the center of mass. We shall now further place the $\zeta$-axis into such a direction that at some definite time $t_0$ both $\zeta$ and its time derivative $\dot\zeta$ vanish. It follows that $\zeta_s$ and $\dot\zeta_s$ vanish at the same time, because of eq. (44). We can now show that for all times to come, $\zeta$ and $\dot\zeta$ will remain zero, in other words, that the whole motion takes place in a plane. At the time $t_0$, the only component of the (intrinsic) angular momentum which does not vanish is the one about the $\zeta$-axis ($I_{12}$). Because of the conservation law for angular momentum, the other two components must remain permanently zero. However, the angular momentum about any given axis vanishes only if the instantaneous tangent of the motion intersects that axis or is parallel to it. If this condition is to be satisfied both for the $\xi$-axis and for the $\eta$-axis, then the motion must be wholly in the $\xi,\eta$-plane. In what follows we may, therefore, treat our system like a system with only two degrees of freedom (as a problem in two dimensions only), restricting ourselves to the $\xi,\eta$-plane.

We may now write down the conservation laws for the intrinsic angular momentum $I_{12}$ and for the intrinsic energy. They are

$$m(\xi\dot\eta - \eta\dot\xi) + M(\xi_s\dot\eta_s - \eta_s\dot\xi_s) = I \tag{45}$$

and
$$\frac{m}{2}(\dot\xi^2 + \dot\eta^2) + \frac{M}{2}(\dot\xi_s^2 + \dot\eta_s^2) - \frac{G\,M\,m}{r} = E,$$
$$r^2 = (\xi - \xi_s)^2 + (\eta - \eta_s)^2. \tag{46}$$

With the help of eqs. (44), we can eliminate completely the coordinates referring to the sun. Equations (45) and (46) then assume the form

$$m'(\xi\dot\eta - \eta\dot\xi) = I,$$
$$\frac{m'}{2}(\dot\xi^2 + \dot\eta^2) - \frac{G\,M'\,m'}{r'} = E$$
$$m' = \left(1 + \frac{m}{M}\right)m,$$
$$M' = \left(1 + \frac{m}{M}\right)^{-2}M,$$
$$r' = \left(1 + \frac{m}{M}\right)^{-1} r = \sqrt{\xi^2 + \eta^2}. \tag{47}$$

In other words, if we replace $m$ and $M$ by appropriately modified quantities, our two-body problem assumes the exact form of the single-body problem in which the central star is assumed to be fixed.

By means of the conservation laws, we have already been able to replace the second-order differential equations of motion (15) by two first-order differential equations, which must, of course, contain two constants of integration, $E$ and $I$. The remaining task of integration will be simplified if we go over to polar coordinates $r'$ and $\theta$. In terms of polar coordinates, eqs. (47) assume the form

$$m' \, r'^2 \, \dot{\theta} = I,$$
$$\frac{m'}{2} (\dot{r}'^2 + r'^2 \, \dot{\theta}^2) - \frac{G \, m' \, M'}{r'} = E. \tag{48}$$

It is possible to integrate these equations by substituting $\dot{\theta}$ from the first into the second equation. If we were to follow this method, we should obtain a differential equation for $r'$ as a function of $t$, which can be solved by separating the variables. However, this method of solution, though apparently most straightforward, leads to an algebraic relationship between $r'$ and $t$ which cannot be solved readily with respect to $r'$. That is why we shall follow the customary method of solution, which consists of eliminating the time $t$ as the argument and replacing it by the angle $\theta$. We can do this by setting $\dot{r}'$ equal to $(dr'/d\theta) \cdot \dot{\theta}$ and then substituting $\dot{\theta}$ from the first equation (48). If we do so, we obtain the following differential equation for $r'$ as a function of $\theta$:

$$\frac{I^2}{2m' \, r'^4} \left[ \left( \frac{dr'}{d\theta} \right)^2 + r'^2 \right] - \frac{G \, m' \, M'}{r'} = E. \tag{49}$$

This equation can be further simplified if we introduce the reciprocal of $r'$,

$$\frac{I^2}{2m'} \left[ \left( \frac{dx}{d\theta} \right)^2 + x^2 \right] - Gm' \, M' \, x = E,$$
$$x = \frac{1}{r'}. \tag{50}$$

In this equation, we can now readily separate the variables $x$ and $\theta$ and integrate:

$$\theta = \theta_0 + \int_{x_0}^{x} \left[ \frac{2m'}{I^2} (E + G \, m' \, M' \, \rho) - \rho^2 \right]^{-\frac{1}{2}} d\rho. \tag{51}$$

The constant of integration $\theta_0$ is trivial. We can dispose of it as well as of the lower limit of the integral, $x_0$, by specifying that the angle $\theta$ is to be counted from the perihelion (that point along the path at which $x$ assumes its largest value).

In the integration of the integral, we must distinguish between two cases, whether the energy $E$ is positive or negative. If the energy is negative, the radicand in the bracket has two positive roots, corresponding to a path which possesses both perihelion and aphelion. For values of $x$ outside the range between these two positive roots, the square root under the integral is no longer real, and no physically meaningful path can lie outside these limits for $x$. If, on the other hand, the energy is positive, then the radicand has a positive and a negative root. Since negative values of $x$ have no physical significance, the values of $x$ along an actual path will lie between 0 and the positive root. For values of $x$ greater than the positive root, the integrand again becomes imaginary.

Let us consider the case of negative energy first. In that case, the two positive roots of the radicand are

$$x_{1,2} = \frac{m'^2 G M'}{I^2} \left( 1 \pm \sqrt{1 + \frac{2 I^2 E}{m'^3 G^2 M'^2}} \right), \tag{52}$$

and the integral of eq. (51) (with the normalization of $\theta_0$ described above) is

$$\theta = \arccos \left( \frac{x - \dfrac{m'^2 G M'}{I^2}}{\dfrac{m'^2 G M'}{I^2} \sqrt{1 + \dfrac{2E I^2}{m'^3 G^2 M'^2}}} \right). \tag{53}$$

If we solve this equation with respect to $x$ and if we reintroduce $r'$, the distance of the planet from the center of mass of our system, we obtain the following relationship between $r'$ and $\theta$:

$$r' = \frac{I^2}{G m'^2 M'} \left\{ 1 + \sqrt{1 + \frac{2E I^2}{m'^3 G^2 M'^2}} \cos \theta \right\}^{-1}. \tag{54}$$

This expression is the equation of an ellipse in polar coordinates, provided that the origin ($r'' = 0$) is located at one focus.

So far, we have derived from the equations of motion the first two of Kepler's laws of planetary motion. The second law, which states that the straight line connecting the sun with the planet

sweeps out equal areas in equal time intervals, is nothing but the
conservation law of angular momentum. According to the first
law of Kepler, the planetary orbit is an ellipse, with the sun (actually
the center of mass) at one focus. The third law relates the time
of revolution to the major axis. This third law can be most conveniently derived from geometric considerations. If we write the
orbital equation in the abbreviated form

$$r' = \frac{p}{1 + \epsilon \cos \theta},$$ (55)

where the values of the two constants $p$ and $\epsilon$ are given by eq. (54),
it is well known that the major and the minor axis of the ellipse are
given by the two expressions

$$a = \frac{p}{1 - \epsilon^2}, \qquad b = \frac{p}{\sqrt{1 - \epsilon^2}}.$$ (56)

We can now compute the area of the ellipse in alternative ways,
either in terms of the major and the minor axes,

$$A = \pi a b = \frac{\pi p^2}{(1 - \epsilon^2)^{3/2}},$$ (57)

or, because of Kepler's second law by means of the area swept out
per unit time and the total time of revolution, $T$,

$$A = \frac{1}{2} \frac{I}{m'} T.$$ (58)

Eliminating the area $A$, we obtain for the time of revolution the
expression

$$T = \frac{2\pi m'}{I} \frac{p^2}{(1 - \epsilon^2)^{3/2}},$$ (59)

from which both $\epsilon$ and $p$ can be eliminated by means of the substitutions from (54) and (56):

$$T = \frac{2\pi m'}{I} a^{3/2} p^{1/2} = \frac{2\pi}{\sqrt{G M'}} a^{3/2}.$$ (60)

This final equation gives us Kepler's third law, to the effect that the
time of revolution of a planet is proportional to the $\frac{3}{2}$th power of
the major axis of the ellipse but depends otherwise only on the
magnitude of the mass of the sun (more accurately $M'$).

Let us turn briefly to the case in which the energy is positive. The integration procedure remains exactly the same as in the first case, up to eq. (54). The only difference is that now the eccentricity comes out greater than unity and that, as a result, $r'$ becomes infinite for certain angles in the second and third quadrants. These angles are given by the condition that

$$\cos \theta = -\frac{1}{\epsilon} = -\frac{1}{\sqrt{1 + \dfrac{2I^2 E}{G\,m'^3\,M'^2}}}. \tag{61}$$

The orbit is now a hyperbola, or rather one branch of a hyperbola. The center of gravity lies at that focus inside the planetary orbit.

## Problems

**1.1.** Determine the trajectory of an alpha particle (charge $2e$) which is repelled by a heavy atomic nucleus of charge $Ze$, if its velocity at a great distance is $v_0$ (or its positive energy $E = \frac{1}{2}m\,v_0^2$) and if its distance of closest approach from the deflecting nucleus, if undeflected, would have been $a$. $a$ is called the *collision parameter*.

When the alpha particle has left the vicinity of the deflecting nucleus, it will again travel very nearly straight. Determine the angle between the initial direction of approach and the final direction of travel; this angle can be determined experimentally and is called the *angle of deflection*.

**1.2.** Consider a collimated stream of alpha particles passing the atomic nucleus of Problem 1.1. If the density of particles in the approaching beam is uniform and if all the particles have the same direction of approach and the same initial velocity, determine the distribution-in-angle of the deflected particles. If the experiment is carried out in practice, the single deflecting nucleus is replaced by a thin scatterer containing a large number of heavy nuclei per cm² of target area, which, however, scatter almost independently of each other. Your final result should be the number of particles per steradian per second as a function of energy $E$, the number of scattering atoms per cm² ($N$), and the density of the initial beam ($n$ particles per cm² per second). This result is well known as *Rutherford's scattering formula*.

# Chapter 2

# Analytical Mechanics

## 2.1. Lagrange's equations of motion

Chapter 1 contains all the essential statements which together define the scope of Newtonian mechanics. However, the mathematical formulation of these statements is restricted insofar as the form of the equations of motion (1.15) has validity only if the coordinates $x_i$ belong to a Cartesian (rectilinear) inertial coordinate system. The form which the equations of motion would assume if we introduced some different type of coordinate system cannot be readily predicted. Nevertheless, non-Cartesian coordinate systems are of practical importance. In the one example of Newtonian mechanics which we treated, we found that the equations could be integrated most conveniently if written in terms of polar coordinates. The question arises whether there are methods by which the equations of motion can be transformed uniformly and independently of the special character of the coordinate system used. Such methods have in fact been found and are now known collectively as *analytical mechanics*. We shall devote a whole chapter to the discussion of these methods, not so much because we propose to do a great deal of problem work in the mechanics of systems of mass points but rather because analytical mechanics has helped to develop new concepts which have assumed great importance in present-day quantum mechanics.

**Condition of static equilibrium.** In order to approach analytical mechanics, we shall start with the conditions of static equilibrium of an isolated mechanical system. The first condition is, of course, that none of the members of the mechanical system should experience a net force. If, in addition, at the time $t_0$ all velocity components vanish, then we are assured that the system will be in equilibrium. We may, if we wish, express the necessary and sufficient conditions of equilibrium in this form: If at all times the partial derivatives of the potential energy of the system with respect to all the particle coordinates vanish, then the system is at equilibrium,

$$\frac{\partial V}{\partial x_i}_n = 0 \qquad (n = 1, \cdots, N; \quad i = 1, 2, 3). \tag{1}$$

Equation (1) stands for a set of $3N$ separate conditions. These $3N$ conditions may be formally combined into one if we introduce the concept of *virtual displacements*, $\delta x_i$. Since $V$ is a function of all $3N$ coordinates $x_i$, it follows from eq. (1) that the potential energy of the system would not change its value if each mass point of the system were removed from its actual location an infinitesimal distance, the rectilinear components of which are designated by $\delta x_i$.

Whether or not we have to deal with an equilibrium situation, the change in potential energy is given by the expression

$$\delta V = \sum_{n=1}^{N} \sum_{i=1}^{3} \frac{\partial V}{\partial x_i}_n \delta x_i_n. \tag{2}$$

$\delta V$ vanishes if the partial derivatives satisfy eq. (1). The condition that $\delta V$ vanish is equivalent to eq. (1), provided that it holds for all infinitesimal but otherwise arbitrary virtual displacements $\delta x_i$. If we wish to express the further condition that the partial derivatives of $V$ must vanish throughout a finite time interval, from $t_1$ to $t_2$, we can do so by replacing the condition $\delta V = 0$ by the stronger condition

$$\delta \int_{t_1}^{t_2} V \, dt = \int_{t_1}^{t_2} \sum_{n=1}^{N} \sum_{i=1}^{3} \frac{\partial V}{\partial x_i}_n \delta x_i_n \, dt = 0, \tag{3}$$

where the $\delta x_i$ are now infinitesimal but otherwise arbitrary functions of the time. In other words, the integral $\int_{t_1}^{t_2} V \, dt$ must be stationary with respect to infinitesimal changes in the path of integration in the symbolical space of $3N$ dimensions which is made up of all the coordinates $x_i$ describing the configuration of the mechanical system under consideration.

Since this symbolical space has frequent applications in analytical mechanics, it has been given a special designation, *configuration space*. The form (3) of the condition of equilibrium possesses the important property of being independent of the particular choice of coordinates in configuration space. If, by means of $3N$ arbitrary transformation equations having the form

$$q_k = q_k(\underset{1}{x_1}, \underset{1}{x_2}, \underset{1}{x_3}; \underset{2}{x_1}, \underset{2}{x_2}, \underset{2}{x_3}; \cdots, t), \qquad (k = 1, \cdots, 3N)$$
$$\det \left| \frac{\partial q_k}{\partial \underset{n}{x_i}} \right| \neq 0, \tag{4}$$

we introduce a set of $3N$ quantities $q_k$ which together determine the original coordinates $\underset{n}{x_i}$ in configuration space, we can now describe our mechanical system in terms of the $q_k$; these quantities are called *generalized coordinates*. They represent a set of curvilinear coordinates in configuration space, a set which may even be in motion. If we now express $V$ in terms of the $q_k$, it must still be true that for equilibrium the integral is stationary, or

$$\delta \int_{t_1}^{t_2} V \, dt = \int_{t_1}^{t_2} \sum_{k=1}^{3N} \frac{\partial V}{\partial q_k} \, \delta q_k \, dt = 0, \tag{5}$$

where the $\delta q_k$ represent infinitesimal but otherwise arbitrary virtual displacements, expressed in terms of the generalized coordinates $q_k$. The condition (5) will be satisfied if at all times

$$\frac{\partial V}{\partial q_k} = 0 \qquad (k = 1, \cdots, 3N). \tag{6}$$

**General case.** If we wish to extend our method to the general problem of describing motion in accordance with the laws of mechanics, it appears reasonable to start with the equations of motion (1.15), multiply each equation by $\delta \underset{n}{x_i}$, add, and integrate the resulting differential expression from $t_1$ to $t_2$. We thus obtain a condition in the form

$$\int_{t_1}^{t_2} \sum_{n=1}^{N} \sum_{i=1}^{3} \left\{ \underset{n}{m} \, \underset{n}{\ddot{x}_i} + \frac{\partial V}{\partial \underset{n}{x_i}} \right\} \delta \underset{n}{x_i} \, dt = 0, \tag{7}$$

where the integral is to be extended over a path in configuration space. In order to carry out the analogous steps which led in the case of static equilibrium to the conditions (5) and (6), we shall have to find a function $F$ of which the expression (7) is the infinitesimal variation. In attempting to find such a function, we encounter no difficulty with the terms containing the derivatives of the potential energy; we can write eq. (7) immediately in the form

$$\int_{t_1}^{t_2} \left\{ \sum_{n=1}^{N} \sum_{i=1}^{3} \underset{n}{m} \, \ddot{\underset{n}{x}}_i \, \delta \underset{n}{x}_i + \delta V \right\} dt = 0. \tag{8}$$

The remainder can be transformed as well, by means of an integration by parts. If we write $\ddot{\underset{n}{x}}_i$ in the form $\dfrac{d}{dt}(\dot{\underset{n}{x}}_i)$, we see that

$$\int_{t_1}^{t_2} \sum_{n=1}^{N} \sum_{i=1}^{3} \underset{n}{m} \, \ddot{\underset{n}{x}}_i \, \delta \underset{n}{x}_i \, dt = \left[ \sum_{n=1}^{N} \sum_{i=1}^{3} \underset{n}{m} \, \dot{\underset{n}{x}}_i \, \delta \underset{n}{x}_i \right]_{t=t_1}^{t_2} - \int_{t_1}^{t_2} \delta T \, dt$$

$$\left( T = \tfrac{1}{2} \sum_{n=1}^{N} \sum_{i=1}^{3} \underset{n}{m} \, \dot{\underset{n}{x}}_i^2 \right). \tag{9}$$

The first term on the right-hand side depends only on the values of $\dot{\underset{n}{x}}_i$ and $\delta \underset{n}{x}_i$ at the end points of integration. In order to be rid of this term, we shall restrict our virtual displacements by the requirement that the virtual displacements, as functions of the time $t$, shall vanish at both ends of the interval of integration but shall remain arbitrary in its interior. With this restriction, we find that

$$\int_{t_1}^{t_2} \sum_{n=1}^{N} \sum_{i=1}^{3} \left\{ \underset{n}{m} \, \ddot{\underset{n}{x}}_i + \frac{\partial V}{\partial \underset{n}{x}_i} \right\} \delta \underset{n}{x}_i \, dt = -\delta \int_{t_1}^{t_2} L \, dt,$$

$$L = T - V, \qquad \delta \underset{n}{x}_i(t_1) = \delta \underset{n}{x}_i(t_2) = 0. \tag{10}$$

For paths obeying the laws of mechanics, the integral $\int_{t_2}^{t_1} L \, dt$ in configuration space is stationary with respect to arbitrary virtual displacements, which are merely subject to the restriction that the end points of the path of integration are to be kept fixed. In other words,

$$\delta S = \delta \int_{t_1}^{t_2} L \, dt = 0. \tag{11}$$

The function $L$, which equals the difference between the kinetic and potential energy of the mechanical system, is called its *Lagrangian*.

By means of eq. (11), we have succeeded in expressing the laws of motion in a form in which it is possible to introduce the generalized coordinates $q_k$. If we express the Lagrangian of the system in terms of the $q_k$, their first derivatives with respect to $t$, $\dot{q}_k$, and $t$ itself, it must still be true that the integral $S$ is stationary with respect to arbitrary infinitesimal virtual displacements, provided only that the end points of the integral are being kept fixed. However, we must now determine the form of the differential equations which will assure the stationary character of the integral. To do so requires a brief mathematical discussion.

**The Euler-Lagrange equations.** Consider a series of functions $y_i(x)$ of a single argument $x$, $i = 1, \cdots, n$, and a function $F(y_1, \cdots, y_n; y_1', \cdots y_n'; x)$ of the $y_i$, their derivatives with respect to $x$, and $x$ itself. A branch of mathematics called the *calculus of variations* deals with the following problem: If $F$ is given as a function of *its* arguments but the $y_i$ are as yet undetermined, then determine these functions $y_i(x)$ so that the integral $J$,

$$J = \int_{x_1}^{x_2} F(y_i, y_i', x) \, dx, \qquad y_i(x_1) = y_i \atop 1, \qquad y_i(x_2) = y_i \atop 2 \qquad (12)$$

becomes stationary with respect to arbitrary small changes in the functions $y_i$, provided, however, that at the two boundaries of the integral, $x_1$ and $x_2$, the values of all the $n$ functions $y_i$ are given beforehand.

This problem can be approached with the help of the ordinary methods of differential and integral calculus. Whether or not the integral $J$ is stationary, its variation, resulting from the variation of the arguments $y_i$ is certainly given by the expression

$$\delta J = \int_{x_1}^{x_2} \delta F(y_i, y_i', x) \, dx = \int_{x_1}^{x_2} \sum_{i=1}^{n} \left( \frac{\partial F}{\partial y_i} \delta y_i + \frac{\partial F}{\partial y_i'} \delta y_i' \right) dx. \quad (13)$$

In this expression, the $\delta y_i$ and the $\delta y_i'$ are not independent of each other. Since $\delta y_i$ is the difference between two possible functions $y_i(x)$ and since $\delta y_i'$ is the difference between their derivatives, we can use the rule that the differential quotient of a difference equals the difference between the differential quotients and conclude that

$$\delta(y_i') = \frac{d}{dx} (\delta y_i). \qquad (14)$$

Substituting in the expression (13) and integrating by parts, we get

$$\delta J = \int_{x_1}^{x_2} \sum_{i=1}^{n} \frac{\partial F}{\partial y_i} \delta y_i \, dx + \left[ \int_{x_1}^{x_2} \sum_{i=1}^{n} \frac{\partial F}{\partial y_i'} \delta y_i \right]$$
$$- \int_{x_1}^{x_2} \sum_{i=1}^{n} \frac{d}{dx} \left( \frac{\partial F}{\partial y_i'} \right) \delta y_i \, dx. \quad (15)$$

Because of the requirement that at the end points $x_1$ and $x_2$ the values of all the $y_i$ are given and cannot be varied, the second term on the right-hand side vanishes, and we are left with the result that for infinitesimal variations of the functions $y_i(x)$ not involving the points $x_1$ and $x_2$, the variation of $J$ is given by the integral

$$\delta J = \int_{x_1}^{x_2} \sum_{i=1}^{n} \left[ \frac{\partial F}{\partial y_i} - \frac{d}{dx} \left( \frac{\partial F}{\partial y_i'} \right) \right] \delta y_i \, dx. \quad (16)$$

The condition for the integral being stationary must be that the coefficients of the $\delta y_i$ vanish separately and for all values of $x$ between the limits of integration, since the $\delta y_i$ are arbitrary (infinitesimal) functions of $x$, except at the end points themselves. Thus the condition that $\delta J$ vanish is equivalent to the $n$ differential equations

$$\frac{\partial F}{\partial y_i} - \frac{d}{dx} \left( \frac{\partial F}{\partial y_i'} \right) = 0. \quad (17)$$

These equations are called the *Euler-Lagrange equations* of the *variational problem* (12).

**The equations of motion in generalized coordinates.** We can now return to our original problem, that of expressing the condition (11) in generalized coordinates. Since $L$, the difference between the kinetic and the potential energy of a mechanical system, is a function of the $q_k$, $\dot{q}_k$, and $t$, the integral $S$ has the same form as $J$ in eq. (12). It follows that $S$ will be stationary with respect to infinitesimal virtual changes in the paths of the particles if the following set of $3N$ differential equations is satisfied:

$$\frac{\partial L}{\partial q_k} - \frac{d}{dt} \left( \frac{\partial L}{\partial \dot{q}_k} \right) = 0 \quad (k = 1, \cdots, 3N). \quad (18)$$

These equations are then the equations of motion in terms of the generalized coordinates $q_k$. Incidentally, the second term in these equations, when written *in extenso*, takes the form

$$\frac{d}{dt}\left(\frac{\partial L}{\partial \dot{q}_k}\right) \equiv \sum_{l=1}^{3N} \frac{\partial^2 L}{\partial \dot{q}_k \, \partial q_l}\, \dot{q}_l + \frac{\partial^2 L}{\partial \dot{q}_k \, \partial \dot{q}_l}\, \ddot{q}_l + \frac{\partial^2 L}{\partial \dot{q}_k \, \partial t}. \tag{19}$$

If the coordinates employed are the $x_i$, the equations (18) are the ordinary equations of motion (1.15).

## 2.2. The Canonical Equations of Motion

Lagrange's form of the equations of motion (18) describes the behavior of a mechanical system in terms of the generalized coordinates $q_k$ in configuration space. In that $3N$-dimensional configuration space, the whole system is represented at each instant of time by a single representative point with the $3N$ coordinates $q_k$. The motions of the particles which belong to the system are represented by the single curve on which the representative point travels in the course of time. Given the configuration (the values of all $3N$ coordinates $q_k$) at a time $t_0$, the further motion will be determined uniquely only if at the same time the initial values of the $\dot{q}_k$ are given as well. In other words, through each point in configuration space there passes an infinity of curves representing possible paths for a given mechanical system.

For many purposes, this infinite number of mechanical trajectories through each point in configuration space is awkward. We should like to have available a representation in a different sort of symbolical space, in which one and only one trajectory passes through each point. Such a field of curves must obey differential equations of the first order, not second-order equations like the Euler-Lagrange equations. Systems of differential equations of arbitrary order can always be replaced by systems of the first order if we are willing to increase the number of variables as well as the number of equations. $3N$ equations of the second differential order are equivalent to $6N$ first-order equations. The additional variables must be algebraically determined by the $3N$ generalized velocity components, the $\dot{q}_k$. If we add some such variables to the $q_k$, we shall have generated a new type of symbolical space, which is $6N$-dimensional. Each point in that space describes a complete set of locations $(q_k)$ plus velocities $(\dot{q}_k)$. If these $6N$

quantities are given at a particular time, then the future behavior of the mechanical system, and with it the motion of its representative point in the new symbolical space, is completely determined. Thus, in the new symbolical space, there will be only one mechanical trajectory through each point.

**The generalized momenta.** We could, of course, introduce the generalized velocities $\dot{q}_k$ themselves as the additional variables. Instead, it proves more convenient to introduce certain closely related quantities, namely, the derivatives of $L$ with respect to the $\dot{q}_k$. The $3N$ quantities $p_k$,

$$p_k = \frac{\partial L}{\partial \dot{q}_k}, \tag{20}$$

are called the *generalized momenta* which are canonically conjugate to the $q_k$. Since the right-hand sides of the defining equations (20) are known functions of the generalized coordinates $q_k$, their derivatives $\dot{q}_k$, and the time $t$, they can be solved with respect to the $\dot{q}_k$, at least in principle, resulting in $3N$ equations having the form

$$\dot{q}_k = \dot{q}_k(q_l, p_l, t). \tag{21}$$

If we are to carry out our program, we shall have to obtain $6N$ equations of the first differential order which contain the $q_k$ and the $p_k$ as the unknown functions of $t$.

**The canonical equations of motion.** In the Lagrangian, we shall eliminate the $\dot{q}_k$ by substituting the expressions (21). The result is a function of the $q_k$, the $p_k$, and $t$, which is numerically equal to the Lagrangian and which we shall designate by $L^*$. In other words, we have

$$L^*(q_k, p_k, t) = L(q_k, \dot{q}_k, t). \tag{22}$$

We are now able to express the partial derivatives of $L^*$ with respect to $q_k$ and with respect to $p_k$ in terms of the partial derivatives of $L$ with respect to its arguments. We find

$$\frac{\partial L^*}{\partial q_k} = \frac{\partial L}{\partial q_k} + \sum_{l=1}^{3N} \frac{\partial L}{\partial \dot{q}_l} \frac{\partial \dot{q}_l}{\partial q_k} = \frac{\partial L}{\partial q_k} + \sum_{l=1}^{3N} p_l \frac{\partial \dot{q}_l}{\partial q_k}$$

$$= \frac{\partial L}{\partial q_k} + \frac{\partial}{\partial q_k}\left(\sum_{l=1}^{3N} p_l \dot{q}_l\right) \tag{23}$$

and

$$\frac{\partial L^*}{\partial p_k} = \sum_{l=1}^{3N} \frac{\partial L}{\partial \dot{q}_l} \frac{\partial \dot{q}_l}{\partial p_k} = \sum_{l=1}^{3N} p_l \frac{\partial \dot{q}_l}{\partial p_k}$$
$$= \frac{\partial}{\partial p_k} \left( \sum_{l=1}^{3N} p_l \dot{q}_l \right) - \dot{q}_k. \tag{24}$$

The partial derivatives on the right-hand sides of these equations are to be taken in the sense that the $\dot{q}_l$ have been expressed as functions of the $q_k$ and $p_k$ in accordance with eqs. (21). If we collect the functions of $q_k$ and $p_k$ on one side and the remaining terms on the other, we obtain the relations

$$\frac{\partial}{\partial q_k} \left( L^* - \sum_{l=1}^{3N} p_l \dot{q}_l \right) = \frac{\partial L}{\partial q_k},$$
$$\frac{\partial}{\partial p_k} \left( L^* - \sum_{l=1}^{3N} p_l \dot{q}_l \right) = -\dot{q}_k \tag{25}$$

Herewith our task is almost completed. All that remains to be done is to substitute the expressions for $(\partial L / \partial q_k)$ in the Lagrangian equations of motion (18), which can also be written in the form

$$\frac{\partial L}{\partial q_k} - \dot{p}_k = 0, \tag{26}$$

and to introduce a new function $H(q_k, p_k, t)$, defined by the equation

$$H(q_k, p_k, t) = -L^*(q_k, p_k, t) + \sum_{l=1}^{3N} p_l \dot{q}_l(q_k, p_k, t). \tag{27}$$

By combining the first equation (25) with (26) and (27) and introducing $H$ also into the second equation (25), we obtain the *canonical equations of motion*,

$$\dot{p}_k = -\frac{\partial H}{\partial q_k}, \qquad \dot{q}_k = \frac{\partial H}{\partial p_k}. \tag{28}$$

These equations are not only $6N$ equations of the first order; what is more, they are already solved with respect to the first-order derivatives of the $6N$ coordinates involved. Given the values of the $q_k$ and $p_k$ at a time $t_0$, the canonical equations of motion uniquely determine the $q_k$ and $p_k$ at all other times.

The function $H$ is called the *Hamiltonian*.  Giving the Hamiltonian as a function of its $(6N + 1)$ arguments is obviously one way of completely characterizing a mechanical system.  If we wish to examine the physical significance of $H$, we can do so most expeditiously by reintroducing into eqs. (27) and (20) the original coordinates $x_i$.  We find that with respect to these coordinates the generalized momenta are simply the ordinary momenta,

$$p_i \underset{n}{=} m_n \dot{x}_i \qquad (29)$$

and that $H$ is

$$H = -L^* + \sum_{n=1}^{N} \sum_{i=1}^{3} m_n \dot{x}_i^2 = -T + V + 2T = T + V, \quad (30)$$

the total energy of the mechanical system.

The symbolical space of the generalized coordinates and momenta, which is, as we have seen, a $6N$-dimensional space, has also been given a name; it is called the *phase space* of the system.  Through each point of phase space passes exactly one mechanical trajectory.

**Poisson brackets.**  Suppose some dynamical variable, such as the kinetic energy of one particular particle, is given in terms of the $q_k$, the $p_k$, and $t$.  Call the variable in question $G$.  Then we can express the change of $G$ with time in terms of its partial derivatives with respect to its arguments.  We have

$$\frac{dG}{dt} = \sum_{k=1}^{3N} \left( \frac{\partial G}{\partial q_k} \dot{q}_k + \frac{\partial G}{\partial p_k} \dot{p}_k \right) + \frac{\partial G}{\partial t}. \qquad (31)$$

By substituting eqs. (28), we can put this expression into the form

$$\dot{G} = \sum_{k=1}^{3N} \left( \frac{\partial G}{\partial q_k} \frac{\partial H}{\partial p_k} - \frac{\partial G}{\partial p_k} \frac{\partial H}{\partial q_k} \right) + \frac{\partial G}{\partial t}. \qquad (32)$$

In many cases of practical importance, the generalized coordinates are chosen so that the physically interesting variables do not depend on the time explicitly.  In such a case, the last term in eq. (32) vanishes, and the time derivative of $G$ can be expressed without explicit reference to the time at all.

Expressions of the type occurring in eq. (32) are called *Poisson brackets.* Specifically, the Poisson bracket of two dynamical variables $F$ and $G$ is defined as the expression

$$[F, G] \equiv \sum_{k=1}^{3N} \left( \frac{\partial F}{\partial q_k} \frac{\partial G}{\partial p_k} - \frac{\partial F}{\partial p_k} \frac{\partial G}{\partial q_k} \right). \tag{33}$$

Eq. (32) may be written in the form

$$\dot{G} = [G, H] + \frac{\partial G}{\partial t}. \tag{34}$$

A specific application can be made to the rate of change of the energy. We have

$$\dot{H} = [H, H] + \frac{\partial H}{\partial t} = \frac{\partial H}{\partial t}, \tag{35}$$

since the bracket $[H, H]$ obviously vanishes. In a conservative mechanical system, in which the expression for the energy does not contain the time explicitly, it follows that $H$ is constant. Furthermore, any other constant of the motion, such as the angular momentum, must have a vanishing Poisson bracket with $H$. In passing, we may note that the Poisson bracket satisfies identically the relations

$$[F, G] + [G, F] \equiv 0 \tag{36}$$

and

$$\Big[F, [G, I]\Big] + \Big[G, [I, F]\Big] + \Big[I, [F, G]\Big] \equiv 0. \tag{37}$$

The Poisson brackets of the coordinates themselves have the values

$$\begin{aligned} [q_k, q_l] = 0, \qquad [q_k, p_k] = 1, \\ [p_k, p_l] = 0, \qquad [q_k, p_l] = 0, \qquad (k \neq l). \end{aligned} \tag{38}$$

## 2.3. Canonical transformations

The form of Lagrange's equations of motion (18) is invariant with respect to arbitrary transformations in configuration space. That is to say, if instead of the $3N$ coordinates $q_k$ we introduce new coordinates $q_l'$ by means of transformation equations,

$$q_l' = q_l'(q_k, t), \tag{39}$$

then with respect to the new coordinates we shall have equations of motion having exactly the same form as eqs. (18),

$$\frac{\partial L'}{\partial q_i'} - \frac{d}{dt}\left(\frac{\partial L'}{\partial \dot{q}_i'}\right) = 0. \tag{40}$$

$L'$ is the same physical quantity as $L$, but kinetic and potential energy are now expressed in terms of the new coordinates $q_i'$ and their derivatives $\dot{q}_i'$.

The question arises what coordinate transformations in phase space will carry the canonical equations (28) over into new equations possessing the same form in terms of the new coordinates. There is, of course, a restricted group of such transformations, namely those in which the new $q_i'$ are functions of the old $q_k$ only, not involving the $p_k$. These are just the same transformations permissible in configuration space. However, there is a much more general type of transformation, in which the $q_i'$ are functions of both the old $q_k$ and the $p_k$. This more general type of transformation is of interest in many considerations, but most of all in quantum mechanics. We shall now investigate whether there are coordinate transformations of this general type which carry the canonical equations (28) in phase space over into new equations of the same kind.

**Variational principle in phase space.** From our experience in the preceding section, we know that such transformation properties can be examined very conveniently if it is possible to represent the equations in question as the Euler-Lagrange equations of a variational principle. It turns out that the canonical equations (28) can in fact be so represented. The variational principle is the following:

$$\delta \int_{t_1}^{t_2}\left[\sum_{k=1}^{3N} p_k \dot{q}_k - H(q_k, p_k, t)\right] dt = \delta \int_{t_1}^{t_2} \tilde{L}\, dt = 0, \tag{41}$$

in which the $q_k$ and the $p_k$ are to be considered as independent variables; in other words, the variations to be considered are arbitrary virtual displacements of the path of integration *in phase space*. (The end points are, of course, again fixed and must not be varied.) A little calculation shows that really the canonical equations (28) are the appropriate Euler-Lagrange equations, because we find that

$$\frac{\partial \tilde{L}}{\partial q_k} = -\frac{\partial H}{\partial q_k}, \qquad \frac{\partial \tilde{L}}{\partial \dot{q}_k} = p_k,$$

$$\frac{\partial L}{\partial p_k} = \dot{q}_k - \frac{\partial H}{\partial p_k}, \qquad \frac{\partial L}{\partial \dot{p}_k} = 0. \tag{42}$$

Substitution of these expressions into eq. (17) yields eqs. (28).

But the function $\tilde{L}$ is not the only integrand of a variational principle of which the canonical equations are the Euler-Lagrange equations. If we add to the integrand an arbitrary function which is the exact derivative (with respect to time) of some function $F$ of the arguments $q_k$, $p_k$, the contribution of this additional term to the integral would depend only on the value of $F$ at the end points and, as a result, the variation of this part of the integral (with fixed end points) would contribute nothing. Thus, we could, for instance, subtract from $L$ the expression $\dfrac{d}{dt}\left(\displaystyle\sum_k p_k\,q_k\right)$ and obtain the integral

$$T = -\int_{t_1}^{t_2}\left(H + \sum_{k=1}^{3N} q_k\,\dot{p}_k\right)dt. \qquad \delta T = 0, \qquad (43)$$

of which the Euler-Lagrange equations are again the equations (28).

**The transformation conditions.** After this preparation, we can formulate the transformation conditions. The equations of motion, expressed in terms of the new canonical coordinates $q'$ and $p'$,

$$q_l' = q_l'(q_k,\,p_k,\,t), \qquad p_l' = p_l'(q_k,\,p_k,\,t), \qquad (44)$$

will again assume the form (28) if the integrand $\tilde{L}$, expressed in terms of the new canonical coordinates, differs from the form indicated in eq. (41) only by an exact derivative,

$$\sum_{k=1}^{3N} p_k\,\dot{q}_k - H(q_k,\,p_k,\,t) \equiv \sum_{l=1}^{3N} p_l'\,\dot{q}_l' - H'(q_l',\,p_l',\,t) + \frac{dF}{dt}. \quad (45)$$

Here $F$ is an arbitrary (differentiable) function which must be defined for all points of phase space and for all values of the time $t$. It would seem sensible to represent it as a function of the $q_k$, $p_k$, and $t$, or else as a function of $q_l'$, $p_l'$, and $t$. Actually, the formulas turn out to be simpler if the points of phase space are identified by a combination of old (unprimed) and new (primed) coordinates.

If we give $F$ as a function of the $q_k$, $q_l'$, and $t$, then eq. (45) may be written in the form

$$\sum_{k=1}^{3N}\left(p_k - \frac{\partial F}{\partial q_k}\right)\dot{q}_k - \sum_{l=1}^{3N}\left(p_l' + \frac{\partial F}{\partial q_l'}\right)\dot{q}_l' + \left(H' - H - \frac{\partial F}{\partial t}\right) = 0.$$

$$(46)$$

This relation will hold for arbitrary paths of integration only if the coefficients of the $(6N)$ independent time derivatives and the last parenthesis vanish separately. We obtain the conditions

$$p_k = \frac{\partial F}{\partial q_k}, \qquad p_l' = -\frac{\partial F}{\partial q_l'}, \qquad H' = H + \frac{\partial F}{\partial t}. \qquad (47)$$

In these equations, with $F$ given arbitrarily but then known, it is possible to solve the first $3N$ equations with respect to the $q_l'$ and, thus, to obtain them as functions of the old coordinates and the time. Then the next $3N$ equations determine the $p_l'$, and the last equation furnishes the new Hamiltonian $H'$. If the function $F$ is independent of time, then the Hamiltonian is invariant with respect to that transformation.

The arbitrary function $F$ is often referred to as the *generating function* of the canonical transformation (44).

Sometimes the generating function is chosen as a function of the $q_k$, $p_l'$, and $t$. In that case, the condition (45) must be replaced by the equation

$$\sum_{k=1}^{3N} p_k \dot{q}_k - H = -\sum_{l=1}^{3N} q_l' \dot{p}_l' - H' + \frac{dG(q_k, p_l', t)}{dt}, \qquad (48)$$

in which the new function $G$ is related to $F$ by the equation

$$G(q_k, p_l', t) = F(q_k, p_l', t) + \sum_{l=1}^{3N} q_l' p_l'. \qquad (49)$$

$G$ is, of course, also a suitable generating function. The resulting equations, taking the place of the conditions (47), are

$$p_k = \frac{\partial G}{\partial q_k}, \qquad q_l' = \frac{\partial G}{\partial p_l'}, \qquad H' = H + \frac{\partial G}{\partial t}. \qquad (50)$$

To obtain the transformation equations (44), it is necessary to solve the first $3N$ equations with respect to the $p_l'$; the remaining equations then determine the $q_l'$ and also $H'$.

## 2.4. Hamilton-Jacobi partial differential equation

Cyclic coordinates. Frequently it happens that in the expression for the Hamiltonian, $H(q_k, p_k, t)$, certain of the $q$-coordinates do not appear at all. For instance, in the case of a central force, when the potential energy of a particle depends only on $r$ (in spherical coordinates), then one of the angles, $\phi$, will not enter into the expression for the energy of the system. In such a case, the canonically conjugate momentum will possess a zero time derivative,

$$\frac{dp_k}{dt} = - \frac{\partial H}{\partial q_k} = 0. \tag{51}$$

In other words, that momentum will be constant along a mechanical path; it will be a *constant* or *integral of the motion*. In the case of central motion, the vanishing of the time derivative of $p_\phi$ implies simply that the angular momentum about the $z$-axis is constant. Since the azimuth angle furnishes one of the most important examples of "invisible" coordinates, such coordinates (that is, coordinates that do not occur in the expression for the Hamiltonian) are called *cyclic coordinates*.

Suppose now that we should attempt to introduce cyclic coordinates by means of a canonical transformation, in fact, that we should try to make all coordinates cyclic. Then all the conjugate momenta would have to be constants of the motion,

$$p'_l = a_l, \tag{52}$$

where the $a_l$ are $3N$ constants. In addition, it is possible to require that the new Hamiltonian, $H'$, vanish, by appropriately disposing of the time dependence of the function which generates the canonical transformation. Without proving at the moment that it is possible to carry out such a transformation, we shall assume that such transformations exist, and we shall formulate the conditions which must be satisfied by them.

The generating function $G$ which was introduced at the end of Section 2.3 would then be a function of $q_k$, $a_l$, and $t$, where the $a_l$ would not change in the course of time along a particular mechanical path. Since

$$p_k = \frac{\partial G}{\partial q_k}, \qquad H = - \frac{\partial G}{\partial t}, \tag{53}$$

in accordance with eq. (50), the function $G(q_k, a_l, t)$ must satisfy the partial differential equation

$$H\left( q_k, \frac{\partial G}{\partial q_k}, t \right) + \frac{\partial G}{\partial t} = 0. \tag{54}$$

This equation is known as the *Hamilton-Jacobi partial differential equation*. It contains partial derivatives of $G$ only with respect to the $q_k$ and $t$, not with respect to any of the new coordinates $a_l$, $q'_l$. If we could find a solution of eq. (54) which contains $3N$ constants of integration, these could be considered as the $a_l$, and the conjugate $q'_l$ could be found by means of the equations

$$q'_l = \frac{\partial G}{\partial a_l}. \tag{55}$$

Their time derivatives would be given by the expressions

$$\dot{q}'_l = \frac{\partial H'}{\partial a_l} = 0. \tag{56}$$

In other words, if all $q'_l$ are cyclic, their time derivatives vanish as well, and they are constants of the motion. If we can express the old $q_k$ and $p_k$ in terms of the new canonical variables, a task that is essentially solved if we have found an appropriate function $G(q_k, a_l, t)$, the integration of the equations of motion has been accomplished. Our task has been reduced to the finding of a solution of eq. (54), plus a series of algebraic manipulations. ("Algebraic" in this sense means operations not involving integrations.) Unfortunately, in most practical cases, it is just as difficult to find a solution of eq. (54) as it is to integrate the equations of motion directly. Nevertheless, the Hamilton-Jacobi equation is of great significance, in that it provides an important connecting link between classical and wave mechanics. We shall, therefore, devote the remainder of this chapter to a discussion of its relationship to the equations of motion.

**Generation of mechanical trajectories.** Suppose we consider eq. (54) on its own merits and consider it as a partial differential equation which has some relationship to a mechanical system with the Hamiltonian function $H(q_k, p_k, t)$. That is, we shall no longer refer to canonical transformations, but rather consider the relationship between solutions of the Hamilton-Jacobi equation to mechanical trajectories directly. Since we are now no more interested in the role of $G$ as a generating function, we shall also change its name and call it the "action function" $S$, which satisfies the equation

$$H\left(q_k, \frac{\partial S}{\partial q_k}, t\right) + \frac{\partial S}{\partial t} = 0, \tag{57}$$
$$S = S(q_k, t).$$

In this formulation, the constant parameters $a_l$ no longer appear.

First of all, we shall prove that *any solution of eq. (57) generates a field of mechanical trajectories which satisfy the equations of motion and which cover the configuration space* so that through each point of configuration space passes at each instant of time one and only one trajectory of the set. The significance of this statement is as follows: We can, for each set of values of the $q_k$ and $t$, determine a set of $3N$ values of the $\dot{q}_k$, so that a field of velocities is defined in configuration space. This field determines, of course, a set of trajectories which covers the configuration space in the sense defined above. We can then prove that, on the basis of our determination of the field of the $\dot{q}_k$, these trajectories satisfy the equations of motion.

We determine the $\dot{q}_k$ by the $3N$ equations

$$\dot{q}_k = \frac{\partial H}{\partial \left(\dfrac{\partial S}{\partial q_k}\right)}, \tag{58}$$

where the partial derivatives on the right-hand side are to be taken in the sense that $H$ is a function of the $(6N + 1)$ independent arguments $q_k$, $\partial S/\partial q_k$, $t$. This definition of the $\dot{q}_k$ has been chosen in accordance with the second half of the canonical equations of motion (28). We must now show that the first half of the equations of motion is also satisfied. To this end, we compute the change of the momenta in the course of time along the generated trajectories. The momenta themselves, which are known algebraic expressions of the $\dot{q}_k$ and the $q_k$, must equal the partial derivatives of $S$ with respect to the $q_k$, because of eqs. (58) and the second half of (28), which latter are the solutions of the defining equations (20). In other words, we have

$$p_k = \frac{\partial S}{\partial q_k}, \tag{59}$$

because of our equations (58). The rate of change of these expressions with time along a generated trajectory is given by

$$\dot{p}_k = \frac{d}{dt}\left(\frac{\partial S}{\partial q_k}\right) = \sum_l \frac{\partial^2 S}{\partial q_k\, \partial q_l}\, \dot{q}_l + \frac{\partial^2 S}{\partial q_k\, \partial t}. \tag{60}$$

We shall now make use of the fact that $S$ is a solution of eq. (57)

and set the last term equal to

$$\frac{\partial^2 S}{\partial q_k \, \partial t} = -\frac{\partial H(q_l, t)}{\partial q_k}. \tag{61}$$

The derivative on the right-hand side must be understood in the same sense as those on the left-hand side; that is to say, the independent variables are $q_k$ and $t$. On the other hand, $H$ is originally defined as a function of $q_k$, $\partial S/\partial q_k$, and $t$, where the partials, as a matter of fact, are in turn functions of $q_k$ and $t$. We shall, therefore, re-express the partial derivatives on the right-hand side of eq. (61) in terms of the partial derivatives of $H(q_k, \partial S/\partial q_k, t)$.

$$\frac{\partial H(q_l, t)}{\partial q_k} = \frac{\partial H\left(q_l, \dfrac{\partial S}{\partial q_l}, t\right)}{\partial q_k} + \sum_l \frac{\partial H}{\partial\left(\dfrac{\partial S}{\partial q_l}\right)} \frac{\partial^2 S}{\partial q_l \, \partial q_k}. \tag{62}$$

If we now substitute this expression into eq. (60), we find that, because of eq. (58), the remaining second derivatives of $S$ cancel and $\dot{p}_k$ is given by the expression

$$\dot{p}_k = -\frac{\partial H\left(q_l, \dfrac{\partial S}{\partial q_l}, t\right)}{\partial q_k}, \tag{63}$$

which is the first half of the equations of motion (28). Thus, our original assertion is proven, and the generated trajectories really obey the equations of motion.

**Construction of a field of trajectories.** We shall now turn to the converse question and ask under what circumstances a field of mechanical trajectories defines a function $S$ which will obey the Hamilton-Jacobi eq. (57). We shall prove that *it is always possible to construct such a field of mechanical trajectories which contains any one arbitrarily chosen mechanical trajectory*. On the other hand, it is not true that just any field of mechanical trajectories which covers the configuration space defines an action function $S$. In general a field of $p_k (q_l)$ at some initial time $t_0$, when the momenta may be chosen freely, cannot be represented as the partial derivatives (with respect to $q_k$) of any "potential function" $S$. Such a possibility of representation imposes stringent requirements on the functional dependence of the $p_k$ on their arguments.

When is it possible to find a function $S$ at the time $t_0$ of which a field of $p_k(q_l)$ are the partial derivatives? The necessary and sufficient condition is that any integral of the form

$$\oint \sum_k p_k \, dq_k = 0, \tag{64}$$

taken over an arbitrary closed path in configuration space at the fixed time $t_0$, vanish.[1] The condition (64) is *necessary*. For if at the time $t_0$ eq. (59) is satisfied, the integrand of eq. (64) is an exact differential, namely $dS$, so that an open-path integral

$$\int_{\frac{1}{q_k}}^{\frac{2}{q_k}} \sum_k p_k \, dq_k = S(\overset{2}{q}_k) - S(\overset{1}{q}_k) \equiv \Delta S \tag{65}$$

equals the difference of $S$ at the two end points of the path of integration. If the two end points coincide—if the path of integration is closed—then this difference $\Delta S$ must vanish. At the same time, the condition (64) is *sufficient*, because if it is satisfied, we can find a function $S$ of which the momenta are the partial derivatives, by giving the function $S$ at a point $\bar{q}_k$ the value

$$S(\bar{q}_k) = \overset{0}{S} + \int_{\overset{0}{q_k}}^{\bar{q}_k} \sum_k p_k \, dq_k. \tag{66}$$

Here the point $\overset{0}{q}_k$ is a fixed point of reference, for instance the point on the one arbitrarily chosen mechanical trajectory occupied at the time $t_0$, and $\overset{0}{S}$ is the value of $S$ at the point $\overset{0}{q}_k$. This initial value $\overset{0}{S}$ can be chosen at will even after the choice of the point $\overset{0}{q}_k$ has been made. The path of integration is any path connecting the two indicated end points, and the value of the integral is independent of the particular choice of the connecting path, because of eq. (59).

Now that we know that the condition (64) is both necessary and sufficient for the existence of the function $S$ at the time $t_0$, we can easily construct a proper field of $p_k(q_k)$ which at the point $\overset{0}{q}_k$ has

---

[1] The symbol $\oint$ is generally used in connection with path integrals to express the fact that the path is closed, or in connection with surface integrals also to express the fact that the surface of integration is a closed surface.

certain preassigned values $\overset{0}{p_k}$. (It is the $6N$ constants $\overset{0}{q_k}$, $\overset{0}{p_k}$ which characterize the one path which was initially chosen at will and about which we wish to construct our field of paths.) All we need to do is to pick any function $S_0(q_k)$ the partial derivatives of which assume the values $\overset{0}{p_k}$ at the point with the coordinates $\overset{0}{q_k}$. The $p_k$ elsewhere are the partial derivatives of this function $S_0$. Obviously, the variety of choice of appropriate fields, although not completely unrestricted, is still enormous.

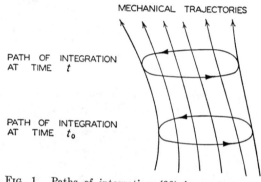

FIG. 1.    Paths of integration (66) in configuration
space at two different times.

Suppose, then, that we have constructed a field of paths the momenta of which at an initial time $t_0$ satisfy the condition (64). Will they continue to satisfy this condition in the course of time? This question can be answered in the affirmative, on the basis of a much more general relationship. For an *arbitrary* covering field of mechanical trajectories [not necessarily satisfying (64)], it is true that a closed-path integral

$$A = \oint \sum_k p_k \, dq_k, \qquad (67)$$

taken at a time $t_0$, will retain its value $A$ constant if each point on the path of integration is displaced along its mechanical trajectory to the proper location at a time $t$ and the integral (67) taken at that time (Fig. 1). To examine the change of the integral under the influence of such a displacement in configuration space and in time, we shall introduce a parameter, say $\lambda$, along the path of integration, so that

$$A = \oint \sum_k p_k \, q_k' \, d\lambda, \qquad q_k' = \frac{\partial q_k(\lambda, t)}{\partial \lambda}. \tag{68}$$

In the displacement, we shall arrange matters so that the parameter $\lambda$ retains its value along each mechanical trajectory. The rate of change of the integrand, $\sum_k p_k \, q_k'$, is then given by the expression

$$\frac{d}{dt}\left(\sum_k p_k \, q_k'\right) = \sum_k \dot{p}_k \, q_k' + \sum_k p_k \frac{\partial q_k'}{\partial t}, \tag{69}$$

in which we may make the further transformation

$$\frac{\partial q_k'}{\partial t} = \frac{\partial \dot{q}_k}{\partial \lambda}. \tag{70}$$

If we now use Lagrange's equations of motion in the form (26) and if we replace $p_k$ by the defining equation (20), we find that

$$\frac{d}{dt}\left(\sum_k p_k \, q_k'\right) = \sum_k \frac{\partial L}{\partial q_k} \frac{\partial q_k}{\partial \lambda} + \sum_k \frac{\partial L}{\partial \dot{q}_k} \frac{\partial \dot{q}_k}{\partial \lambda} = \frac{\partial L}{\partial \lambda}. \tag{71}$$

The expression on the right-hand side represents the change of the Lagrangian $L$ along the path of integration. We find that the change of $A$ with time,

$$\frac{dA}{dt} = \oint \frac{\partial}{\partial t}\left(\sum_k p_k \, q_k'\right) d\lambda = \oint \frac{\partial L}{\partial \lambda} \, d\lambda = 0, \tag{72}$$

vanishes. If *all* closed-path integrals satisfy the condition (64) initially, they will continue to do so, and it will be possible to find some function $S^*(q_k, t)$ which has the property that the $p_k(q_l, t)$ of the mechanical trajectories, chosen with appropriate initial conditions at the time $t_0$, are the partial derivatives. Moreover, it is possible to assign to $S^*$ arbitrary values along the originally chosen trajectory, since, at every time $t$, $S^*$ is determined by eq. (66) only up to an arbitrary constant. Thus, $S^*$ is determined by our field of curves only up to an arbitrary function of $t$; if the $p_k$ are the partial derivatives of a function $S^*$, they will also be the partial derivatives of another function $S^{**}$,

$$S^{**} = S^* + f(t), \tag{73}$$

where $f(t)$ is that arbitrary function of $t$. We shall now make use of this arbitrariness to find a particular function $S^*$ which satisfies eq. (57).

**Determination of S.** Let us substitute a function $S^*(q_k, t)$ into the left-hand side of the Hamilton-Jacobi equation (57) and determine to which extent it fails to satisfy that equation. We find that the right-hand side, instead of being zero, equals

$$R(q_k, t) = H\left(q_k, \frac{\partial S^*}{\partial q_k}, t\right) + \frac{\partial S^*}{\partial t}. \tag{74}$$

The right-hand side, though not zero, possesses another property: it is a function of $t$ only and independent of the coordinates of our configuration space, the $q_k$. For proof, we can form the partial derivatives $\partial R/\partial q_k$. We find for them the expressions

$$\frac{\partial R(q_l, t)}{\partial q_k} = \frac{\partial^2 S^*}{\partial t\, \partial q_k} + \frac{\partial H}{\partial q_k} + \sum_{l=1}^{3N} \frac{\partial H}{\partial\left(\dfrac{\partial S^*}{\partial q_l}\right)} \frac{\partial^2 S^*}{\partial q_l\, \partial q_k}. \tag{75}$$

But since the mechanical trajectories and the function $S^*$ have been chosen so that

$$\frac{\partial S^*}{\partial q_k} = p_k \tag{76}$$

and so that, because of the canonical equations (28),

$$\frac{\partial H}{\partial\left(\dfrac{\partial S^*}{\partial q_l}\right)} = \frac{\partial H}{\partial p_l} = \dot{q}_l, \tag{77}$$

eq. (75) may be given the form

$$\frac{\partial R}{\partial q_k} = \frac{\partial p_k(q_l, t)}{\partial t} - \dot{p}_k + \sum_{l=1}^{3N} \dot{q}_l \frac{\partial p_k}{\partial q_l}. \tag{78}$$

In this expression we encounter both the expression $\partial p_k/\partial t$ and the expression $\dot{p}_k$; the two are not equivalent. The dot designates the change of $p_k$ in time as we proceed along a mechanical trajectory. The partial derivative, on the other hand, equals the change of $p_k$ in time if we remain at the same point (with the coordinates $q_k$)

in configuration space. The two quantities are related to each other by the formula

$$\dot{p}_k \equiv \frac{\partial p_k}{\partial t} + \sum_{l=1}^{3N} \frac{\partial p_k}{\partial q_l}\, \dot{q}_l. \tag{79}$$

The last term takes account of the displacement which a point traveling along a mechanical trajectory experiences during the time interval $dt$; it represents the resulting change in $p_k$ which must be added to the local change in order to obtain the total change.

Comparison of eq. (79) with (78) shows that the partial derivative of $R$ with respect to $q_k$ really vanishes. This property enables us to cause $R$ to vanish by means of an appropriate transformation (73). If we replace $S^*$ by $S^{**}$, the partial derivatives with respect to $q_k$ remain unchanged, and $H$ will remain unchanged as a result. The new value of $R$ will be

$$\bar{R} = H + \frac{\partial S^{**}}{\partial t} = R + \frac{df}{dt}. \tag{80}$$

The choice of the function $f(t)$ is arbitrary. If we choose it in particular to be

$$f(t) = -\int_{t_0}^{t} R(\tau)\, d\tau, \tag{81}$$

which is possible because $R$ is a function of $t$ only, then $\bar{R}$ will vanish. Thus, we have completed the construction of a function $S(q_k, t)$ which satisfies all requirements: it satisfies the Hamilton-Jacobi equation, and its partial derivatives with respect to $q_k$ are the generalized momenta of a field of mechanical trajectories which includes the one trajectory which was chosen at the beginning.

To summarize: any particular solution of the Hamilton-Jacobi partial differential equation generates a set of trajectories that satisfy the equations of motion. On the other hand, given a single arbitrary mechanical trajectory, it is possible to construct fields of trajectories containing the one chosen originally which belong to a function $S$ satisfying the Hamilton-Jacobi equation. In this sense, the totality of all solutions of the Hamilton-Jacobi equation is equivalent to the totality of all mechanical trajectories satisfying a given set of equations of motion (as represented by its Hamiltonian). Finally, along any single trajectory the function $S$

is the value of that integral which is stationary with respect to virtual displacements.[1]

It is worth remarking that whereas the totality of all solutions of eq. (57) is equivalent to the totality of all solutions of eqs. (28), there is no one-to-one correspondence between particular solutions. On the contrary, every particular solution of the Hamilton-Jacobi equation generates a whole set of trajectories. On the other hand, each single trajectory which satisfies the canonical equations of motion is generated by an infinite number of different solutions of the Hamilton-Jacobi equation.

## Problems

**2.1.** Derive the Euler-Lagrange equations of motion for a single particle in spherical coordinates, on the special assumption that the potential energy is a function of $r$ only, $V(r)$. Physically, this condition represents the case in which a center of attraction or repulsion is permanently located at a particular point, which has been chosen as the origin of the coordinate system.

Compare the Euler-Lagrange equations with the equations which are obtained if the equations of motion are first written down in Cartesian coordinates $x$, $y$, $z$ and then transformed term by term into equations for spherical coordinates.

**2.2.** Integrate the Euler-Lagrange equations of the preceding problem step by step, showing first that the angular momentum about the pole axis is a constant and then that the square of the total angular momentum remains constant. The equations can be reduced to the point where only the radial equation remains to be solved.

The radial equation can also be integrated for special cases.

(a) Assume that the potential energy $V$ is inversely proportional to the distance $r$. $V = c/r$ is the potential energy belonging to the inverse-square field. Your results should agree with those obtained in Chapter 1.

(b) Set the potential energy equal to $\frac{k}{2} r^2$. This expression for $V$ corresponds to an attractive force which is proportional to the distance from the center (harmonic oscillator). The trajectories are found to be ellipses,

---

[1] In analogy to eq. (79), the time derivative of $S$ along a trajectory is

$$\dot{S} = \frac{\partial S}{\partial t} + \sum_{l=1}^{3N} \frac{\partial S}{\partial q_l} \, \dot{q}_l = -H + \sum_{l=1}^{3N} p_l \dot{q}_l = L.$$

It follows that

$$S = \int L \, dt,$$

provided that the path of integration is a mechanical trajectory.

with the origin at the center. The time of revolution is independent of the dimensions of the ellipse.

**2.3.** Obtain expressions for the generalized momenta of a single particle in spherical coordinates. Identify the angular momentum about the polar axis and the squared total angular momentum. Finally set up the expression for the Hamiltonian in spherical coordinates and obtain the canonical equations of motion, assuming that the field of force has spherical symmetry (is a central force field).

**2.4.** Repeat the steps of the preceding problem for different types of coordinate system, such as cylinder coordinates, confocal elliptic, and confocal parabolic coordinates.

**2.5.** Integrate the canonical equations of motion in spherical coordinates for the inverse-square force field and compare the steps of your integration procedure with those required in Problem 2.2(a).

**2.6.** Set up the Hamilton-Jacobi partial differential equation for a single particle in spherical coordinates for the central force field. This equation can be solved, or its solution can at least be reduced to quadratures, if $S$ is chosen as the sum of four terms of which each is a function of one argument only, $t$, $r$, and the two angles.

Having obtained such a special solution, examine the field of trajectories generated.

**2.7.** Solve the Hamilton-Jacobi equation for the inverse square field, once in spherical coordinates and once in confocal parabolic coordinates (plus an azimuth angle). In both coordinate systems, the problem can be solved by the separation of variables. Compare the fields of trajectories generated by these two different types of solutions.

**2.8.** Examine the canonical transformation which is generated by means of the generating function

$$F(q_k, q_l', t) = \sum_k q_k q_k'. \tag{82}$$

This particular transformation is known in quantum mechanics as the *transition to momentum space*.

Set up the Hamilton-Jacobi equation in terms of the new coordinates $q_k'$. The space of the $q_k'$ is known as *momentum space*. Solve completely the problem of the one-dimensional harmonic oscillator in terms of these new coordinates.

# Chapter 3
# Matter in Bulk

In the development of modern physics, the treatment of matter in bulk plays a peculiar role. Naturally, most of the matter with which the physicist comes in contact in his laboratory consists of very large numbers of molecules, atoms, or elementary particles. To apply to such complex systems the formalisms developed in the first two chapters is out of the question, since the number of differential equations to be solved simultaneously would be overwhelming. Nevertheless, we are not completely helpless in the face of large accumulations of mass points.

The reader will recall the form of the conservation laws. The motion of the center of mass of any mechanical system is determined by the external forces. So are changes in angular momentum and in energy. If we define appropriately a number of average or bulk properties, we can make at least partial predictions concerning the behavior of bulk matter. This idea has been followed up in a number of directions. If matter is considered in bulk, we can discern at every point in its interior a prevalent state of motion, its *local (average) velocity*. This velocity field determines, as we shall see, the changes in *density* which result from the streaming along of the particles. Individual particles, however, may possess velocities which differ widely from the local velocity; these deviations are called *random motion*. The kinetic energy of matter consists additively of a term which depends only on the local velocity and one which involves only the random motion. All those laws in whose formulation the random motion enters only through its contribution to the kinetic energy can be summarized as the laws of *mechanics* of matter in bulk, whereas the treatment of the random motion itself and the laws governing it leads to the theory of *heat*.

In this chapter, we shall restrict ourselves to the development of the *mechanical* laws. Depending on the type of interaction which the particles exert on each other, matter is classified as *solid* or *fluid;* the latter term includes the liquid and the gaseous state of matter. Strictly speaking, there is no sharp dividing line between the solids and the fluids. Although a solid is defined as matter which on deformation will produce internal stresses that tend to restore its original shape, and a fluid is defined as matter which has no resistance to changes in shape (provided that they take place sufficiently slowly), all solids are actually subject to *plastic flow* if subjected to sufficient stress for a sufficiently long time, and many fluids will exhibit "springiness" when the applied stress acts only for a short time. But since actual matter frequently approaches the properties which are by definition those of solids or fluids, respectively, these two concepts are very useful, in spite of their obvious limitations. The mechanics of solids is known as *elastomechanics*, the mechanics of fluids as *fluid dynamics*.

### 3.1. Density and local velocity

Before we can begin to work out the laws of mechanics in the form in which they can be applied to bulk matter, we must introduce the average quantities which have already been mentioned, the density and the local velocity.

Let us start with the density $\rho$. Everybody knows that density is defined as mass per unit volume. But how shall we choose the volume in which the mass will be determined? If we have an appreciably homogeneous, fairly sizable chunk of some material such as pure gold in the solid state, we can determine, with great accuracy, the number of grams of gold contained in one cm³ under standard conditions. If we now subdivide the original gold bar into smaller and smaller fragments, the density will remain sensibly constant up to a certain order of magnitude, of the order of $10^3$ Å³. When we reach this limit, by considering minute colloidal particles of gold, the density will gradually become subject to fluctuations until it loses all significance for amounts of gold comprising only very few atoms. In other words, the density of gold, $\rho_{Au}$, has significance only for sufficiently large crystallized amounts of the material.

On the other hand, if we consider a highly turbulent mass of air, we know that its density is by no means constant throughout the space region filled by this air mass; $\rho$ is a function of both the spatial coordinates and the time, dependent on the instantaneous local values of temperature and pressure. To obtain reasonably meaningful values for the local density, the ratio of mass to volume must be formed for regions which are neither too large nor too small (the dimensions must be small compared to distances over which the density changes measurably, but large compared to the average distance between closest molecules). Whether there are regions that satisfy both of these bounding conditions depends, of course, on the special nature of the case under consideration. There are cases of a practical nature where no such regions exist, as in the immediate vicinity of so-called shock waves. But ordinarily, regions of the right order of magnitude to satisfy both conditions can in fact be found. In that case, it is possible to describe the forces acting in the interior of the matter, the distribution of mass points and their state of motion, by appropriate average quantities.

As for the average local velocity, we shall define it as the ratio between the total linear momentum and the total mass of all the particles inside an appropriately chosen volume. The choice of the volume is governed by the same considerations as in the case of the density. If the volume is too small, the average is subject to large fluctuations; if too large, it may average over regions in which the prevalent state of motion is markedly different. In dividing the total linear momentum through by the total mass, we average, in effect, the velocities of all the particles inside, but so that the contribution of each particle to the average is weighted by its mass. Thus, if we consider a piece of electric wire through which an electric current is passing, the contribution of the rapidly moving electrons to the local velocity is small, even though their average velocity is considerable: their mass is a very small proportion of the mass of the wire as a whole.

We have indicated that the velocity of an individual particle may differ considerably from the average local velocity. If we have occasion to consider the random motion, we shall designate the deviation of the particle velocity from the average total velocity by the symbol $\mathbf{u}$. If we sum the total linear momentum of all the particles in a "suitable" volume (suitable for the taking of averages as discussed above), we obtain the expression

$$\mathbf{P} = \Sigma m(\mathbf{v} + \mathbf{u}) = \mathbf{v} \, \Sigma m. \qquad (1)$$

The right-hand side merely follows from the definition of average local velocity.   By canceling the identical expressions left and right, we find that the (weighted) average of the random velocities vanishes, a result which we shall use repeatedly.

### 3.2. The stress tensor

In Chapter 1, we established the notions of internal and external forces acting on the member mass points of a nonisolated mechanical system.   We found that the rate of change of the total linear momentum $P_i$ of a system depends on the external forces only and is independent of the internal forces.   Let us now consider an arbitrary region $V$ in the interior of matter in bulk. Call its surface $S$ and designate as a mechanical system the set of mass points inside $S$ (that is, in $V$) at the time $t$ (see Fig. 2).

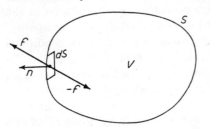

FIG. 2.   The volume $V$ and the forces across its surface $S$.

The external forces acting on the points inside $S$ are then those forces which the molecules outside $S$ exert on those molecules inside $S$. We shall now assume that molecules will exert forces of appreciable magnitude on each other only if they are quite close to each other, say within 10 Å for a solid or liquid.   With this assumption, it will be possible to describe the total external force acting on the matter in $V$ by means of a surface integral,

$$F_i^* = - \oiint_S f_i \, dS, \tag{2}$$

where $-f_i$ is the force per unit area which the molecules on the outside of the surface element $dS$ exert on those inside.   Because of Newton's third law, $f_i$ will then be the force per unit area which the molecules on the inside of $dS$ will exert on the molecules outside. The values of the components $f_i$ depend, of course, on the location of the surface element $dS$, and also on its orientation, which we shall always characterize by means of the unit normal **n** pointing away from the interior of $V$.

We shall now study the dependence of $f_i$ at a given location on the direction of the normal of the surface element $dS$, $n_i$.   Incidentally, $n_i$ is defined as a unit vector, so that its components satisfy the relationship

$$\sum_i n_i^2 = 1. \tag{3}$$

In fact, $n_i$ is nothing but the cosine of the angle between the normal direction and the $x_i$-axis. In order to approach our problem, we shall examine the immediate vicinity of $dS$ and study the intermolecular forces across the plane $Q$, which is tangential to $S$ at the location $dS$ (see Fig. 3).

We shall take a piece of the plane $Q$ having the total area $A$ and then enclose this piece in a closed surface $R$ which includes enough of the region on both sides of $Q$ that almost all of the force across

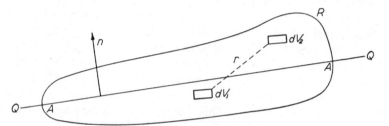

Fig. 3.　Forces across the plane $Q$.

the piece $A$ of $Q$ is due to molecules inside $R$. The total force across shall be called $F_i$. It is the sum of all the forces which molecules below $Q$ exert on molecules above $Q$.

To obtain an expression for $F_i$, we shall consider the force which the molecules inside a volume element $dV_1$ below $Q$ exert on the molecules inside another volume element $dV_2$ which lies above $Q$. This force will depend on the locations of the two volume elements involved, and it will be proportional to the magnitudes of both. Its direction must be in the connecting straight line. If we call the coordinates of the two volume elements $x_i$ and $x_i$, respectively,
$\phantom{xxxxxxxxxxxxxxxxxxxxxxxxxxxxxxxxxxxxxxxxxxxxxxxxxxxxxxxxx}_1\phantom{xxxxx}_2$
then the infinitesimal force contributed by their interaction is given by an expression having the form

$$d^6F_i = \phi(x_k, x_k) \frac{x_i - x_i}{r} dV_1 dV_2,$$
$$r^2 = \sum_i (x_i - x_i)^2 \tag{4}$$

Because of Newton's third law, the function $\phi$ will not change its value if the arguments $x_i$ and $x_i$ are interchanged; the force exerted by the molecules in $dV_1$ must be equal to $-d^6F_i$, and the change in sign is accomplished by the change in the direction cosine, $(x_i - x_i)/r$. It will now be necessary to integrate this force over all $dV_1$ lying inside $R$ below $Q$ and over all $dV_2$ lying inside $R$ above $Q$. This task can be accomplished only if we add another assumption to those already made, an assumption which might be called the *assumption of local homogeneity*. We shall assume that within $R$ the value of the function $\phi$ depends appreciably only on the *relative* location of the two volume elements involved; in other words, while the volume elements $dV_1$ and $dV_2$ are sufficiently large that $\phi$, an average force per unit volume square, is a smooth function of the coordinates (fluctuations of this average being negligibly small), the whole region $R$ is sufficiently small that any two volume elements of the same size as $dV_1$ and $dV_2$ which have also the same relative location with respect to each other will exert very nearly the same force on each other. This assumption of local homogeneity can be expressed in the form that within $R$,

$$\phi(x_1, x_2, x_3; x_1, x_2, x_3) = \phi(x_1 - x_1, x_2 - x_2, x_3 - x_3). \tag{5}$$

With this assumption, it is now possible to carry out the necessary integrations without too much difficulty.

As the first step, it is convenient to introduce new variables of integration. We shall introduce the coordinate differences, $x_i - x_i$, as new variables,

$$x_i - x_i = \xi_i. \tag{6}$$

The expression for $d^6F_i$ then becomes

$$d^6F_i = \phi(\xi_k)\frac{\xi_i}{r}\,d\xi_1\,d\xi_2\,d\xi_3\,dx_1\,dx_2\,dx_3 \tag{7}$$
$$r^2 = \sum_i \xi_i^2$$

the $x_i$ having been eliminated. This expression must now be integrated over the range of the six coordinates $x_i, \xi_i$. If we carry out

the integration over the $x_i$ first, with some fixed triplet of $\xi_i$-values,
it is clear that the possible range is a slab of constant thickness
directly adjacent to the plane $Q$ (Fig. 4). The thickness of the
slab equals the magnitude of the vector with the components $\xi_i$,
multiplied by the cosine of its angle with the normal. The lateral
extension of the slab is $A$, and therefore its total volume equal to[1]

$$V_1 = A \sum_s \xi_s n_s. \tag{8}$$

In other words, the partial integration of the expression (7) results

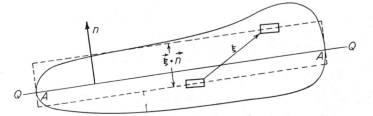

Fig. 4. Details of the integration. The dashed lines indicate the
volume of the "slab" over which the $x_i$ are to be integrated with
fixed $\xi_i$.

in the triple integral

$$F_i = A \int\!\!\int\!\!\int_{\xi_k} \phi(\xi_k) \frac{\xi_i}{r} \sum_s \xi_s n_s \, d\xi_1 \, d\xi_2 \, d\xi_3$$
$$= A \sum_s n_s \int\!\!\int\!\!\int \phi(\xi_k) \frac{\xi_i \, \xi_s}{r} \, d\xi_1 \, d\xi_2 \, d\xi_3. \tag{9}$$

The range of integration is that of all possible relative locations of
volume elements inside $R$ above to elements below $Q$. We shall
find it convenient, however, to extend the limits of integration.
If the envelope $R$ was chosen originally to include all molecules
within the reach of intermolecular forces across $Q$, then nothing will
be changed if the integration is now carried out over the whole

---

[1] The expression for the thickness, used in eq. (8), is the so-called *dot product*
of the two vectors with the components $\xi_s$ and $n_s$. Those readers who are not
familiar with the elementary aspects of vector calculus should refer at this
point to Section 3.3, which is devoted to this topic.

half space of values $(\xi_1, \xi_2, \xi_3)$ in which the angle $(\xi, \mathbf{n})$ is acute or, in other words, where the expression $\sum_s \xi_s n_s$ is positive.

After this extension of the interval of integration, we may go still one step farther. If we consider that range of values of $\xi_i$ which are at present excluded, we find that to every permissible triplet of values corresponds an excluded triplet, namely $-\xi_i$. At that excluded point, the integrand has exactly the same value, because of Newton's third law. In other words, we may carry out the integral (9) over all of $\xi$-space if we divide the result by a factor 2. We finally obtain an expression for $F_i$:

$$F_i = A \sum_k T_{ik} n_k,$$

$$T_{ik} \equiv \frac{1}{2} \int\int\int_{\xi_1, \xi_2, \xi_3 = -\infty}^{\infty} \frac{\phi(\xi_s)}{r} \xi_i \xi_k \, d\xi_1 \, d\xi_2 \, d\xi_3. \tag{10}$$

The force per unit area of $R$, $f_i$, is given by the expression

$$f_i = \frac{F_i}{A} = \sum_k T_{ik} n_k. \tag{11}$$

In this form, the dependence of $f_i$ on the orientation is explicit. The expressions $T_{ik}$ are completely independent of the orientation, merely functions of the location of $dS$. They have the further property of being symmetric in the subscripts $i$ and $k$,

$$T_{ik} = T_{ki}, \tag{12}$$

as is evident from eq. (10).

If the expression (11) is substituted in eq. (2), we finally obtain for the total external force acting on the system of molecules inside $S$ the integral

$$F_i^* = - \oiint_S \sum_k T_{ik} n_k \, dS. \tag{13}$$

### 3.3. Vector and tensor calculus

In the preceding section, we have made use of a typical formation of vector calculus, the dot (or scalar) product. Although we could develop many of the formulas in what follows practically without reference to vector methods, knowledge of the theory of vectors and tensors is an enormous help in penetrating rather lengthy derivations. The reason is simple. Physics is a science dealing with the laws of nature in a three-dimensional space. Almost all the laws of physics relate changes in time with distributions in space. For instance, the force law relates the acceleration of a single member of a mechanical system to the distribution in space of the system as a whole. In the first chapter, we have found that among all conceivable systems of coordinates in which we might describe happenings in space and time, there is a special set, called *inertial systems*, in which the laws of mechanics are particularly simple, that is, in which they assume the standard form. At that time, we did not discuss whether there might be more than one inertial system, and if there were several, what relationship they would have to each other. The fact is that, given one inertial system, we can construct an infinity of others; with respect to every one of them a body which is not subject to external forces will move without acceleration. Starting with one inertial system, we can obtain additional ones by choosing (Cartesian) coordinate systems whose origin moves uniformly (straight and without acceleration) in terms of the first system and whose axes have constant orientation with respect to the original axes. By this method, we can obtain *all* inertial systems in existence.

For a statement of the general laws of nature, all the inertial systems should be equally suitable. That is, those laws of nature which for their mathematical formulation require the introduction of a coordinate system (because they deal with locations, velocities, and accelerations) should assume the same form no matter which of the infinitely many inertial systems is used in the formulation. This is indeed the case. The three laws of Newton assume the same form in every inertial system. If we carry out a transition from one coordinate system to another, a so-called *Galilean coordinate transformation*, then the mathematical equations (1.2), (1.5) with (1.6), and (1.11), are recovered without change. We say that these laws and the equations expressing them are *covariant* with respect to Galilean transformations. The term *invariant* is also used with the same meaning.

Covariance of the three laws of Newton with respect to Galilean transformations is not the only type of covariance we have encountered so far. In Chapter 2, we discussed the equations of motion in generalized coordinates. By introducing the notion of configuration space, we found that the Euler-Lagrange equations assume

the same form in terms of any and all generalized coordinates $q_k$.
The equations of motion in the Euler-Lagrange form are covariant
with respect to arbitrary (nonsingular) coordinate transformations
in configuration space. Finally, the canonical equations (2.28) are
covariant with respect to the canonical coordinate transformations
(2.45), in phase space.

Vector and tensor calculus is concerned with the covariance of
mathematical relationships with respect to a much more restricted
group of coordinate transformations in ordinary space, namely,
those leading from one Cartesian coordinate system to another
without involving the time; these transformations are usually
called *orthogonal transformations*. Since orthogonal transformations
lead from one inertial system to another and thus form a small fraction of the Galilean transformations, the general laws of nature
must also be covariant with respect to orthogonal transformations;
though necessary, this condition is in general not sufficient.

**Transformation law of vectors.** The relative location of two
fixed points provides a convenient starting point. If with respect
to some Cartesian system their coordinates are designated by $\underset{1}{x_i}$
for the one point and by $\underset{2}{x_i}$ for the other, the three differences
between corresponding coordinates,

$$\Delta x_i = \underset{2}{x_i} - \underset{1}{x_i}, \tag{14}$$

provide complete information concerning the spatial relationship
between the two points. Their distance $\Delta s$ is given by the expression

$$\Delta s^2 = \sum_i \Delta x_i^2, \tag{15}$$

and the three expressions $(\Delta x_i/\Delta s)$ are the cosines of the angles which
the straight line connecting the two points forms with the three
coordinate axes.

Let us now introduce another Cartesian coordinate system,
designated, let us say, by coordinates $y_k$. The coordinate values
of any point in space in terms of the new system are linear functions
of the coordinate values in terms of the original system,

$$y_k = \overset{0}{y_k} + \sum_{i=1}^{3} c_{ki} x_i. \tag{16}$$

The constants $\overset{0}{y_k}$ are the $y$-coordinate values of the origin of the $x$-system; each of the nine constant coefficients $c_{ki}$ is the cosine of an angle between the appropriate $y_k$- and $x_i$-axes. As for coordinate differences, such as our $\Delta x_i$, the constants $\overset{0}{y_k}$ of eq. (16) drop out of the transformation law. The new coordinate differences are not only linear but are also homogeneous functions of the old ones,

$$\Delta y_k = \sum_i c_{ki} \, \Delta x_i. \tag{17}$$

Because of the geometrical significance of the constant coefficients $c_{ki}$ as the cosines of angles between the new and the old coordinates, we have also the further relationship that the coefficients of the inverse transformation,

$$\Delta x_i = \sum_k c_{ik}^+ \, \Delta y_k, \tag{18}$$

are identical with those of the transformation (17),

$$c_{ik}^+ = c_{ki}. \tag{19}$$

From this simple fact follows a further property of the coefficients $c_{ki}$: if we substitute the expressions (18) into the right-hand side of eq. (17), we obtain a relationship which contains the $\Delta y_k$ on both the left-hand side and the right-hand side,

$$\Delta y_k = \sum_{i,l=1}^{3} c_{ki} \, c_{li} \, \Delta y_l. \tag{20}$$

This relationship can be valid for arbitrary sets of coordinate differences only if the products of coefficients $c_{ki}$ satisfy the nine equations

$$\sum_{i=1}^{3} c_{ki} \, c_{li} = \delta_{kl}, \tag{21}$$

where the symbol on the right-hand side is the so-called *Kronecker symbol* and has the significance

$$\delta_{kl} = \begin{cases} 1 & (\text{if } k = l), \\ 0 & (\text{if } k \neq l). \end{cases} \tag{22}$$

The relative position of the two points with the coordinates $x_i$ and

$x_i$ (or $y_k$ and $y_k$), respectively, provides a typical example of a
$\quad_2 \qquad_1 \qquad_2$
vector, an object which possesses both magnitude (in this case the
distance between the points) and a definite direction, independent
of the choice of a coordinate system.   Mathematically, a vector **V**
is represented by its three components $V_i$ with respect to some
chosen coordinate system.   Its components with respect to another
coordinate system, $V_k^*$ (which is, of course, likewise assumed to
be Cartesian) are connected with the first set of components by a
transformation law identical with that for coordinate differences,

$$V_k^* = \sum_i c_{ki} V_i. \tag{23}$$

The magnitude of the vector, $V$, is given by an expression analogous
to eq. (15),

$$V^2 = \sum_i V_i^2 = \sum_k V_k^{*2}. \tag{24}$$

The value of $V$ cannot depend on whether we use the components
$V_i$ or the components $V_k^*$.   This fact, which is intuitively necessary
if "magnitude of a vector" is to have the customary significance,
can be proved formally by means of the transformation equations
(23), coupled with the properties of the transformation coefficients,
(21).   For we have

$$\sum_{i=1}^{3} V_i^2 = \sum_i \left( \sum_k c_{ki} V_k^* \right)^2 = \sum_i \sum_k \sum_l c_{ki} c_{kl} V_k^* V_l^*$$
$$= \sum_k \sum_l \delta_{kl} V_k^* V_l^* = \sum_k V_k^{*2}. \tag{25}$$

In other words, the sum of the squares of the components of a
vector is invariant with respect to orthogonal coordinate transformations (16).   The individual vector components $V_i$ are not invariant,
but the set of the three may be said to be covariant in that they
transform in accordance with a definite transformation law, (23),
which permits their determination in terms of any chosen Cartesian
coordinate system if the components with respect to some one
Cartesian coordinate system are known.

Every orthogonal transformation may be thought of as the
combination of a *translation* and a *rotation*.   A *translation* is a
transformation in which the origin of the coordinate system is dis-

placed but the new coordinate axes are parallel to the old ones. In a *rotation*, on the other hand, the origins of both coordinate systems coincide, but the axes of the two coordinate systems are not parallel.

Some important quantities behave as vectors with respect to one type of orthogonal transformation but not with respect to the other. We call *radius vector* the triplet of the coordinates of any arbitrary point, $x_i$. The radius vector transforms like a vector with respect to rotations but not with respect to translations. Its magnitude (the distance of the point in question from the origin of the coordinate system) is, therefore, invariant only with respect to rotations, but it will change its value as the result of a translation.

The so-called *unit axis vectors*, **i, j,** and **k,** provide an example of a different kind. With respect to translations, they behave like vectors; with respect to rotations they do not. Although many workers like to perform vector calculations with the help of these quantities [which are defined as the three triplets of numbers (1,0,0), (0,1,0), and (0,0,1), respectively], their combinations will be covariant only if the calculations could also have been carried out without their help. Since we shall be interested very much in the transformation character of all physical relationships to be formulated, we shall avoid use of **i, j,** and **k,** and instead develop a notation in which true vectors [that is, triplets of quantities which transform in accordance with eq. (23)] are manipulated so that transformation properties are apparent at every stage.

**Covariant algebraic operations, summation convention.** What algebraic operations with vectors lead to quantities with similar simple transformation laws? There is, first of all, the multiplication of a vector by a number: if each component of a vector, $V_i$, is multiplied by the same number (invariant with respect to coordinate transformations), say $a$, then the three products $a V_i$ form the components of a new vector,

$$(a V_k^*) = \sum_i c_{ki}(a V_i). \qquad (26)$$

The magnitude of the new vector is $a$ times that of the vector **V**, a fact which is proved formally by direct substitution in the defining equation (24). Its direction is the same as that of **V**.

Next, we can obtain new vectors by adding corresponding components of two or more given vectors. If $V_i$ and $W_i$ are the components of two vectors, then the three expressions

$$T_i = V_i + W_i \qquad (27)$$

are the components of a new vector, which is called the *vector sum* of the two vectors **V** and **W**. The proof consists of explicitly computing the components $T_k^*$,

$$
\begin{aligned}
T_k^* = V_k^* + W_k^* &= \sum_i c_{ki} V_i + \sum_i c_{ki} W_i \\
&= \sum_i c_{ki}(V_i + W_i) = \sum_i c_{ki} T_i.
\end{aligned}
\qquad (28)
$$

Two vectors may be combined in a multiplicative operation known as the *dot product* or *scalar product*. If $V_i$ and $W_i$ are again the components of two vectors, then the expression

$$U = \sum_i V_i W_i = \sum_k V_k^* W_k^* \equiv \mathbf{V} \cdot \mathbf{W} \qquad (29)$$

is invariant with respect to orthogonal transformations. The proof can be carried out along the lines of eq. (25). By the choice of a suitable coordinate system (in which, for instance, one of the two vectors has only a single component), one can further show that the value of the scalar product $\mathbf{V} \cdot \mathbf{W}$ equals the product of the magnitudes of the two vectors, $V$ and $W$, multiplied by the cosine of the angle formed by the two vectors.

In order to simplify the writing of formulas in component notation, it has become customary to drop all summation symbols. Ambiguity can be avoided if it is agreed once and for all that any index which occurs twice in a product is to be understood as a summation index, but that indices which occur only once in a product (or, what is the same, once in each term of a sum) are not to be summed over. Looking over the preceding equations of this section, the reader will find that in fact every summation index occurs twice in each product and all other indices once. From now on, summation symbols will no longer be employed unless it becomes necessary to write down an equation which is not adequately covered by the above *summation convention*.

**Tensors.** Vectors and scalars are not the only types of quantities which are needed to express physical laws in three-dimensional space.  In the second section of this chapter, for instance, we found, that according to eq. (11) the force per unit area across a surface $S$, with the components $f_i$, is a linear homogeneous function of the $n_i$, the components of the surface normal.  The relationship between the two vectors $\mathbf{f}$ and $\mathbf{n}$, which in any one coordinate system is completely determined by the values of the coefficients $T_{ik}$, must be independent of the choice of coordinate system.  This condition imposes a particular law of transformation on the $T_{ik}$ themselves, which we shall now proceed to determine.  With respect to a new coordinate system, $y_k$, we must have a set of three equations

$$f_m^* = T_{mn}^* \, n_n^*, \tag{30}$$

where the new coefficients $T_{mn}^*$ must have values so that eq. (30) is equivalent to (11).  (Because of the summation convention, the index $n$ is to be summed over, even though summation is not explicitly indicated in the equation.)  If we now express the $f_m^*$ and the $n_n^*$ in terms of the unstarred components, we obtain

$$c_{mi} f_i = T_{mn}^* \, c_{nk} \, n_k \tag{31}$$

and further

$$c_{mi} T_{ik} \, n_k = T_{mn}^* \, c_{nk} \, n_k,$$
$$(c_{mi} T_{ik} - T_{mn}^* \, c_{nk}) n_k = 0, \tag{32}$$

by substituting eq. (11) on the left-hand side.  The three eqs. (32) (corresponding to $m = 1$, 2, and 3) must be satisfied for all possible normal directions $\mathbf{n}$; that is possible only if the coefficients of the components of $\mathbf{n}$ are all zero,

$$c_{mi} T_{ik} = T_{mn}^* \, c_{nk}. \tag{33}$$

These equations can now be solved with respect to the quantities $T_{mn}^*$, simply by multiplying them by $c_{sk}$ and summing over the index $k$.  The result of this operation is

$$c_{mi} c_{sk} T_{ik} = c_{nk} c_{sk} T_{mn}^* = \delta_{ns} T_{mn}^*, \tag{34}$$

because of eqs. (21).  On the right-hand side, $n$ is a summation index.  In the sum indicated, all terms but one will vanish, because of the definition of the Kronecker symbol, (22).  We get a contribution different from zero only when $n$ equals $s$, and its value is $T_{ms}$.  We find, therefore, that

$$T_{ms}^* = c_{mi} c_{sk} T_{ik} \tag{35}$$

is the transformation law for the $T_{ik}$.  It is identical with the transformation law for vectors, except that the $T_{ik}$ carry two indices and that they must be transformed with respect to each index separately. We call the $T_{ik}$ the components of a *tensor*, and define a tensor as a set of components $V_{ik}...$ with $N$ indices (called the *rank* of the tensor) which transform with respect to each tensor index like a vector; in other words,

$$V^*_{mn} = c_{mi}\, c_{nk} \cdot\, \cdot\, \cdot\, V_{ik}.... \qquad (36)$$

Although it is logical to call vectors tensors of rank one and to call scalars tensors of rank 0, the terms "vector" and "scalar" have never been completely displaced by the "systematic" designations. However, all general laws relating to tensors and tensor operations apply to vectors and scalars as well.

Just like vectors, tensors can be multiplied, component by component, by a common factor, and this operation leads to a new tensor of the same rank. Likewise, several tensors of the same rank can be added (that is, corresponding components can be added), and the sums will form a new tensor of the same rank. Finally, a tensor may be *contracted* if its rank is at least 2. Any two of its indices may be made equal and summed over, and the result will be a new tensor of a rank lower by 2; for instance, **u** with the components $u_i$,

$$u_i = u_{iss}, \qquad (37)$$

is a vector if the $u_{ikl}$ are the components of a tensor of rank 3. The proof of the tensor character of the contracted tensor follows by direct verification, using in particular eq. (21).

Given two tensors $u_{ik}...$ and $v_{mn}...$ of ranks $M$ and $N$, respectively, it is possible to construct a new tensor of rank $M + N$, by simply multiplying every component of the first tensor by every component of the second,

$$w_{ik...mn...} = u_{ik}... v_{mn}.... \qquad (38)$$

The proof of the tensor character of $w_{ik...mn...}$ is again straightforward. This multiplication may be combined in a number of ways with contraction; the dot product of two vectors is one example.

**Tensor analysis.** So far, we have considered only algebraic combinations of scalars, vectors, and tensors: the addition, the multiplication, and the contraction. Let us now turn to operations involving differentiation as well.

A tensor (or vector or scalar) may have components each of which is the function of some scalar parameter. Take, as an example, the velocity of a particle. Its three components undoubtedly form a vector. Each of the components is, furthermore, a function of the time $t$. If we differentiate each of these three functions once, then the three resulting derivatives form again a vector, the acceleration. More generally, we can formulate the principle that the derivatives of a tensor with respect to a (scalar) parameter form a new tensor of the same rank.

A much more involved situation is encountered if the components of a tensor are functions of the coordinates themselves. Such a tensor is generally known as a *tensor field*. An example of a scalar field is a temperature distribution, such as the temperature in the atmosphere. The temperature at a particular point in space is undoubtedly a scalar; the measurement certainly does not depend on the choice of coordinate system (though it does on the temperature scale employed). But the temperature has different values at different points in space, and that is what makes it a field. The local velocity $\mathbf{v}$ in a streaming fluid is, at each point, a vector. Its components (at a fixed point in the fluid) transform in accordance with eq. (23). At the same time, each of the components $v_i$ is a function of the three coordinates $x_1$, $x_2$, $x_3$, and this functional dependence makes $\mathbf{v}$ a vector field. Finally, the tensor $T_{ik}$ is a tensor field, since its components vary from point to point and are again functions of the coordinates.

A field and its components may be not only functions of the coordinates but also, at the same time, may depend on some other, scalar, parameter. In fact, most fields encountered in physics depend not only on the spatial coordinates but on the time as well. Take, as another instance of a scalar field, the local density $\rho$. In a streaming fluid, the density will not only change from point to point (at a fixed time); also, at a given point in space, it will change its value in the course of time. That is,

$$\rho = \rho(x_1, x_2, x_3, t) \equiv \rho(x_i, t). \tag{39}$$

Now the derivative $\partial\rho/\partial t$ denotes the time rate of change of the density for fixed $x_i$. Like $\rho$ itself, it is a scalar field; that is, at a particular point in space and at a particular time its value is independent of the coordinate system chosen. Not so its derivative with respect to one of the coordinates, $x_2$ for instance, $\partial\rho/\partial x_2$. This partial derivative denotes the change in $\rho$ per unit distance in the $x_2$-direction, with the time fixed. Naturally, if we go over to a new coordinate system, the significance of "the $x_2$-direction" changes, and so will the value of the partial derivative. However, the value of the derivative in the $y_2$-direction is completely determined by the *three* partial derivatives $\partial\rho/\partial x_i$, together with the direction cosines $c_{ki}$. For we have

$$\frac{\partial\rho}{\partial y_2} = \frac{\partial\rho}{\partial x_i}\frac{\partial x_i}{\partial y_2} = c_{i2}^+\frac{\partial\rho}{\partial x_i} = c_{2i}\frac{\partial\rho}{\partial x_i}, \tag{40}$$

because of eqs. (18) and (19). If we carry out that same computation for the other two partial derivatives of $\rho$, with respect to $y_1$ and $y_3$, we find that

$$\frac{\partial\rho}{\partial y_k} = c_{ki}\frac{\partial\rho}{\partial x_i}. \tag{41}$$

But this law of transformation is just the defining property of a vector field. The three spatial derivatives of a scalar field transform together as a vector, and this vector is known as the *gradient field* or simply as the *gradient*.

The infinitesimal difference between the density values at two neighboring points with the coordinate values $x_i$ and $x_i + dx_i$, respectively (with the time again fixed), is given by the fundamental law of partial differential calculus,

$$d\rho = \frac{\partial\rho}{\partial x_i}dx_i. \tag{42}$$

The right-hand side looks like, and in fact is, the scalar product of two vectors, the density gradient and the infinitesimal displacement vector. In the so-called direct notation of vector calculus, we should write the right-hand side in the form

$$d\rho = \text{grad } \rho \cdot \mathbf{dx}. \tag{43}$$

The equations (42) and (43) express fully the geometrical significance of the gradient: it represents in magnitude and in direction the "slope" of the scalar field. The rate of change of $\rho$ in any direction (per unit distance) equals the magnitude of the gradient, multiplied by the cosine of the angle between the directions of the gradient and the displacement.

Gradients can also be formed of vector and tensor fields. Suppose we wish to examine the infinitesimal change in a component of the tensor **T** with the components $T_{ik}$ when we travel from the point $(x_i)$ to the point $(x_i + dx_i)$. Again, we have

$$dT_{ik} = \frac{\partial T_{ik}}{\partial x_l} \, dx_l, \tag{44}$$

and the right-hand side appears as a dot product. In fact, straightforward computation shows that the 27 quantities $\partial T_{ik}/\partial x_l$ together form a tensor of rank 3. The proof, being completely analogous to earlier ones, will be left to the reader. Generally speaking, gradients of tensors are again tensors, of a rank higher by one than that of the original tensor. Since $l$ is actually a tensor index, as far as transformation properties are concerned, we shall find it convenient to write spatial derivatives in the form

$$\frac{\partial T_{ik}}{\partial x_l} \equiv T_{ik,l}. \tag{45}$$

Only the comma indicates that the index on its right has been added through differentiation. A symbol $W_{i,mn}$ is short for

$$W_{i,mn} \equiv \frac{\partial^2 W_i}{\partial x_m \, \partial x_n}. \tag{46}$$

Again, all three indices $i$, $m$, $n$ are indices of a tensor of rank 3, which satisfies the appropriate transformation law.

Certain types of contraction combined with differentiation occur again and again in physical laws; they have been given names of their own, and special symbols are in common use in the direct notation. We have, first, the *divergence* of a vector field,

$$\frac{\partial u_s}{\partial x_s} \equiv u_{s,s} \equiv \operatorname{div} \mathbf{u} \equiv \nabla \cdot \mathbf{u}, \tag{47}$$

which is a scalar. The contraction of a tensor gradient is also usually called a divergence. The "direct notation" for the divergence of a tensor is inconvenient or even ambiguous, since the contraction may be carried out between the differentiation index and any one of the tensor indices; naturally, the two expressions $t_{is,s}$ and $t_{si,s}$ are in general not equal.

If we differentiate the components of a field twice and then contract with respect to the two indices of differentiation, we are taking, in effect, the divergence of a gradient. This operation, which leads from a tensor field to a tensor field of the same rank, is called the *Laplacian*. The Laplacian of a scalar field can be designated in any one of these notations:

$$\rho_{,ss} \equiv \text{div grad } \rho \equiv \nabla^2 \rho. \tag{48}$$

The significance of divergences, including the Laplacian, stems from their occurrence in Gauss's theorem, which we shall take up next.

**Gauss's theorem.**   Gauss's theorem enables us to convert certain types of integrals which are to be taken over a closed surface into an integral over the volume in the interior of the surface, and vice versa. The kind of surface integral to which the theorem applies has the form

$$I = \oint_S V_{\ldots s \ldots} n_s \, dS. \tag{49}$$

The dots indicate the possibility of further indices of the tensor field in the integrand. One of the indices, however, here designated by $s$, is contracted with the subscript of the unit normal to the surface, **n**, with the components $n_s$. By custom, we always let the unit normal of a closed surface point outside. $dS$ is the area of an infinitesimal surface element. (Some authors denote the product **n** $dS$ by **dS**, but we shall keep the two factors separated.)

For what follows, we shall specialize the tensor field and work with a vector field **V**, just to avoid the ballast of additional indices which contribute nothing to the calculations. Nevertheless, our conclusions will be valid for all kinds of vector and tensor fields. In the integral

$$I = \oint V_s \, n_s \, dS \equiv \oint (V_1 n_1 + V_2 n_2 + V_3 n_3) \, dS \tag{50}$$

we shall integrate each of the three terms separately, by means of a specially adapted grating.

Figure 5 shows the grating suitable for the integration of the third term. It is a grating in the $x_1,x_2$-plane, projected on the closed surface $S$. Each of the lines parallel to the $x_3$-axis which generate the projection pierces $S$ twice (or, in the case of a more involved surface, at least an even number of times). Thus, two surface elements $dS$ correspond to the same base rectangle with the area $dx_1 \, dx_2$. Let us consider two such corresponding surface elements. For the upper of these two elements in Fig. 5, we see that the angle between **n** and the $x_3$-direction equals the angle which $dS$ makes with the $x_1x_2$-plane. Since $n_3$ is the cosine of that angle,

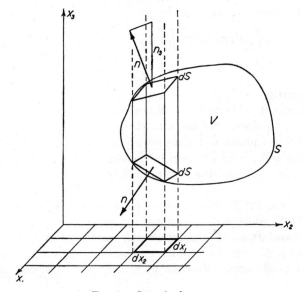

FIG. 5.  Gauss's theorem.

it follows that

$$n_3 \, dS = dx_1 \, dx_2. \tag{51}$$

The same conclusion holds for the lower surface element, with the difference that here **n** points downward, $n_3$ is negative, and $n_3 \, dS$, therefore, equals $-dx_1 \, dx_2$.

Let the superscripts $(u)$ and $(l)$ denote the upper and the lower location, respectively. Then the contribution of the two surface elements indicated to the integral $I_3$,

$$I_3 = \oint V_3 \, n_3 \, dS, \tag{52}$$

is

$$dI_3^{(u)} + dI_3^{(l)} = (V_3^{(u)} - V_3^{(l)}) \, dx_1 \, dx_2 = \int_{x_3^{(l)}}^{x_3^{(u)}} \frac{\partial V_3}{\partial x_3} \, dx_3 \, dx_1 \, dx_2. \tag{53}$$

If we now integrate over the whole surface $S$, we obtain

$$I_3 = \int \int \int_V \frac{\partial V_3}{\partial x_3} \, dx_1 \, dx_2 \, dx_3. \tag{54}$$

All we need to do now is to repeat the same argument for the other two terms on the right-hand side of eq. (50). When they are all added together, we find the identity

$$\oint_S V_s \, n_s \, dS \equiv \int \int \int_V V_{s,s} \, dx_1 \, dx_2 \, dx_3,$$

$$\oint_S \mathbf{V} \cdot \mathbf{n} \, dS \equiv \int \int \int_V \operatorname{div} \mathbf{V} \, dx_1 \, dx_2 \, dx_3. \tag{55}$$

This equation is Gauss's theorem for a vector field. It holds for other kinds of fields as well. Whenever a surface integral is to be taken over a closed surface and when the integrand possesses the form of a dot product of the unit normal $\mathbf{n}$ and some tensor field, then that surface integral can be converted into a volume integral over the interior, and the integrand is the divergence of the tensor field.

Later on, in the discussion of electromagnetic fields, we shall require two additional operations, the cross product and the curl. Their transformation properties are, however, slightly different from those of ordinary vectors, and we shall defer their treatment until we need them. Now, let us return to our physical problem.

### 3.4. The equations of motion

At the end of Section 3.2, we found that the total external force acting on the molecules inside a closed surface $S$ is given by eq. (13). This expression may be transformed with the help of Gauss's theorem, and the total external force expressed by the volume integral

$$F_i^* = - \int \int \int_V T_{is,s} \, dx_1 \, dx_2 \, dx_3. \tag{56}$$

By virtue of the conservation law of linear momentum, which was derived in eq. (1.21), this total external force must equal the rate of change in total linear momentum of all the molecules inside $S$ at the time $t$. If we could identify these molecules and number them from one through $N$, we should equate

$$- \int \int \int_V T_{is,s} \, dx_1 \, dx_2 \, dx_3 = \sum_{n=1}^{N} m_n \, \ddot{x}_i \tag{57}$$

But in this form the relationship is useless. Though the left-hand side contains only bulk averages, the right-hand side cannot be evaluated except in terms of individual particles. We must strive to replace the summation over identifiable particles by an integral over local averaged quantities. Such a transformation of the right-hand side is rendered difficult because even during a short time interval a certain number of particles will pass through the surface $S$ and, hence, leave or enter the domain $V$. As a result, the particles inside $V$ at the time $t$ are not identical with the particles inside $V$ at the time $t + dt$, and we shall have to allow for this difference. The change in momentum called for on the right-hand side of eq. (57) is a change in momentum of the particles *initially* inside $V$, not the change in momentum inside $V$, regardless of to which particles it is attached. That is why the expression

$$\frac{dP_i}{dt} \equiv \int \int \int_V \frac{\partial}{\partial t} (\rho v_i)\, dx_1\, dx_2\, dx_3 \tag{58}$$

differs from what we want to the extent that momentum is carried bodily across $S$ by particles entering or leaving $V$. We shall now determine these "transport terms."

We shall consider a surface element $dS$ and the particles in its vicinity. Each of the particles involved possesses a mass $m$ and a velocity $V$,

$$\mathbf{V} = \mathbf{v} + \mathbf{u}. \tag{59}$$

As before, $\mathbf{v}$ is the local average velocity and $\mathbf{u}$ the random velocity. We shall now introduce a notation for averaging, the carets $\langle \ \rangle$, and give them this meaning: Any mechanical quantity which is defined for individual particles, such as mass, velocity, or the like, when enclosed in carets, shall be added for all the particles in a small volume $\Delta V$, suitably chosen, and the sum divided by $\Delta V$. In other words, for quantities enclosed in carets we shall take the average values per unit volume. In accordance with this notation, we have, for instance, the relations

$$\langle m \rangle = \rho, \tag{60}$$
$$\langle m\,\mathbf{V} \rangle = \langle m \rangle\,\mathbf{v}, \tag{61}$$
and
$$\langle m\,\mathbf{u} \rangle = 0. \tag{62}$$

Let us now consider an individual particle with the mass $m$ and the velocity $\mathbf{V}$. If it should cross the surface element $dS$ during the time $dt$ and pass from the inside out, then it would carry a linear momentum

$$\mathbf{p} = m\,\mathbf{V} \tag{63}$$

away from the interior of $V$. What are the chances of its doing so? Figure 6 shows the small volume $\Delta V$ and in its interior the surface element $dS$. Below $dS$ in the figure is the interior of $V$, above the outside. Now the particle under consideration will cross $dS$ only if it is initially somewhere inside the inclined prism with the base $dS$ and with the lengthwise edges $\mathbf{V}\,dt$. The volume of this inclined

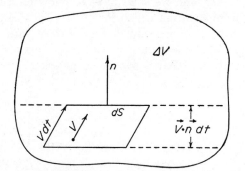

Fig. 6.   Momentum transport.

prism equals $(\mathbf{n} \cdot \mathbf{V}\,dt\,dS)$. Now the probability that our particle (which is one of the particles inside $\Delta V$) should be inside the prism equals the ratio between the volume of the prism and the volume $\Delta V$. That is, the ratio between all the particles with a certain mass $m$ and with a certain velocity $\mathbf{V}$ inside the prism and those particles with the same properties inside $\Delta V$ equals the ratio between the two volumes, because of our standing assumption of local homogeneity inside $\Delta V$.

Thus the *average* momentum carried by a particle of mass $m$ and velocity $V$ across $dS$ during the time interval $dt$ is

$$p_i^* = m\,V_i\,\frac{V_s\,n_s}{\Delta V}\,dS\,dt. \tag{64}$$

If we add the contributions of all the particles inside $\Delta V$ and compute the linear momentum that is carried across $dS$ per unit time, we find, for the rate of this transport out of $V$,

$$P_i^* = \langle m\,V_i\,V_s\rangle\,n_s\,dS. \tag{65}$$

In this expression, we can separate the contributions of the prevalent state of motion from those of the random motion. We have, first of all,

$$P_i^* = \langle m(v_i + u_i)(v_s + u_s) \rangle \, n_s \, dS. \tag{66}$$

Before we carry out the product inside the carets, let us note that in every term factors which are common to all the particles may be placed outside the carets. With this rule in mind, we find that

$$\langle m(v_i + u_i)(v_s + u_s) \rangle = \langle m \rangle \, v_i \, v_s + \langle m \, u_i \rangle \, v_s + \langle m \, u_s \rangle \, v_i$$
$$+ \langle m \, u_i \, u_s \rangle \tag{67}$$
$$= \rho \, v_i \, v_s + \tau_{is}, \qquad \tau_{is} \equiv \langle m \, u_i \, u_s \rangle.$$

This expression, substituted into eq. (66) and then integrated over the whole surface $S$ of the volume $V$, is the amount of linear momentum lost per unit time because of transport. Lacking any particular knowledge about the random motion, we cannot evaluate the tensor $\tau_{is}$. It is a symmetric tensor of rank 2, and we shall soon find that in the macroscopic equations it is always combined with the tensor $T_{is}$, which we have obtained in Section 3.2.

The rate at which the total momentum inside $V$ changes in the course of time must be determined by the combination of external forces and transport of momentum. We set

$$\iiint_V \frac{\partial(\rho v_i)}{\partial t} \, dx_1 \, dx_2 \, dx_3 = - \iiint_V T_{is,s} \, dx_1 \, dx_2 \, dx_3$$
$$- \oint_S (\rho \, v_i \, v_s + \tau_{is}) \, n_s \, dS. \tag{68}$$

If we now apply Gauss's theorem to the last integral, we can combine all the volume integrals into one and get

$$\iiint_V \left[ \frac{\partial}{\partial t} (\rho \, v_i) + (\rho \, v_i \, v_s)_{,s} + t_{is,s} \right] dx_1 \, dx_2 \, dx_3 = 0,$$
$$t_{is} = T_{is} + \tau_{is}. \tag{69}$$

To obtain the desired relationship in its final form, we observe that the choice of the domain of integration $V$ was arbitrary and that the integral (69) must vanish when extended over any domain in the interior of our bulk piece of matter. But an integral can vanish over arbitrary domains only if the integrand itself vanishes everywhere in the interior,

$$\frac{\partial}{\partial t} (\rho \, v_i) + \frac{\partial}{\partial x_s} (\rho \, v_i \, v_s + t_{is}) = 0. \tag{70}$$

This set of three partial differential equations is the final form of the equations of motion of matter in bulk. The tensor $t_{ik}$, called the *stress tensor*, contains in condensed form all we need to know about the internal relations of the individual particles.

**The equation of continuity.** The three partial differential equations (70) do not determine the behavior of the velocity field in time completely insofar as they contain the time derivative of $\rho$ in addition to those of the three quantities $v_i$. Therefore it is necessary to adjoin a fourth partial differential equation to the three equations (70) in order to determine completely the future behavior of a given initial density-velocity distribution.

Such a partial differential equation can be obtained quite easily by means of the law of conservation of mass. All that needs to be done is to express in the form of a partial differential equation the fact that the combined mass of the $N$ particles initially filling the domain $V$ remains constant. This mass is initially represented by the integral

$$M = \int \int \int_V \rho \, dV. \tag{71}$$

The change in $M$ after an infinitesimal time interval $dt$ must be determined completely by the transport of mass across the surface $S$. We proceed exactly as before. A particle will carry the mass $m$ across a surface element $dS$ during the interval $dt$ only if it is within the prism shown in Fig. 6. The probability of its being there is determined in the same manner as before, and the average mass carried across $dS$ during the time interval $dt$ by a single particle in $\Delta V$ is

$$m^* = m \frac{\mathbf{V} \cdot \mathbf{n}}{\Delta V} \, dt \, dS. \tag{72}$$

Adding the contributions of all the particles in $\Delta V$, we get, for the total mass transport out of $V$ across $dS$ per unit time,

$$M^* = \langle m \, V_s \rangle \, n_s \, dS = \rho \, v_s \, n_s \, dS, \tag{73}$$

and the decrease of mass in $V$ because of transport must be given by the surface integral

$$\int \int \int_V \frac{\partial \rho}{\partial t}\, dx_1\, dx_2\, dx_3 = \frac{dM}{dt} = - \oint_S \rho\, v_s\, n_s\, dS. \qquad (74)$$

If we convert this surface integral into a volume integral with the help of Gauss's theorem, we get

$$\int \int \int_V \left[ \frac{\partial \rho}{\partial t} + (\rho\, v_s)_{,s} \right] dx_1\, dx_2\, dx_3 = 0 \qquad (75)$$

and finally

$$\frac{\partial \rho}{\partial t} + (\rho\, v_s)_{,s} = 0, \qquad (76)$$

the so-called *equation of continuity*. With the help of this equation, we can eliminate the time derivative of $\rho$ from the three equations of motion (70), a procedure which is sometimes convenient. As the result of this elimination, we can obtain the equations of motion in the alternative form

$$\rho \left( \frac{\partial v_i}{\partial t} + v_s\, v_{i,s} \right) + t_{is,s} = 0. \qquad (77)$$

The four equations (70) and (76) contain the complete formulation of the laws of mechanics in a form in which they can be applied to the treatment of matter in bulk. The stress tensor $t_{ik}$ depends, as we have seen, both on the internal configuration and force laws of the elementary particles and on their velocity distribution. Without the help of statistical mechanics, the latter cannot be predicted from the "microscopic" picture, but the stress tensor as a macroscopic entity can be determined experimentally in its dependence on the composition of matter—its density, temperature, and macroscopic motion. This specific dependence will determine completely the mechanical properties of the matter considered. For the "perfect" solid, the stress depends only on the internal deformation, and in the fluid without rigidity the stress is a function of the density and the state of (macroscopic) motion only. Actual materials will behave in an intermediate fashion. In any case, into our equations as well as into our observations will always enter $t_{ik}$, not $T_{ik}$ or $\tau_{ik}$ separately.

### 3.5. The strain tensor

Internal stress in matter is primarily the result of deformation. If an unstrained piece of material, be it rubber or be it steel, is subjected to external forming forces, it will yield and change its shape, but the result of the relative displacement of its elementary constituents will be the emergence of internal restoring forces, which are described by means of the stress tensor $t_{ik}$. In general, if the external forces are relaxed, the internal stresses will bring about partial restoration of the original shape. Depending on the degree of completeness of this restoration, we speak of "elastic" and of "plastic" deformation. We shall not develop in this book the complete theory of partially elastic, partially plastic deformations. We shall restrict ourselves to the mathematical formulation of the two extreme situations, both of which have great practical importance. They are, on the one hand, the *elastic solid*, in which restoration of the original shape is complete, and, on the other, the *fluid*, in which restoration takes place only with respect to the volume but not at all with respect to the shape.

**The elastic solid.** An elastic solid can be characterized by the fact that it has a certain equilibrium shape to which it will return if all external forces are relaxed. In this relaxed shape there are no internal stresses. We can characterize this relaxed shape mathematically by "engraving" on the relaxed chunk of matter a Cartesian coordinate system, $y_i$, and by retaining the $y_i$ as labels which will help to identify material domains within the chunk even if through deformation the $y_i$ are no longer Cartesian (that is, straight lines and at right angles to each other).

If we now consider the same piece of matter in a strained condition, the material point which is characterized by the "labels" $y_i$ will be found at a location characterized by the coordinate values $x_i$, which refer to a set of Cartesian coordinates that are defined independently of the instantaneous position and shape of our chunk. If the $x_i$ equal $y_i$ throughout the piece, then the material is at its original location and possesses its equilibrium shape. Otherwise, the $y_i$ will be some functions of the $x_i$ and, if there is motion, of the time $t$ as well. Knowledge of these functions implies complete information regarding the (macroscopic) motion of all the portions of our piece of matter.

For our purposes, we are chiefly interested in internal deformations, not so much in motions of the piece as a whole. If the functions $y_i(x_1, x_2, x_3, t)$ are, for instance, of the form (16), (21), with the $\overset{0}{y}_k$ and $c_{ki}$ functions of $t$ only, then our chunk would move *rigidly* through space without any internal deformation; this is the kind of information which, in this connection, is of *no* interest to us. We should like to obtain mathematical expressions which characterize exclusively internal, local deformations.

In considering the exact significance of this term "internal, local deformation," we are led to the following consideration. If, by means of the $y$-coordinates, we define a small geometrical figure at some spot inside our chunk and consider this same figure after deformation, we should consider the internal deformation zero if the original and the changed figure are congruent, that is, if all lengths and angles making up the figure have remained unchanged.

Conversely, if of any angle and any distance inside our piece we can tell how it is affected by the deformation, then we know all we care to know concerning internal relative displacements. It is not too difficult to obtain a mathematical expression for these changes, now that we know that this is what we want. Suppose we consider some particular point inside our material which is identified both by its $y$- and its $x$-coordinates. If we now draw two infinitesimal displacement vectors originating at that point, characterized by the coordinate differentials $d'x_i$ and $d''x_i$, respectively, their dot product, $d^2P$,

$$d^2P = d'x_k \, d''x_k, \tag{78}$$

is a scalar. Now if, for arbitrary points $(x_i)$ and arbitrary infinitesimal displacement vectors $d'x_i$, $d''x_i$, we can determine the change in $d^2P$ as the result of the deformation, then we know the changes of both distances and angles. In order to obtain an infinitesimal distance (or its change because of deformation), we must simply let $d'$ and $d''$ coincide. In order to obtain angles, we let the two infinitesimal displacements form the legs of the desired angle; the expression $d^2P$, divided by the product of the magnitudes of the two infinitesimal vectors, then equals the cosine of the desired angle.

In the relaxed position, the value of the above dot product shall be denoted by $d^2Q$,

$$d^2Q \equiv d'y_i \, d''y_i. \tag{79}$$

The change in the dot product is then given by the difference

$$d^2P - d^2Q = d'x_k \, d''x_k - d'y_i \, d''y_i, \tag{80}$$

where the $dy_i$ are connected with the $dx_k$ through the equations

$$d'y_i = \frac{\partial y_i}{\partial x_k}\, d'x_k, \qquad d''y_i = \frac{\partial y_i}{\partial x_k}\, d''x_k. \qquad (81)$$

We find, therefore, that the change of the dot product is given by the product

$$d^2P - d^2Q = \left(\delta_{kl} - \frac{\partial y_i}{\partial x_k}\frac{\partial y_i}{\partial x_l}\right) d'x_k\, d''x. \qquad (82)$$

The coefficients of the differentials

$$s_{kl} = \frac{1}{2}\left(\delta_{kl} - \frac{\partial y_i}{\partial x_k}\frac{\partial y_i}{\partial x_l}\right) \qquad (83)$$

form a tensor with respect to orthogonal transformations of the $x_i$-coordinates.[1] It is symmetric with respect to its two indices $k$ and $l$, and is known as the *strain tensor of an elastic solid*.

**The fluid.**  In a fluid, it is not practical to indicate the original shape of the flowing mass by means of a system of $y$-coordinates, because once the fluid is at rest, its only internal stress is an isotropic pressure which depends only on its density, not on its shape. In other words, a changed shape giving the fluid mass the same volume as the original provides a new "equilibrium" shape, physically equivalent to the first shape.  Therefore it is preferable to characterize the state of the fluid exclusively by means of "instantaneous" quantities, $\rho$ and $v_i$, which are defined irrespective of the previous history.

As a matter of fact, in the typical fluid internal stresses arise for two different reasons, one being changes in density and the other finite *shear velocities*.  Shear velocity is called the rate at which changes in shape take place.

Consider, again, the scalar product of two infinitesimal displacement vectors $d'x_i$ and $d''x_i$, calling it, as before, $d^2P$.  We may now ask how the value of $d^2P$ changes in the course of time if both the origin and the end points of these displacement vectors are made to move with the local velocity **v** of the streaming fluid.  If the velocity

[1] Its components are invariant with respect to orthogonal transformations of the $y$-coordinates, that is to say, with respect to transformations in which the new $y$-coordinates are connected with the original ones by equations possessing the form (16), (21).

field were constant rather than a function of the $x_i$, nothing would change. As it is, the components of each vector will change at a rate which depends on the gradient of the velocity field:

$$\frac{d}{dt}(d'x_i) = \frac{\partial v_i}{\partial x_k}d'x_k, \qquad \frac{d}{dt}(d''x_i) = \frac{\partial v_i}{\partial x_k}d''x_k. \tag{84}$$

As a result, $d^2P$ will also change, at the rate

$$\frac{d}{dt}(d^2P) = \left(\frac{\partial v_i}{\partial x_k} + \frac{\partial v_k}{\partial x_i}\right)d'x_i\,d''x_k. \tag{85}$$

Again, the coefficients of the bilinear form of the differentials $d'$ and $d''$ form a symmetric tensor,

$$s_{ik} = \frac{1}{2}\left(\frac{\partial v_i}{\partial x_k} + \frac{\partial v_k}{\partial x_i}\right), \tag{86}$$

which is appropriately called the *strain tensor of a fluid*. It determines the *time rate* at which distances and angles inside the fluid change because of the macroscopic motion.

### 3.6. Diagonal form and trace of symmetric tensors

The next step in our program should consist of setting up force laws which would relate the strain tensor to the resulting stress. Unfortunately, before we can do so, it is necessary to interpolate one more brief mathematical section. This section will deal with some of the properties of symmetric tensors of rank 2. The reader who is getting apprehensive concerning the amount of mathematics piled up in this chapter may find some consolation in the knowledge that the results obtained in this section will be useful later on in the mathematical treatment of modern quantum mechanics.

**Diagonalization.** It will be remembered that the force per unit area across a surface with the normal **n** depends on the orientation of **n** through eq. (11). Likewise, the rate of momentum transfer across a surface (regardless of the mechanism by which momentum is transferred) is connected with the direction of the surface normal by the equation

$$f_i^* = t_{is}\,n_s. \tag{87}$$

Ordinarily, **f**\* will not be parallel to **n** and therefore will not be perpendicular to the surface $S$. Only for certain directions of **n** will the two vectors be parallel. These directions play a special role: if a surface is oriented perpendicular to one of these so-called *principal stress axes*, then the tangential components of **f***, the "shear stresses," will vanish, and only the "normal stress" component will remain. We shall discover that for a given set of components $t_{ik}$ there are at least three such principal axes.

Let us assume that there is at least one direction in which the stress is purely normal to $S$, and let us attempt to determine this direction. The condition that the two vectors **f*** and **n** be parallel can be expressed in the form

$$f_i^* = t\, n_i. \tag{88}$$

$t$ is a constant of proportionality, as yet undetermined. Physically, it represents the magnitude of the stress in the direction of the principal axis. If we substitute the expression (88) into eq. (87), we obtain the conditions for $t$ and $n$:

$$t_{is}\, n_s = t\, n_i, \tag{89}$$

or three equations for the four unknowns $t$, $n_1$, $n_2$, and $n_3$. At first sight, the problem appears insufficiently determined; but this impression is incorrect. If we were to assume that $t$ had been chosen in some arbitrary fashion, then we should retain three *homogeneous, linear* equations for the remaining three unknowns. From the theory of such equations, it is well known that they have either only the identically vanishing solution ($n_i = 0$) or infinitely many; in the case of nonvanishing solutions a new solution can always be obtained by multiplying each $n_i$ by the same but otherwise arbitrary constant. The first case does not represent a meaningful solution, since a "normal" with only zero components does not define a direction. In the latter case, the freedom of multiplying the solution by an arbitrary common factor will enable us to normalize **n** to be a vector of unit magnitude. The question is, which of the two alternatives is realized?

If we bring all the terms of eqs. (89) on one side, we may write them in the form

$$(t_{ik} - t\, \delta_{ik})\, n_k = 0, \tag{90}$$

in which we get a clearer idea of the coefficients of the equations. It is known that the necessary and sufficient condition for the existence of a nonvanishing solution is that the determinant of the coefficients vanish,

$$\det |t_{ik} - t\,\delta_{ik}| \equiv \begin{vmatrix} t_{11} - t, & t_{12}, & t_{13} \\ t_{21}, & t_{22} - t, & t_{23} \\ t_{31}, & t_{32}, & t_{33} - t \end{vmatrix} = 0. \qquad (91)$$

This condition obviously constitutes a determining equation for $t$, which is a cubic equation. It has three roots, not necessarily all different. An equation of this form is often referred to as a *secular equation*.[1]

Once we have obtained a root of the secular equation (91), it is not difficult to find a normalized solution of eqs. (89). $t$, the magnitude of the normal stress in the direction of a principal axis, is called a *principal stress*. Since a cubic equation has generally three roots, we have three principal stresses belonging to a particular set of components $t_{ik}$, and they are usually all different.

We shall now prove two properties of the principal stresses: (a) All the roots of the secular equation are real and are, therefore, physically significant; (b) the principal stress axes which belong to two different roots are at right angles to each other. For both of these properties, the fact that $t_{ik}$ is symmetric in its two indices is crucial.

In order to prove that the roots are real, we shall write down the conjugate complex of eq. (89), with the understanding, of course, that the given values of $t_{ik}$ are real:

$$t_{ik}\, n_k^* = t^*\, n_i^*. \qquad (92)$$

(The asterisk shall be used consistently to indicate transition to the conjugate complex, in line with current practice in quantum mechanics.) If we now multiply eq. (89) by $n_i^*$ and eq. (92) by $n_i$ and then subtract,

$$t_{ik}(n_i^*\, n_k - n_k^*\, n_i) = n_i^*\, n_i(t - t^*), \qquad (93)$$

we find that, because of the symmetry of $t_{ik}$, the left-hand side vanishes. Since the scalar product $n_i^*\, n_i$ is a nonvanishing positive definite number, it follows that $t$ must equal $t^*$; therefore $t$ is real.

Having proved our first assertion, we can now proceed to the second one. Suppose that we have obtained two roots of the

---

[1] The name is derived from the circumstance that equations of this type were first encountered in celestial mechanics in connection with the theory of secular (long-term) perturbations of the planetary orbits.

secular equation, say $t_I$ and $t_{II}$, and two corresponding normals, $n_i$ and $n_i$, respectively. If we now write eq. (89) down twice, for
    I     II
each solution separately, then multiply the first equation (for **n**) by
                                                              I
$n_i$ and the second by $n_i$, and subtract, the result of these operations
II           I
will be:

$$t_{ik}(n_k\, n_i - n_k\, n_i) = n_i\, n_i(t_I - t_{II}).$$
$$\quad\;\, \text{I II}\;\; \text{II I} \quad\;\; \text{I II} \qquad\qquad (94)$$

Again the left-hand side vanishes, because of the symmetry of $t_{ik}$. The right-hand side is the product of $n_I \cdot n_{II}$ by the difference $(t_I - t_{II})$. Two cases must be distinguished. In the first, the two roots are different; then the dot product of the two normals must vanish, and they must be at right angles to each other [which is the gist of our assertion (b)]. Otherwise we have the second case, in which the two roots $t_I$ and $t_{II}$ are numerically equal. The presence of such a double root is the necessary and sufficient condition for the existence of two different solutions **n** belonging to the same numerical value of $t$. By "*different* solutions" is meant two solutions which are linearly independent of each other, that is, where one is not proportional to the other. Likewise, a triple root is the necessary and sufficient condition for the existence of three linearly independent (that is, noncoplanar) solutions **n** belonging to the same value of $t$. These proofs will not be offered here but can be found elsewhere.[1] Once it is established that there are two or three linearly independent solutions, it is easy to see that any linear combination of solutions belonging to the same value of $t$ is again a solution and that we can, in particular, always find two (or three, as the case may be) such solutions which are unit vectors and perpendicular to each other.

Geometrically, these results may be interpreted as follows. Suppose that in a three-dimensional graph are plotted both a sphere of unit radius and the figure which contains the end points of all the resulting stresses (with a given array of values $t_{ik}$). This construction is shown two-dimensionally in Fig. 7. The stress envelope will be an ellipsoid (the *stress ellipsoid*), with the principal stresses as the three semiaxes. As long as all three semiaxes are

---

[1] See, for instance, H. Margenau and G. Murphy, *The Mathematics of Physics and Chemistry*, Van Nostrand, 1943, Chapter 10.

different in magnitude, they are uniquely determined. But if two, or three, of them should be equal, we shall have the ellipsoid degenerate into an ellipsoid of revolution or even into a sphere. In the former case, there will be a whole plane in which $f^*$ is parallel to the corresponding $n$, and it is obviously possible to choose two mutually perpendicular solutions in that plane in an infinity of ways; whereas in the latter case, of a sphere, $f^*$ will be parallel to $n$ in all directions, and any three mutually perpendicular directions can be chosen as directions of principal stress.

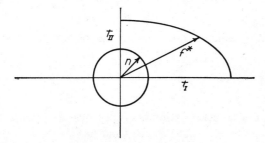

Fɪɢ. 7.  The stress ellipsoid.

Once we have found three directions of principal stress which are mutually perpendicular to each other, it can be shown that in terms of them the tensor $t_{ik}$ can be represented in the form

$$t_{ik} = t_{\mathrm{I}}\, n_i\, n_k + t_{\mathrm{II}}\, n_i\, n_k + t_{\mathrm{III}}\, n_i\, n_k. \qquad (95)$$
$$\quad\ \ \ {}_{\mathrm{I}\ \ \mathrm{I}} \qquad {}_{\mathrm{II}\ \mathrm{II}} \qquad {}_{\mathrm{III}\ \mathrm{III}}$$

The proof can be carried out in the form that we show that the tensor

$$\mathfrak{F}_{ik} = t_{ik} - t_{\mathrm{I}}\, n_i\, n_k - t_{\mathrm{II}}\, n_i\, n_k - t_{\mathrm{III}}\, n_i\, n_k \qquad (96)$$
$$\qquad\qquad {}_{\mathrm{I}\ \ \mathrm{I}} \qquad {}_{\mathrm{II}\ \mathrm{II}} \qquad {}_{\mathrm{III}\ \mathrm{III}}$$

has the same three directions of principal stress $n_{\mathrm{I}}$, $n_{\mathrm{II}}$, $n_{\mathrm{III}}$ but the $f^*$-vector belonging to each one of these is zero. The stress ellipsoid of the tensor $\mathfrak{F}_{ik}$ is, therefore, a sphere of zero radius; that is, for any direction whatsoever,

$$\mathfrak{F}_{ik}\, n_k \equiv 0. \qquad (97)$$

That means that all components of $\mathfrak{F}_{ik}$ vanish. The form (95) shows that for an arbitrary direction $n$, the corresponding vector $f^*$ may be obtained by representing $n$ as the vector sum of three vectors parallel to $n_{\mathrm{I}}$, $n_{\mathrm{II}}$, and $n_{\mathrm{III}}$, multiplying each component by the appropriate value of $t$, and adding the results,

$$f_i^* = \sum_{A=\text{I,II,III}} t_A(\mathbf{n} \cdot \mathbf{n}_A)\, n_i. \tag{98}$$

If we carry out a coordinate transformation so that the directions of $\mathbf{n}_\text{I}$, $\mathbf{n}_\text{II}$, and $\mathbf{n}_\text{III}$ become the directions of the new coordinate axes, then the components of the tensor $t_{ik}$ will take the form

$$t_{ik} = \begin{pmatrix} t_\text{I}, & 0, & 0 \\ 0, & t_\text{II}, & 0 \\ 0, & 0, & t_\text{III} \end{pmatrix}, \tag{99}$$

with the three principal normals having the **components**

$$\begin{aligned} \mathbf{n}_\text{I} &= (1, \quad 0, \quad 0), \\ \mathbf{n}_\text{II} &= (0, \quad 1, \quad 0), \\ \mathbf{n}_\text{III} &= (0, \quad 0, \quad 1). \end{aligned} \tag{100}$$

This particular transformation is often called *diagonalization* of the tensor $t_{ik}$ and the form (99) its *diagonal form*.

**Trace.** Together with the tensor $t_{ik}$ is defined the scalar $t_{ss}$, the sum of the three components $t_{11}$, $t_{22}$, and $t_{33}$. This scalar is often called the *trace*. It is numerically equal to the sum of the three principal stresses, because of the possibility of introducing the coordinates in which the tensor assumes its diagonal form (99).

Given the tensor $t_{ik}$, it is always possible to construct a tensor with vanishing trace by forming the new tensor

$$t_{ik}^* = t_{ik} - \tfrac{1}{3}\delta_{ik}\, t_{ss}. \tag{101}$$

With its help, the stress tensor $t_{ik}$ may be represented as the sum of a completely isotropic tensor and one with zero trace,

$$t_{ik} = \tfrac{1}{3}t_{ss}\, \delta_{ik} + t_{ik}^*. \tag{102}$$

This decomposition is not only an invariant one (independent of the coordinate system chosen, since $t_{ss}$ is a scalar) but is also of some physical interest. The isotropic part of the stress tensor, $\tfrac{1}{3}t_{ss}\delta_{ik}$, is what we usually call the *pressure*. If the stress tensor has only this isotropic part, then the stress is normal to any surface $S$ (the stress ellipsoid degenerates into a sphere). In a fluid at rest, the stress tensor assumes the isotropic form. The remainder, $t_{ik}^*$, which has a zero trace, generally represents the reaction of the material to shear. Deformations taking place in response to a stress tensor having a vanishing trace will not affect the density of the material but will merely change its shape. A contraction in one direction is offset by an expansion in others. In a fluid, the part $t_{ik}^*$ represents the viscous resistance of the material to shearing flow, whereas the isotropic part of the stress tensor represents the reaction to compression or expansion.

### 3.7. The Fluid

After these lengthy preparations, we shall finally proceed to write down the force law for the above-mentioned two extreme cases, the fluid and the elastic solid. This section will be devoted to the fluid.

**The force law.** In a fluid, the isotropic and the anisotropic parts of the stress tensor are determined by quite different factors: the isotropic part (the pressure) is a function of the density (and the temperature), whereas the shear stress is determined by the shear velocity. Therefore, it is appropriate and in accordance with customary notation to replace $t_{ss}$ by $3p$. We shall not attempt to treat the difficult case in which the local temperature is an additional variable and is determined by a third differential equation (the equation of heat conduction), but we shall dispose of it by restricting ourselves to cases in which the pressure is a function of the density only, be it because the processes considered are isothermic (in which case the temperature is constant) or because they are adiabatic (in that case the temperature is a unique function of the density). Finally, we shall consider shear velocities small enough that the pure shear stress $t_{ik}^*$ is *proportional* to the anisotropic part of the strain tensor (86), $\sigma_{ik}$,

$$\sigma_{ik} \equiv \tfrac{1}{2}(v_{i,k} + v_{k,i}) - \tfrac{1}{3}\delta_{ik}\, v_{s,s}. \tag{103}$$

If we call the constant of proportionality $\eta$, the *coefficient of viscosity* of the medium,

$$t_{ik}^* = -2\eta\, \sigma_{ik} \tag{104}$$

(where the numerical coefficient has been chosen in agreement with the usual definition of $\eta$), then the stress tensor of the fluid takes the form

$$t_{ik} = p(\rho)\, \delta_{ik} - \eta(v_{i,k} + v_{k,i} - \tfrac{2}{3}\delta_{ik}\, v_{s,s}). \tag{105}$$

If the function $p(\rho)$ is known, then eq. (105) is the complete force law of a (viscous) fluid.

With the help of this force law, we shall make two applications. We shall derive Bernoulli's law, and we shall briefly discuss the propagation of acoustic waves in a fluid.

**Bernoulli's law.** Bernoulli's law is the law of conservation of energy, applied to the special case of the *perfect fluid;* a perfect fluid is one in which the coefficient of viscosity $\eta$ vanishes. For its derivation, we require the force law (with $\eta$ vanishing),

$$t_{ik} = p(\rho)\,\delta_{ik}, \tag{106}$$

the equation of continuity (76), and the equations of motion (77). The derivation is quite similar to the derivation of the conservation law of energy in Chapter 1.

Substituting for $t_{is}$ in eq. (77) the expression (106), we multiply the resulting equation by $v_i$, leading to

$$\frac{\rho}{2}\left[\frac{\partial(v^2)}{\partial t} + v_s\frac{\partial(v^2)}{\partial x_s}\right] + v_s\frac{\partial p}{\partial x_s} = 0. \tag{107}$$

To this equation we add the equation of continuity, multiplied by $\frac{1}{2}v^2$ ($v^2$ is short for $v_i\,v_i$). When we combine terms as much as possible, we obtain the equation

$$\frac{\partial}{\partial t}\left(\frac{1}{2}\rho v^2\right) + \frac{\partial}{\partial x_s}\left(\frac{1}{2}\rho v^2\,v_s\right) + v_s\frac{\partial p}{\partial x_s} = 0. \tag{108}$$

In this equation there appears an expression which may be described as the (macroscopic) kinetic energy density. It appears twice, once differentiated with respect to time and once in the form that the divergence is taken of its product by the velocity vector. The remaining term has neither the form of a time derivative nor that of a divergence. It is possible, though, to modify it until it assumes that form. To this end, we shall first differentiate by parts,

$$v_s\frac{\partial p}{\partial x_s} = \frac{\partial}{\partial x_s}(p\,v_s) - p\frac{\partial v_s}{\partial x_s}, \tag{109}$$

and then work on the remainder. Using once more the equation of continuity,

$$\frac{\partial v_s}{\partial x_s} + \frac{1}{\rho}\left(\frac{\partial\rho}{\partial t} + v_s\frac{\partial\rho}{\partial x_s}\right) = 0, \tag{110}$$

to which (76) can easily be reduced, we may convert eq. (109) into the form

$$v_s \frac{\partial p}{\partial x_s} = \frac{\partial}{\partial x_s} (p \, v_s) + \frac{p}{\rho} \left( \frac{\partial \rho}{\partial t} + v_s \frac{\partial \rho}{\partial x_s} \right), \tag{111}$$

Further progress can be made if we introduce a new function, which has the significance of a *potential energy density*. To obtain this function, we consider the amount of energy which is stored up in a unit mass of our fluid when it is compressed from some initial standard density $\rho_0$ to the density $\rho$. If we denote the volume occupied by the unit mass by $V'$,

$$V' = \frac{1}{\rho}, \tag{112}$$

then the amount of work done in an infinitesimal compression equals

$$dW = -p \, dV' = +\frac{p}{\rho^2} \, d\rho \tag{113}$$

$(-dV'$ being the dot product of normal direction and displacement, integrated over the whole surface). The energy per unit mass accumulated during compression is, therefore,

$$W = \int_{\rho' = \rho_0}^{\rho} \frac{p(\rho')}{\rho'^2} \, d\rho', \tag{114}$$

and the energy accumulated per unit volume is

$$P(\rho) = \rho \, W = \rho \int_{\rho_0}^{\rho} \frac{p(\rho')}{\rho'^2} \, d\rho'. \tag{115}$$

If this defining equation for the function $P(\rho)$ is differentiated, we obtain

$$d \left( \frac{P(\rho)}{\rho} \right) = \frac{p}{\rho^2} \, d\rho, \tag{116}$$

an expression which we shall introduce into eq. (111). The immediate result is

$$v_s \frac{\partial p}{\partial x_s} = \frac{\partial}{\partial x_s} (p v_s) + \rho \left[ \frac{\partial}{\partial t} \left( \frac{P}{\rho} \right) + v_s \frac{\partial}{\partial x_s} \left( \frac{P}{\rho} \right) \right], \tag{117}$$

which, on further transformation, becomes

$$v_s \frac{\partial p}{\partial x_s} = \frac{\partial}{\partial x_s}(pv_s) + \left(\frac{\partial P}{\partial t} + v_s \frac{\partial P}{\partial x_s}\right) - \frac{P}{\rho}\left(\frac{\partial \rho}{\partial t} + v_s \frac{\partial \rho}{\partial x_s}\right)$$
$$= \frac{\partial}{\partial x_s}(pv_s) + \left(\frac{\partial P}{\partial t} + v_s \frac{\partial P}{\partial x_s}\right) + P \frac{\partial v_s}{\partial x_s}. \tag{118}$$

In the last step, eq. (76) has been used a second time. All that need to be done now is to collect terms and substitute into eq. (108). Our final result is

$$\frac{\partial}{\partial t}\left(\frac{\rho}{2}v^2 + P\right) + \frac{\partial}{\partial x_s}\left(\frac{\rho}{2}v^2 v_s + P v_s + p v_s\right) = 0, \tag{119}$$

an equation valid for the motion in any perfect fluid.

For an arbitrary finite geometrical volume $V$, with the surface $S$, inside our fluid we have the equality:

$$\frac{d}{dt}\left\{\int\int\int_V \left(\frac{\rho}{2}v^2 + P\right)dV\right\}$$
$$= -\oiint_S \left(\frac{\rho}{2}v^2 v_s + P v_s + p v_s\right)n_s\, dS. \tag{120}$$

This integral relationship expresses the conservation of energy. The total energy in $V$ changes only as the result of an energy flow across $S$. This energy flows consists of two parts: the "transport" flow of energy takes place because energy streams across $S$ attached to matter (the first two terms are the transport terms); the last term represents energy which is exchanged because the matter on one side of $S$ does work on the matter on the other side.

We shall briefly consider the case of *stationary flow*, which is a flow pattern in which none of the local quantities, $\rho$, **v**, or $p$, depend on the time. In stationary flow, it is quite possible for a given material element to change its density and its velocity in the course of time as it passes through various points along its path. But we require that subsequent elements of the fluid passing along the same path shall go through exactly the same combinations of density and velocity at the same points as their predecessors. Stationary flow patterns have technical significance because laminar flow, at least, may be considered stationary about a ship or an airplane in a coordinate system which is rigidly connected with the vessel.

In this case, eq. (119) reduces to

$$\left[\left(\frac{\rho}{2}v^2 + P + p\right)v_s\right]_{,s} = 0$$
$$= v_s\left(\frac{\rho}{2}v^2 + P + p\right)_{,s} + v_{s,s}\left(\frac{\rho}{2}v^2 + P + p\right). \quad (121)$$

We can again transform the last term with the help of eq. (110) (where the term $\partial\rho/\partial t$ vanishes, because of the stationary character of the flow pattern):

$$v_s\left(\frac{\rho}{2}v^2 + P + p\right)_{,s} - v_s\frac{\rho_{,s}}{\rho}\left(\frac{\rho}{2}v^2 + P + p\right) = 0. \quad (122)$$

If we factor $v_s$, we obtain *Bernoulli's law:*

$$v_s\left[\frac{1}{\rho}\left(\frac{\rho}{2}v^2 + P + p\right)\right]_{,s} = 0. \quad (123)$$

According to this last equation, the derivative of the expression

$$U \equiv \frac{1}{\rho}\left(\frac{\rho}{2}v^2 + P + p\right), \quad (124)$$

taken along a streamline (parallel to **v**) vanishes. $U$ is the energy density per unit mass.

**Acoustic waves.** Given an equilibrium distribution of fluid matter (in which **v** vanishes), a small disturbance of the equilibrium will spread with a finite velocity throughout the medium. Such a disturbance is called an *acoustic wave.* Specifically, acoustics deals with disturbances so small that it is sufficient to treat the deviation from the equilibrium distribution by means of *linearized* equations, neglecting higher-order terms.

We shall call the equilibrium density $\rho_0$ and the corresponding pressure $p_0$. The deviation from equilibrium we shall characterize by the quantities

$$v_i, \qquad \sigma = \rho - \rho_0, \qquad \pi = p - p_0. \quad (125)$$

Furthermore, we shall consider that the function $p(\rho)$ can be expanded into a power series about the equilibrium point,

$$p = p_0 + \frac{\kappa}{\rho_0}\sigma + \cdots \quad (126)$$

The coefficient $\kappa$ is called the *bulk modulus* of the fluid. It is defined as

$$\kappa = \frac{\rho_0 \pi}{\sigma} = \left\{ \rho \frac{dp}{d\rho} \right\}_{\rho = \rho_0} \tag{127}$$

With these quantities, the equations which determine the motion take the following forms:

$$\frac{\partial \sigma}{\partial t} + \rho_0 \frac{\partial v_s}{\partial x_s} = 0, \tag{128}$$

the equation of continuity;

$$\rho_0 \frac{\partial v_i}{\partial t} + \frac{\partial t_{is}}{\partial x_s} = 0, \tag{129}$$

the equations of motion;

$$t_{ik} = \delta_{ik}(p_0 + \pi) - \eta[v_{i,k} + v_{k,i} - \tfrac{2}{3} v_{s,s} \delta_{ik}], \tag{130}$$

the force law; and eq. (126), which provides the necessary algebraic relationship between the two scalar fields $\pi$ and $\sigma$. Making the necessary substitutions, we may combine these equations into equations which, apart from constants, contain only the fields $\pi$ and $v_i$,

$$\frac{1}{\kappa} \frac{\partial \pi}{\partial t} + v_{s,s} = 0,$$
$$\rho_0 \frac{\partial v_i}{\partial t} + \pi_{,i} - \eta(v_{i,ss} + \tfrac{1}{3} v_{s,si}) = 0. \tag{131}$$

The task of acoustics (in fluid media) consists then of finding and discussing solutions of these equations.

We shall restrict ourselves to the simplest possible case, in which the disturbance is a function of one coordinate only, say $x_1 = x$, in other words, where the disturbance is a plane wave. In particular, we shall consider the case of a progressive harmonic wave of the angular frequency $\omega$, and we shall attempt to find a solution of the form

$$\pi = \pi_0 \, e^{i(\omega t - kx)},$$
$$v_x = v_0 \, e^{i(\omega t - kx)} \qquad v_y = v_z = 0. \tag{132}$$

We shall find that the unknown constant $k$ in these two expressions is complex.

Substituting our plane-wave expressions into eqs. (131), we obtain the algebraic conditions

$$\frac{\omega}{\kappa}\pi_0 - k\,v_0 = 0,$$

$$\rho_0\,\omega\,v_0 - k\,\pi_0 - \tfrac{4}{3}i\,\eta\,k\,v_0 = 0. \tag{133}$$

In this set of equations, $k$ can be determined as a function of $\omega$ by the elimination of both $\pi$ and $v$. The value of $k$ turns out to be

$$k = \frac{\omega}{c_0}\left(1 + \frac{4}{3}\,i\,\eta\,\frac{\omega}{\kappa}\right)^{-1/2} \qquad c_0 = \sqrt{\frac{\kappa}{\rho_0}} \tag{134}$$

If the viscosity is not too high or the frequency too great, this expression can be expanded into a power series with ascending powers of $\omega$ or $\eta$, leading to

$$k = \frac{\omega}{c_0} - \frac{2}{3}\,i\,\frac{\eta}{\kappa\,c_0}\,\omega^2 + \cdots . \tag{135}$$

In other words, the expression for $\pi$, for instance, will turn into

$$\pi = \pi_0\,e^{-ax}\,e^{i\omega\left(t - \frac{x}{c_0}\right)} \qquad a = \frac{2}{3}\frac{\eta}{\kappa}\,c_0\,\omega^2. \tag{136}$$

The constant $c_0$ is the velocity with which the pressure wave propagates. It is called the *velocity of sound* in that fluid. The coefficient of $x$ in the amplitude factor, $a$, represents the relative drop in sound pressure amplitude per unit distance of propagation. $2a$ (which equals the relative drop of the square of the sound pressure amplitude per unit distance) is called the *coefficient of absorption.*

Experimental determinations of the velocity of sound in various media have consistently confirmed the expression for $c_0$ in eq. (134). However, experimentally determined absorption coefficients are often considerably higher than those predicted by eq. (136). This deviation indicates that other sources of dissipation must be effective, in addition to shear viscosity.

## 3.8. The elastic solid

In Section 3.5, we found an expression for the strain tensor of an elastic solid, eq. (83). We shall restrict ourselves to the case in which the strain is sufficiently small that the resulting stress is proportional to the strain. This condition is generally known as Hooke's "law." The designation as a law is misleading insofar as Hooke's law expresses nothing but the expandability of the stress as a function of strain into a power series in powers of $s_{ik}$. No matter what solid material is involved, there will be a region of small strain in which Hooke's law is a good approximation, and there will be an "elastic limit" beyond which the linear approximation is no longer valid. Naturally, the elastic limit is not sharply defined but depends on the requirements of accuracy. Frequently, though, measurements show that noticeable deviations from linearity occur first at the same order of magnitude of the applied strain at which the solid undergoes a permanent change of shape, that is, where upon complete relaxation the material no longer recovers its original shape.

In any case we shall consider only situations in which there is no permanent (plastic) deformation and in which Hooke's law is a satisfactory approximation. The components of the stress tensor are, then, linear homogeneous functions of the components of the strain tensor. Since there are six algebraically independent components of the strain tensor ($s_{11}$, $s_{12}$, $s_{13}$, $s_{22}$, $s_{23}$, and $s_{33}$; the remaining components, such as $s_{21}$, are not independent, because of the symmetry conditions) and an equal number of stress components, the total number of coefficients of proportionality $c_{(ik)(mn)}$,

$$t_{ik} = c_{(ik)(mn)} s_{mn}, \tag{137}$$

might be as high as 36. Fortunately, this enormous number of independent parameters is actually reduced to 21 even in crystals with the least possible symmetry, the triclinic crystals. In all other types of crystals, symmetry conditions reduce the number of independent moduli even further. If the solid is isotropic (such as an unstrained glass or a fine-grained steel without a preferred orientation), the number of independent moduli reduces to two, one of which is the bulk modulus, the other the shear modulus.

The bulk modulus is defined by the equation

$$\tfrac{1}{3} t_{ss} = -\kappa \, s_{ss}, \tag{138}$$

and the shear modulus is defined by the equation

$$t_{ik}^* = -2\nu \, \sigma_{ik}. \tag{139}$$

The combination of these two definitions results in the two-parametric relationship

$$t_{ik} = -(\kappa - \tfrac{2}{3}\nu) \, s_{ss} \, \delta_{ik} - 2\nu \, s_{ik}, \tag{140}$$

which will hold for any elastic isotropic solid which obeys Hooke's

law.   It should be noted that with this relationship the directions
of principal stress and those of principal strain are always paralleled.

**Young's modulus.**   Young's modulus is the ratio between the
stress and the strain in one principal direction if the stress (but
not the strain) in the two other principal directions is kept zero.
It is related to the parameters $\kappa$ and $\nu$ above.   If we choose a
coordinate system in which the principal directions are parallel to
the coordinate axes, we find for the principal stresses the expressions

$$t_{11} = -(\kappa + \tfrac{4}{3}\nu)\, s_{11} - 2(\kappa - \tfrac{2}{3}\nu)\, s_{22},$$
$$t_{22} = t_{33} = -2(\kappa + \tfrac{1}{3}\nu)\, s_{22} - (\kappa + \tfrac{2}{3}\nu)\, s_{11} = 0. \qquad (141)$$
$$s_{22} = s_{33}$$

The solutions of these equations are

$$Y = -\frac{t_{11}}{s_{11}} = -3\,\frac{\kappa\,\nu}{\kappa + \tfrac{1}{3}\nu},$$
$$\sigma = -\frac{s_{22}}{s_{11}} = -\frac{1}{2}\frac{\kappa - \tfrac{2}{3}\nu}{\kappa + \tfrac{1}{3}\nu}. \qquad (142)$$

$Y$ is Young's modulus, and the constant $\sigma$ is known as *Poisson's
ratio*.   This ratio is a measure for the transverse contraction of a
stretched wire.

**Elastic waves.**   Just as in a fluid, disturbances of the equilibrium
will also propagate in an elastic solid.   The laws of propagation are
much the same as those found in the preceding section, except for
the added complication that a solid is capable of propagating two
kinds of elastic waves, so-called *compression waves* and *shear waves*.
To find the laws governing both types, we must again assemble a
set of linearized differential equations.

We start by considering the functions $y_i$, which are required for
the determination of the strain tensor.   We assume that the solid
has been deformed only slightly, and we agree that the functions
$y_i$ shall deviate only slightly from the coordinates $x_i$,

$$y_i = x_i - u_i(x_k). \qquad (143)$$

The field $u_i$ represents the displacement of a given material point
from its equilibrium position.   If we substitute this expression into
eq. (83), disregarding all terms which contain higher than first
powers of the field $u_i$, we obtain for the strain tensor the approximate
linearized expression

$$s_{ik} = \tfrac{1}{2}(u_{i,k} + u_{k,i}), \tag{144}$$

and therefore for the force law, because of eq. (140),

$$t_{ik} = -(\kappa - \tfrac{2}{3}\nu)\, u_{s,s}\, \delta_{ik} - \nu(u_{i,k} + u_{k,i}). \tag{145}$$

On the other hand, the velocity field is related to the **u**-field by the equations

$$v_i = \frac{\partial u_i}{\partial t}, \tag{146}$$

except for higher-order terms. If eqs. (145) and (146) are substituted into the equations of motion (77), the result is a set of three differential equations for the three variables $u_i$,

$$\rho_0 \frac{\partial^2 u_i}{\partial t^2} - \left(\kappa + \frac{1}{3}\nu\right) u_{s,si} - \nu\, u_{i,ss} = 0. \tag{147}$$

Again, we shall look for plane-wave harmonic solutions; it is convenient to attempt the form

$$u_i = \overset{0}{u_i} e^{i(\omega t - k_s x_s)} \tag{148}$$

The three quantities $k_s$ form a vector which is normal to the wave fronts (and therefore parallel to the direction of propagation) and which has the magnitude $2\pi/\lambda$. With this attempt, the differential equations turn into algebraic equations for the quantities $\overset{0}{u_i}$ and $k_i$,

$$(\rho_0\,\omega^2 - \nu\,k^2)\,\overset{0}{u_i} - (\kappa + \tfrac{1}{3}\nu)\,k_i\,k_s\,\overset{0}{u_s} = 0. \tag{149}$$

The solutions of these equations can be found most rapidly in a coordinate system in which a coordinate axis is parallel to the vector **k.** We set

$$k_1 = k, \qquad k_2 = k_3 = 0, \tag{150}$$

and obtain immediately the equations

$$\begin{aligned} &[\rho_0\,\omega^2 - (\kappa + \tfrac{4}{3}\nu)k^2]\,\overset{0}{u_1} = 0, \\ &[\rho_0\,\omega^2 - \nu k^2]\,\overset{0}{u_2} = 0, \qquad [\rho_0\,\omega^2 - \nu k^2]\,\overset{0}{u_3} = 0. \end{aligned} \tag{151}$$

From these three equations it appears that, for one value of $k$, $\overset{0}{u_1}$ and $\overset{0}{u_2}$ cannot both be different from zero. We find two different solutions which lead to different values of $k$ and, thereby, of the speed of propagation $c$. They are

$$\overset{0}{u_2} = \overset{0}{u_3} = 0,$$

$$k^2 = \frac{\rho_0}{\kappa + \frac{4}{3}\nu}\,\omega^2, \qquad c = \sqrt{\frac{\kappa + \frac{4}{3}\nu}{\rho_0}}, \tag{152}$$

and

$$\overset{0}{u_1} = 0,$$

$$k^2 = \frac{\rho_0}{\nu}\,\omega^2, \qquad c = \sqrt{\frac{\nu}{\rho_0}}. \tag{153}$$

The waves (152) represent displacements in the direction of propagation, while those corresponding to eq. (153) are at right angles to the direction of propagation. The speed of propagation of the *longitudinal waves* (152) is higher than that of the *transverse waves*. Finally, the transverse waves must have a plane of polarization, whereas the longitudinal waves do not. Both types of waves are well known as the carriers of acoustic energy in solids. They are also commonly observed in seismic disturbances, where the longitudinal or *compression wave* always arrives at the seismographic observatory ahead of the transverse or *shear wave*. This difference of arrival is roughly proportional to the distance traveled (not exactly, because the speed of propagation is also a function of depth) and hence permits conclusions concerning the distance of the origin of the disturbance from the point of observation.

## Problems

**3.1.** If a solid body is submerged in a fluid at rest, each element of its surface is subjected to the hydrostatic pressure of the fluid, which exerts a force per unit area at right angles to the surface element $dS$ and equal in magnitude to $g$ (980 cm-sec$^{-2}$), multiplied by the density of the fluid $\rho$ and by the depth below the free surface of the fluid. Obtain an expression for the total force exerted by the hydrostatic pressure on the submerged body and show that your expression leads to Archimedes' law of buoyancy.

**3.2.** A vector field is given by the expressions

$$v_1 = x_2 f(\rho), \qquad v_2 = -x_1 f(\rho), \qquad v_3 = 0, \qquad \rho^2 = x_1^2 + x_2^2,$$

where $f(\rho)$ is an arbitrary function of its argument. Find the correct expressions for the same vector field with respect to a coordinate system which has the $x_3$-axis in common with the original one and where the new $x_1$- and $x_2$-axes form the angle $\theta$ with the corresponding old axes.

**3.3.** In Problem 3.2, carry out a coordinate transformation in which the $x_2$- and $x_3$-axes remain the same and the $x_1$-axis merely changes the sign.

**3.4.** Prove that the Kronecker symbol is a tensor.

**3.5.** In a special coordinate system, the stress tensor has the components

$$t_{12} = t_{21} = T,$$

all other components being zero. Diagonalize the vector and give not only the principal stresses but also the directions of principal stress and the explicit coordinate transformation which leads to the diagonal form.

**3.6.** (a) Show that the divergence of the vector field $v_i$ of Problem 3.2 vanishes, no matter how $f$ is chosen.

(b) How must the function $f$ be chosen so that the field $v_i$ may be considered (at least locally) as the gradient of a scalar field?

**3.7.** Find the most general form of a function of $r$,

$$r^2 = x_s\, x_s,$$

of which the Laplacian vanishes everywhere, except possibly in a finite number of space points.

**3.8.** Determine all the cases in which (with the elastic moduli given) the stress tensor of an isotropic elastic solid is proportional to the strain tensor.

**3.9.** Prove that the principal stresses of an isotropic elastic solid are always parallel to the principal strains.

**3.10.** For a perfect fluid ($\eta = 0$), derive the conservation law of acoustic energy by starting with eqs. (131).

**3.11.** Derive the conservation law of wave energy for an elastic solid by starting with eqs. (147). Note that the flow of elastic energy (the expression of which the divergence appears in the conservation law) must equal the dot product of the stress tensor (145) by $v_i$.

**3.12.** Consider the case of two perfect fluids separated by a plane interface. At the interface, the sound pressure and the normal component of the velocity must remain continuous. Derive the laws of reflection and refraction of sound waves by combining the incident, the reflected, and the refracted plane waves so that the conditions of continuity across the interface are satisfied. The intensity laws are obtained coincidentally.

**3.13.** Starting with the equations (131), derive a partial differential equation for the sound pressure $\pi$ alone, both for the perfect and for the imperfect fluid. These equations are called *wave equations*. The plane waves treated in the text are special solutions of these equations.

**3.14.** For the perfect fluid, derive a solution which is a periodic function of the time $t$ but which is spherically symmetric in the coordinates; that is, spatially it is to depend on $r$ only.

# Chapter 4

## Summary of Classical Mechanics

In the following chapters, we shall take up Maxwell's theory of the electromagnetic field, which requires some modification of the foundations of mechanics. That is why this chapter will be devoted to a brief review.

In Newtonian mechanics, the deviation of a mass point from straight-line, uniform motion (as described in terms of an inertial frame of reference) is determined completely by the forces which other mass points exert on it, in accordance with the second law: The acceleration of the particle multiplied by its mass equals the sum of the forces caused by the other particles in the universe. Since the force acting on a particular mass point can thus be resolved into the sum of the contributions made by all the other individual mass points, it is appropriate to talk of the interactions between individual pairs of mass points and to build up the resultant forces from pair interactions.

Forces which two mass points exert on each other obey the following laws:

(1) The force which mass point $A$ exerts on $B$ is equal in magnitude and opposite in direction to the force which $B$ exerts on $A$.

(2) This common magnitude depends only on the distance between the two particles, in accordance with a specific law which is called the *force law* applying to these two particles. Examples are Newton's law of gravitation and Coulomb's law of electrostatic interaction.

(3) Directions of the two forces are parallel to the connecting straight line between the two bodies. That is to say, $A$ will exert a force on $B$ which will either point straight toward or straight away from $A$ (attraction and repulsion).

From these basic assumptions, we were able to draw a number of conclusions concerning the behavior of aggregates of particles:

(A) The total linear momentum of a system of particles changes in time in accordance with the total external force acting on the system, irrespective of any internal interaction.

(B) The total angular momentum of a system changes in time in accordance with the total external torque applied, irrespective of internal interactions.

(C) A certain specific function of the coordinates and velocities of a system of particles, called the *total energy* of the system, changes in time according to the work done by the external forces on the constituent particles.

It is these three conclusions (A), (B), and (C), rather than the basic assumptions (1), (2), and (3), which are subject to experimental verification, inasmuch as we are rarely able to carry out experiments on particles that we are certain constitute mass points in the rigorous sense.   This possibility of experimental verification is important to keep in mind in what follows in Part II.   We shall find that the action of the magnetic field on charges cannot be reconciled with Newton's assumptions.   Although, thus, we are forced to modify the basic assumptions, obviously we should not be ready to agree to modifications which will not permit the retention of some conservation laws applying to linear momentum, angular momentum, and energy, because the conservation laws for aggregates can be tested readily and are invariably found to hold.

Next, we must recapitulate the significance of our treatment of matter in bulk.   If we are to treat a problem in mechanics involving only a few mass points (the meaning of "few" being a function of our mathematical ingenuity), then our task is to set up a system of *ordinary* differential equations which involves a number of functions of a *single* argument, the functions $x_i(t)$.   The number of these functions, and the number of differential equations which must be solved, equals the number of degrees of freedom of the system and is ordinarily three times the number of mass points involved.   If now the number of mass point becomes large (and is possibly not even accurately known), we must remove from our laws of nature all quantities referring to the individual particles and replace them by quantities describing average properties of the material.   Naturally, in this process we lose much pertinent information.   But the remarkable fact is that it is possible to set up laws for suitably chosen "average" quantities, the mass density, the local velocity (which is defined as the ratio between momentum density and mass density), the components of the stress tensor, and so on. These quantities are no longer functions of the single argument $t$ only but, being "local" averages, are functions of the coordinates as well. Coordinates no longer identify the location of an individual particle; rather, they identify a particular location in space irrespective of the presence of particles. As a result, the laws of nature in this formalism are *partial* differential equations.

However, as far as our basic physical assumptions (1) through (3) are concerned, nothing has been changed. As a result, the conservation laws (A) through (C) must still hold, though their mathematical form may be quite different. Indeed, we were able to derive differential relationships which express in terms of partial derivatives the fact that local energy or momentum density changes at a time rate determined by the flux of energy or momentum toward or away from the domain under consideration. A similar relationship could have been obtained by essentially the same methods for the angular-momentum density.

Treatment of matter in bulk is called for not only because of the practical importance of such laws—after all, most of the matter which we have to deal with in the laboratory occurs in bulk form —but also for an entirely different reason. Without changing our basic physical assumptions, we have produced a mathematical formalism which is capable of handling physical theories widely different from Newtonian mechanics. In particular, in the chapters which follow we shall be concerned with a *field theory*. A field is a distributed physical quantity, such as temperature or electric potential, that is, a quantity which is defined at any given time at each point within the spatial domain that we are considering. In a mechanical picture of the physical world, we consider as the principal subject of our theories discrete, individual mass points, separated by expanses of empty space, across which they exert forces on each other. In a field theoretical approach, we think of space as being filled everywhere by various fields; and the fields, together with the mass points, become the primary building stones of the physical world.

In our treatment of bulk matter, we have "smeared" out our mass points through the device of averaging. The mass density and the other averages of this formalism are typical *mathematical fields*, even though the underlying physical ideas stem from a mechanical rather than a field theory.    We shall find the techniques which were developed in Chapter 3 very useful when we need to develop the formalism appropriate to genuine field theoretical concepts.

# PART II
# ELECTRODYNAMICS

# Chapter 5

## Electrostatics and Magnetostatics

### 5.1. Coulomb's law

The forces which two charged particles exert on each other vary inversely with the square of the distance, just like gravitational forces. Coulomb's law states that the magnitude of the force which two isolated charged mass points or *point charges* exert on each other equals the product of their charges, divided by the square of the distance between them:

$$|\mathbf{f}| = \frac{e_1 e_2}{r^2}. \tag{1}$$

In thus formulating Coulomb's law, we have already defined the unit of electric charge, the so-called *statcoulomb* (if the force is measured in dynes). The statcoulomb is that charge which exerts on an equal charge at a distance of one centimeter a force of one dyne. Although other systems of units are also in use, we shall in this book consistently use electrostatic units and, in the case of magnetic quantities, Gaussian units.

Both Coulomb's law of electrostatic interaction and Newton's law of gravitation are so-called inverse square laws. However, these two laws have different structures in that in nature we find only positive masses, which attract each other, whereas electric charges occur with both signs. Charges having the same sign repel each other; charges of opposite sign attract each other. Coulomb's law is a typical example of a mechanical force law in that the mutual forces between two particles are equal, opposite, in the direction of the connecting straight line, and, for two given point charges, functions of the distance only.

We have found previously that any force law can also be formulated conveniently in terms of the potential energy associated with a pair of mass points. If we call the potential energy between two point charges $V$, as before, then Coulomb's law may also be written in the form

$$V = \frac{e_1\, e_2}{r}. \tag{2}$$

Equation (2) includes automatically the dependence of the direction of the force on the signs of the two charges involved. As before, the force acting on either of the two particles is the negative gradient of the potential energy $V$ with respect to the coordinates of that particle.

Equation (2) permits a rather convenient representation of the force experienced by one point charge in the presence of several other charges. Instead of adding vectorially the individual contributions to the force, we add the scalar potential energies and subsequently obtain the force by forming the gradient. If we consider a system of $N$ point charges with charges $e_k$, $k = 1, \cdots, N$, then the force acting on the $n$th particle must be the negative gradient of a function which we shall call, for the moment, $V_n$ and which is the sum of the potential energies of all particle pairs including the $n$th point charge,[1]

$$V_n = \sum_{k=1}^{N}{}' \frac{e_k\, e_n}{r_{kn}} = e_n \cdot \sum_{k=1}^{N}{}' \frac{e_k}{r_{kn}}. \tag{3}$$

The prime indicates that in the summation the term with $k = n$ is to be omitted. The force acting on the $n$th particle is then given as

$$f_{i\,n} = - \frac{\partial V_n}{\partial x_{i\,n}} = -e_n \cdot \frac{\partial}{\partial x_{i\,n}} \left( \sum_{k=1}^{N}{}' \frac{e_k}{r_{kn}} \right). \tag{4}$$

No matter how involved the system of point charges, the force acting on the $n$th particle can always be expressed as the product of two factors. The first factor is $e_n$, while the second factor contains only the charges of the other particles and, of course, functions of the relative coordinates. For many purposes, this separation

---

[1] This function, $V_n$, differs from the potential energy of the system, which we introduced in Chapter 1, in that we are now omitting all those pairs in the summation of which the $n$th is not one member.

is desirable. The second factor in eq. (3) can be called the *electrostatic potential* applying to the $n$th particle, while its negative gradient [the second factor in eq. (4)] can be called the *electric field intensity* applying to the $n$th particle. We shall denote these quantities by the symbols $\Phi_n$ and $E_i$, respectively,

$$\Phi_n = \sum_k{}' \frac{e_k}{r_{nk}},$$

$$E_i = - \frac{\partial \Phi_n}{\partial x_i} = - \frac{\partial}{\partial x_i}\left(\sum_k{}' \frac{e_k}{r_{nk}}\right). \tag{5}$$

The dimension of the potential is ergs per statcoulomb, and its unit is called the *statvolt*. The dimension of the field strength is dynes per statcoulomb, but more usually the equivalent expression of statvolts per cm is used instead.

Given our system of point charges, we can introduce functions very similar to $\Phi_n$ and to $E_i$ which do not refer to a particular particle and which can be defined at each point of space. We shall call the function

$$\Phi(x_i) = \sum_k \frac{e_k}{r_k} \qquad (r_k = \sqrt{(x_i - x_i)(x_i - x_i)}), \tag{6}$$

the *electrostatic potential* (without making reference to the $n$th or any other particular particle) and its negative gradient,

$$E_i = - \frac{\partial \Phi}{x_i} = - \frac{\partial}{\partial x_i}\left(\sum_k \frac{e_k}{r_k}\right), \tag{7}$$

the *electric field strength*. These functions are continuous and differentiable everywhere, except at the locations of the constituent point charges, where they become infinite. At the location of a particular point charge (say the $n$th), it is, however, possible to obtain a finite potential function from $\Phi$, simply by subtracting the contribution $e_n/r_n$. The difference remains finite and, at the exact location of the $n$th particle itself, assumes the value $\Phi_n$.

Analogous relations hold for $E_i$ and $E_i$.

## 5.2. Continuous charge distributions

The introduction of the "field" variables $\Phi$ and $E_i$ has little to recommend it as long as we treat only systems consisting of a few charges and as long as we set up and solve the ordinary equations of motion for the individual particles. These functions reveal their usefulness, though, once we go over to the problem of treating large numbers of point charges in accordance with the methods which were developed in Chapter 3. In that case, we may assume without serious error that the contribution of any individual particle to the potential $\Phi$ is negligible and that, therefore, the potential $\underset{n}{\Phi}$ applying to the $n$th particle is very nearly equal to the average value of $\Phi$ in the vicinity of the particle.

It could be argued that at the location of the $n$th particle the function $\Phi$ becomes infinite whereas $\underset{n}{\Phi}$ does not; that the difference between these functions, therefore, is infinite; and that there is no such thing as a "small" or "negligible" infinity. However, in a consideration of bulk matter the locations of individual particles are not accurately known anyway, and what enters into the equations is not the exact value of the potential at the location $\underset{n}{x_i}$ but rather its "average" value in the vicinity of that point. In any such averaging operation, the contribution of the infinity itself remains finite and can, in fact, be made small. If we wish to compute the average value of $e/r$ in a sphere of radius $R$ surrounding the location of the charge in question, we must compute the integral

$$\int \Phi \, dx_1 \, dx_2 \, dx_3 = \int_0^R \frac{e}{r} \cdot 4\pi \, r^2 \, dr = 2\pi \, e \, R^2 \tag{8}$$

and then divide through by the volume of the sphere, $\frac{4}{3}\pi R^3$. The result of this averaging is

$$\langle \Phi \rangle = \frac{3}{2}\frac{e}{R}, \tag{9}$$

This expression becomes the smaller the greater the chosen sphere. How small we can make it obviously depends only on how large we can make the sphere before it includes neighboring point charges. Thus, the replacement of $\Phi$ by the "local average of $\Phi$" involves no serious omission.

In addition to the local (average) potential, we shall require the local charge density, that is, the average number of statcoulombs per unit volume. This average is, of course, subject to all the comments that apply in the case of such other average quantities as the mass density $\rho$ (compare the beginning of Chapter 3). We shall denote the electric charge density by the symbol $\sigma$. In its computation negative charges are, of course, to be offset against positive charges, and $\sigma$ represents the net charge density.

The electrostatic force which is experienced by all the charges present in a small volume element $dV$ must equal the product of the average field strength $E_i$ by the charge present, $\sigma\, dV$. The force per unit volume representing Coulomb interaction is, therefore,

$$f_i = \sigma\, E_i = -\sigma\, \frac{\partial \Phi}{\partial x_i}. \tag{10}$$

This force must be added to forces representing other types of interaction. Offhand, it cannot be incorporated in the stress tensor, because the electrostatic forces do not decrease sufficiently rapidly at large distances to assure the convergence of the integral (3.10). True, the magnitude of the force drops off with the square of the distance; but at the same time the number of particles present at distances between $r$ and $r + dr$ increases with the same power of $r$. To restrict the integration arbitrarily to a neighborhood of, say, 10 Å may mean throwing away an infinite contribution. Nevertheless, we shall find a way to incorporate electrostatic interactions in the stress tensor $t_{ik}$.

Suppose we knew the distribution of charges throughout a large region. Then it must be possible to replace the summation over individual charges in eq. (6) by an integral. If we wish to find the value of $\Phi$ at a point with the coordinates $x_i$, then the contribution of all the charges contained in the volume element $dV$ centered about the point with the coordinates $\bar{x}_i$ must be

$$d\Phi(x_i) = \frac{\sigma(\bar{x}_i)\, dV}{r} \qquad r^2 = (x_i - \bar{x}_i)(x_i - \bar{x}_i). \tag{11}$$

When we integrate over all that region of space in which charges are contained, we obtain the integral expression

$$\Phi(x_i) = \int \frac{\sigma(\bar{x}_i)\, d\bar{x}_1\, d\bar{x}_2\, d\bar{x}_3}{r}. \tag{12}$$

Equations (12) and (10) together enable us to find the electric force per unit volume as a function of the charge distribution throughout our mechanical system.

For many applications, eq. (12) is not particularly satisfactory.

We shall derive a law which expresses the dependence of $\Phi$ on local conditions. This law is commonly known as *Gauss's law*. With its help, we shall be able to express $f_i$ in eq. (10) in the form of a divergence of a symmetric tensor.

Gauss's law states that an integral taken over an arbitrary closed surface of the normal component of the electric field strength, multiplied by the infinitesimal surface element, equals $4\pi$ times the total electric charge contained in the interior of that surface. To derive this law, we shall first prove that in the absence of charges

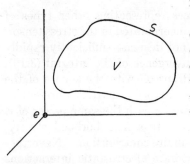

in the interior this integral vanishes. Consider Fig. 8. An arbitrary closed surface $S$ encloses a region $V$ of space, but not the origin $O$ of our coordinate system. Into the origin we place a point charge of magnitude $e$. We shall compute the value of the integral

$$W = \oint_S E_i\, n_i\, dS \equiv \oint_S \mathbf{E} \cdot \mathbf{n}\, dS.$$
(13)

FIG. 8. Gauss's theorem for a surface which encloses no charges.

To do so, we apply Gauss's theorem and convert the surface integral into a volume integral,

$$W = \int_V \frac{\partial E_s}{\partial x_s}\, dV.$$
(14)

With our choice of coordinate system, the components of $\mathbf{E}$ take the values

$$E_s = \frac{e x_s}{r^3} \qquad (r^2 = x_r x_r),$$
(15)

and therefore the divergence is zero,

$$\frac{\partial E_s}{\partial x_s} = e\, \frac{\delta_{ss}}{r^3} - 3\, \frac{x_s x_s}{r^5} = 0 \qquad \delta_{ss} \equiv 3, \qquad \frac{\partial r}{\partial x_s} \equiv \frac{x_s}{r}.$$
(16)

We conclude, therefore, that the surface integral (13) over $S$ vanishes, as long as it does not include the origin.

This result can be generalized without difficulty. Suppose that outside the surface is placed not one charge but instead many different charges at different locations, though none inside $S$. In that case, the total electric field strength at any point on $S$ is the vector sum of the contributions of the individual point charges. The integral (13) must equal the sum of similar integrals, but each representing only the contribution of a single point charge. Each one of these contributions vanishes, as we have just seen. It follows that the integral (13) will vanish irrespective of the distribution

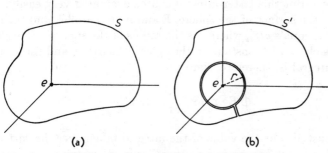

(a)                          (b)

Fig. 9.   Surface enclosing a single charge.

of electric charges outside, provided only that the interior remains free of charges.

We shall now place a single charge inside a closed surface. To consider this case, we can at first again place our single electric charge of magnitude $e$ into the origin of our coordinate system and then choose an arbitrary closed surface $S$ surrounding that origin (Fig. 9a).

The integral (13), extended over this new surface, can be evaluated if we represent it as the sum of two integrals, one over a small spherical surface surrounding the origin, the other a surface that does not contain our charge. To do so, we construct a sphere about the origin, with a radius sufficiently small that all the sphere is well inside $S$. Then we construct a small tube of negligibly small cross section that will connect $S$ with the little sphere. Finally, we eliminate those very small portions of $S$ and the sphere which seal off the two ends of the tube. The result will be a surface of the shape indicated in Fig. 9b. If we integrate $\mathbf{E} \cdot \mathbf{n}$ over this new surface, $S'$, and add to it the integral of $\mathbf{E} \cdot \mathbf{n}$, taken over the same sphere, the sum of these two integrals will equal the integral over $S$ alone. The reason is that the integral over the small sphere is, in effect, being taken twice, but with the normal vector pointing in opposite directions (pointing away from the *interior* of each closed surface). The contribution of the tube is negligible if we will only make its cross section sufficiently small. All that is left now is the contribution of $S$. But the surface $S'$ does not enclose the charge; hence the integral taken over $S'$ must vanish, in accordance with our previous result. In other words, the integral of $\mathbf{E} \cdot \mathbf{n}$, taken over $S$ of Fig. 9a, must equal the integral over the small sphere. But this latter integral can be evaluated very easily.

On the surface of the sphere, $\mathbf{E}$ and $\mathbf{n}$ are parallel, and their dot product equals $e/r^2$, where $r$ is the radius of the sphere. This function is obviously constant on the spherical surface, and the value of the integral is, therefore, simply

$$\oint \mathbf{E} \cdot \mathbf{n} \, dS = \frac{e}{r^2} \cdot 4\pi \, r^2 = 4\pi e. \tag{17}$$

$4\pi e$ must also be the value of the integral taken over the surface $S$.

This result can again be generalized. If we place not one but several charges inside a closed surface, their contributions to the surface integral (13) add, and its value is, therefore, equal to $4\pi$ times the sum of all the charges enclosed by the surface in question. With this conclusion we have completed the proof. If we consider individual point charges, then Gauss's law is expressed by the equation

$$\oint E_s \, n_s \, dS = 4\pi \sum_n e_n, \tag{18}$$

where the summation on the right-hand side is to be carried out over all charges inside $S$ (in $V$) but not over those outside. If we wish to describe the charge distribution by means of the charge density $\sigma$, then the total charge is given by an integral, and we have

$$\oint E_s \, n_s \, dS = 4\pi \int_V \sigma \, dV, \tag{19}$$

which applies to arbitrarily chosen volumes $V$ and their bounding surfaces $S$.

If we now apply Gauss's theorem to eq. (19), we can write the whole equation as a single volume integral

$$\int_V \left( \frac{\partial E_s}{\partial x_s} - 4\pi \, \sigma \right) dV = 0, \tag{20}$$

which must vanish when taken over arbitrary volumes $V$. This can be true only if the integrand vanishes by itself, and we end up with the differential form of Gauss's law:

$$\frac{\partial E_s}{\partial x_s} = 4\pi \, \sigma = - \frac{\partial^2 \Phi}{\partial x_s \, \partial x_s} = -\nabla^2 \, \Phi. \tag{21}$$

With this expression for the divergence of the electric field strength, we can convert the right hand side of eq. (10) into the divergence of a symmetric tensor. We eliminate from this expression $\sigma$ and obtain

$$f_i = \sigma \, E_i = \frac{1}{4\pi} \, E_i \, \frac{\partial E_s}{\partial x_s}. \tag{22}$$

By differentiating by parts, we can transform the right-hand side further into

$$f_i = \frac{1}{4\pi} \left[ \frac{\partial}{\partial x_s} (E_i \, E_s) - E_s \frac{\partial E_i}{\partial x_s} \right]. \tag{23}$$

In order to complete the computation, it will be necessary to make use of the fact that $E_i$ can be represented as the partial derivative of a potential, according to eq. (7), and that, as a result,

$$\frac{\partial E_i}{\partial x_k} - \frac{\partial E_k}{\partial x_i} = - \frac{\partial^2 \Phi}{\partial x_i \, \partial x_k} + \frac{\partial^2 \Phi}{\partial x_k \, \partial x_i} = 0. \tag{24}$$

(In the usual terminology of vector calculus, we say that curl **E** vanishes.) We replace, therefore, $\frac{\partial E_i}{\partial x_s}$ by $\frac{\partial E_s}{\partial x_i}$ and obtain, for the right-hand side of eq. (23),

$$\begin{aligned}
f_i &= \frac{1}{4\pi} \left[ \frac{\partial}{\partial x_s} (E_i \, E_s) - E_s \frac{\partial E_s}{\partial x_i} \right] \\
&= \frac{1}{4\pi} \left[ \frac{\partial}{\partial x_s} (E_i \, E_s) - \frac{1}{2} \frac{\partial}{\partial x_i} (E_s \, E_s) \right] \\
&= \frac{1}{4\pi} \frac{\partial}{\partial x_s} \left[ E_i \, E_s - \frac{1}{2} \, \delta_{is} \, E_r \, E_r \right].
\end{aligned} \tag{25}$$

In other words, the force per unit volume acting on the charges can be represented in the form of a divergence.   The symmetric tensor

$$t_{ik} = \frac{1}{4\pi} \left( \frac{1}{2} \, \delta_{ik} \, E_s \, E_s - E_i \, E_k \right) \tag{26}$$

is sometimes called the *stress tensor* associated with an electrostatic field.   It describes the forces acting on a unit volume containing electric charges formally in the same way that the stress tensor set up in Chapter 3 does.   Nevertheless, there is a very important physical difference.   In Chapter 3, the stress tensor represented the forces per unit area which the particles immediately adjoining a virtual surface on both sides exerted on each other across that surface.   The expression for the electrostatic stress tensor, (26),

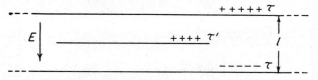

FIG. 10.   Free plate between two fixed condenser plates.

includes forces contributed by particles far removed from that virtual surface.

An example will illustrate the significance of the stress tensor. Suppose that a parallel-plate condenser with very large plates and possessing an area charge density $\tau$ has a plate spacing $l$.   It is well known that the electric field strength between the two condenser plates is everywhere equal to $4\pi \, \tau$.   Now suppose that this arrangement is modified by placing another fairly large plate with area charge density $\tau'$ somewhere between the two condenser plates. This situation is shown in Fig. 10.   The third plate is supposed to be free to move up and down, whereas the two original condenser plates are fixed.   Now the force per unit area acting on the third plate must equal the product of the applied field strength and the charge per unit area,

$$f = \tau' E = 4\pi \, \tau\tau'. \tag{27}$$

This result has been obtained by straightforward elementary considerations.   Let us see how that same answer will be obtained when we apply the concept of the stress tensor.

Because of the presence of the new charged plate, the total field strength above and below the third plate will no longer be given by the simple expression $4\pi\,\tau$. Rather, it will be

$$
\begin{aligned}
E_1 &= 4\pi(\tau + \tfrac{1}{2}\tau') \qquad \text{(below the third plate)}, \\
E_1 &= 4\pi(\tau - \tfrac{1}{2}\tau') \qquad \text{(above the third plate)}.
\end{aligned}
\tag{28}
$$

The components of the tensor $t_{ik}$ of eq. (26), on the other hand, are

$$
t_{11} = -\frac{1}{8\pi}\,E_1^2, \qquad t_{22} = t_{33} = +\frac{1}{8\pi}\,E_1^2,
$$
$$
t_{12} = t_{23} = t_{31} = 0,
\tag{29}
$$

where $x_1$ represents the downward direction. If we interpret these components as positive pressures (pushing apart) in the $x_2$ and $x_3$ directions and as a negative pressure (pulling together) in the $x_1$ direction, we find that the net pull on any volume element (that is, the difference in forces acting on opposite surfaces) vanishes everywhere except where the volume element includes part of the third plate. In that case, there will be a net pull in the downward direction, which will be given by the excess over the pull below that plate over that found above. This excess pull, per unit area of the third plate, is given by the difference

$$
t_{11\,(\text{below})} - t_{11\,(\text{above})}
$$
$$
= \frac{1}{8\pi}\left[4\pi\left(\tau + \frac{1}{2}\tau'\right)\right]^2 - \frac{1}{8\pi}\left[4\pi\left(\tau - \frac{1}{2}\tau'\right)\right]^2
\tag{30}
$$
$$
= 2\pi\cdot 2\tau\tau' = 4\pi\,\tau\tau',
$$

where the expressions (28) have been substituted into $t_{11}$ of eq. (29). This final result equals the result of eq. (27), which had been obtained without reference to the stress tensor.

## 5.3. Dipoles and higher poles.  Polarization

In nature, we often encounter pairs of charges of opposite sign closely tied together. Among the most important examples are molecules consisting of ions of opposite charge, the so-called salts. In the compound NaCl, for instance (sodium chloride, the ordinary cooking salt), the sodium atoms are positively charged, the chlorine atoms negatively, so that the whole molecule is electrically neutral. Nevertheless, the electric field in the vicinity of such a molecule does not vanish, because the two charges of opposite sign are located at different points in space.

Consider a point charge of magnitude $-e$ located at a point with the coordinates $\mathbf{x}_0$ and another point charge $+e$ located at a point with the coordinates $\mathbf{x}_0 + \mathbf{s}$. We shall compute the electric field strength caused by this combination at an arbitrary third point with the coordinates $\mathbf{x}$ (short for $x_i$). The situation is illustrated in Fig. 11. In particular, we are interested in an expression for the

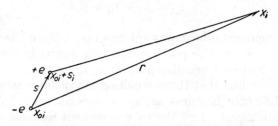

FIG. 11.   Electric dipole.

field which will be valid when the distance $|\mathbf{x} - \mathbf{x}_0|$ is large compared with the distance between the two point charges, $|\mathbf{s}|$. Instead of computing the vector field $\mathbf{E}$, we shall first attack the simpler problem of computing the electric potential $\Phi$. This potential is given by the expression

$$\Phi = \frac{e}{|\mathbf{x} - \mathbf{x}_0 - \mathbf{s}|} - \frac{e}{|\mathbf{x} - \mathbf{x}_0|} = \frac{e}{|\mathbf{r} - \mathbf{s}|} - \frac{e}{|\mathbf{r}|}, \qquad \mathbf{r} = \mathbf{x} - \mathbf{x}_0. \quad (31)$$

The expressions in the denominator are distances. In particular, the first denominator has the value

$$|\mathbf{x} - \mathbf{x}_0 - \mathbf{s}| \equiv \sqrt{(x_i - x_{i_0} - s_i)(x_i - x_{i_0} - s_i)}$$
$$= \sqrt{(r_i - s_i)(r_i - s_i)}. \quad (32)$$

In order to get the expression (31) into a usable form, we shall expand the first term into a power series in ascending orders of the components of the vector $\mathbf{s}$. According to Taylor's theorem (which, in this case, leads to the binomial series), we have

$$[(r_i - s_i)(r_i - s_i)]^{-1/2} = [|r|^2 - 2r_i s_i + |s|^2]^{-1/2}$$

$$= |r|^{-1}\left[1 - 2\frac{r_i s_i}{|r|^2} + \frac{|s|^2}{|r|^2}\right]^{-1/2} \qquad (33)$$

$$= |r|^{-1}\left(1 + \frac{r_i s_i}{|r|^2} + \cdots\right),$$

up to the terms linear in $s_i$. If this power series is substituted into eq. (31), the first term drops out, and the potential is given by the expression

$$\Phi = \frac{e}{|r|^3} r_i s_i = \frac{e}{r^3} \mathbf{r} \cdot \mathbf{s}, \qquad (34)$$

up to first-order terms. The expression (34) approximates the potential well if the distance between the two opposite charges is very small compared to $|\mathbf{r}|$. We can obtain a nonvanishing limiting value if we not only shrink the distance $s$ but also, at the same time, increase the magnitude of the charge $e$ in such a fashion that the product $e|s|$ remains constant. Then the term which has been retained does not change its value at all, whereas all the terms in the expansion which contain higher powers of $|s|$ (but which remain linear in $e$) will tend toward zero.

Frequently, the distance of the measuring equipment from a given pair of charges is so great compared to the mutual distance $|s|$ that only the field (34) will be observed, with all higher terms negligibly small. In that case, we cannot measure the quantities $e$ and $\mathbf{s}$ separately, but only their product, the vector $\mathbf{p}$,

$$\mathbf{p} = e\,\mathbf{s}. \qquad (35)$$

The potential of the dipole is then completely described by the expression

$$\Phi = \frac{1}{r^3}\mathbf{p} \cdot \mathbf{r}. \qquad (36)$$

The vector $\mathbf{p}$ is called the *dipole moment* of the pair of charges considered.

We are now able to consider the distribution of electric charges in bulk matter. All matter is composed of electrically charged particles, the atomic nuclei and the electrons. Ordinarily, there are just enough electrons to offset the positive charges of the nuclei, and a piece of matter has a zero net electric charge (is electrically

neutral).   Moreover, the charges in the interior are so distributed
that there is no preponderance of charges of either sign in any portion of space which is large compared to the size of an atom.   As
a result, if we examine the electric field of a piece of matter at some
distance from the piece, we find neither the field that would be
caused by a net charge nor a field that would correspond to a
resultant dipole moment.   If the charge distribution inside a piece
of matter were unbalanced, the resulting electric field would tend to
restore the balance.

Conditions are changed if we place matter into an electric field,
for instance between the plates of an electric condenser.   The
applied field will pull charges of opposite signs in opposite directions,
and the constituent particles of matter will tend to be displaced from
their normal positions.   As a result, we find that there is a preponderance of negative charge on that side of our piece which faces
the positive condenser plate, and vice versa.   An unbalanced
charge distribution in the interior of matter is called *polarization*.
The polarization is limited by reactive forces; if the applied field
is withdrawn, they will restore the original unpolarized distribution.
Polarization will result in an additional field, both outside and
inside our piece of matter, and this additional field must be added
to the applied field.

If we examine this additional field at a considerable distance
from the polarized piece of matter, we may find that it is a rather
involved function of the coordinates.   Upon proceeding along a
straight line away from our piece, we can expand the observed
additional potential into a power series in descending terms of the
distance.   There will be no term dropping off as $r^{-1}$, because such
a potential is possible only if there is a net electric charge present;
naturally, polarization cannot produce a net charge where there
was none before.   The term with the slowest decrease at great distance will be the $r^{-2}$ term; and if we measure the $r^{-2}$ dependence
of the polarization potential in all directions, we shall find it to be
of the form (36).   In this case, the vector with the constant components $p_i$ will represent the total induced dipole moment of our
piece.   This total dipole moment is the vector sum of the individual moments induced in each atom by the action of the electric
field.   The effective electric field that acts on each atom is the
sum of the original applied field and the additional field caused by

all the other induced dipoles; this effective field is always smaller than the original applied field.

If we could measure the individual dipole moments of the atoms and add up the dipole moments located in a small volume $\Delta V$ in the interior of our piece of matter, then we could determine directly the dipole moment per unit volume, the "dipole moment density." This quantity is called *polarization*. (This is the precise definition of the term.) It has considerable theoretical significance: if we know the polarization, then we can compute the modification which the electric field undergoes because of the presence of matter. Naturally, the measurement of the dipole moment of each individual atom is out of the question. However, it is possible to determine the total dipole moment inside a volume $\Delta V$ merely by examining the electric field on its surface.

Because of Gauss's law, we can determine the total charge contained in a volume $V$ by forming the integral over the surface of $V$ of the integrand $\mathbf{E} \cdot \mathbf{n}$. We shall now derive a similar integral expression that measures the total dipole moment inside a closed surface $S$. For this derivation, we require a special form of Gauss's theorem, which has been distinguished by a name of its own, *Green's theorem*. Consider a vector field $\mathbf{u}$ with the components

$$u_i = \phi \, \psi_{,i} - \psi \, \phi_{,i}, \tag{37}$$

where $\phi$ and $\psi$ are two arbitrary, twice differentiable functions of the coordinates (scalar fields, for instance). If we now apply Gauss's theorem to the field $\mathbf{u}$, we note that the divergence of $\mathbf{u}$ is

$$u_{i,i} = (\phi \, \psi_{,i} - \psi \, \phi_{,i})_{,i} = \phi \, \psi_{,ii} - \psi \, \phi_{,ii}. \tag{38}$$

It follows that

$$\int_V (\phi \, \psi_{,ss} - \psi \, \phi_{,ss}) \, dV \equiv \oint_S (\phi \, \psi_{,s} - \psi \, \phi_{,s}) \, n_s \, dS, \tag{39}$$

and this is Green's theorem.

If both $\phi$ and $\psi$ satisfy the so-called *Laplace equation*,

$$\nabla^2 \phi \equiv \phi_{,ss} = 0, \qquad \nabla^2 \psi = \psi_{,ss} = 0, \tag{40}$$

throughout the interior of $V$, in other words, if they are "*harmonic functions*," then Green's theorem leads to the conclusion that

$$\oint_S (\phi \, \psi_{,s} - \psi \, \phi_{,s}) \, n_s \, dS = 0. \tag{41}$$

Because of eq. (21), we know that the electric potential satisfies Laplace's equation everywhere outside charged particles. If we formulate Green's theorem for the potential $\Phi$ as the one function and some other function $v$ which is harmonic in $V$ (that is, which satisfies Laplace's equation everywhere in $V$), then we are assured that the surface integral

$$I \equiv \oint_S (\Phi\, v_{,s} - v\, \Phi_{,s})\, n_s\, dS \tag{42}$$

depends only on the charge distribution in the interior and that it will vanish if there are no charges inside $S$. Everywhere in empty space, the divergence of the vector field $\mathbf{W}$,

$$W_s = \Phi\, v_{,s} - v\, \Phi_{,s} \tag{43}$$

must vanish. We shall now choose the function $v$ so that the integral (42) will give us information concerning the dipole distribution inside $S$. It will turn out that if we choose for $v$ the coordinate $x_i$ itself, then the surface integral (42) will measure the magnitude of the $i$th component of the enclosed dipole moment.[1] We shall carry the proof out in a sequence similar to the one we employed in the derivation of Gauss's law. First, we shall carry out the integral (42) for a small spherical surface that encloses a single dipole at its center. Then we shall consider an arbitrary closed surface enclosing just one dipole. Finally, we shall generalize our result to an arbitrary surface that encloses several dipoles.

Let us start, then, with a small sphere about the origin of a coordinate system $x_i$, and let us place a dipole with the moment $\mathbf{p}$ into the origin. The potential $\Phi$ will then be given by the expression (36) or, in components, by

$$\Phi = \frac{1}{r^3}\, p_n\, x_n, \qquad r^2 \equiv x_s\, x_s. \tag{44}$$

If we set $v$ equal to $x_i$ and substitute this expression and the expression (44) for $\Phi$ into eq. (43), then we get for $W_s \atop (i)$

$$W_s \atop (i) = \frac{1}{r^3}\, (p_n\, x_n\, \delta_{is} - x_i\, p_s) + \frac{3}{r^5}\, p_n\, x_n\, x_i\, x_s. \tag{45}$$

---

[1] The three functions $x_1$, $x_2$, and $x_3$ are each harmonic; that is, they satisfy Laplace's equation.

Before we can form the surface integral (42), we must multiply $W_s \atop (i)$
by $n_s$, which in our case (a spherical surface with the center at the
coordinate origin) equals $x_s/r$,

$$W_s \atop (i) \, n_s = \frac{3}{r^2} p_s \frac{x_s}{r} \frac{x_i}{r}. \tag{46}$$

The expression (46) must now be integrated over the spherical surface $S$. Since $dS/r^2$ is nothing but the infinitesimal solid angle
subtended by $dS$ at the coordinate origin, the integral (42) can be
written in the form

$$I_i = 3p_s \int_\Omega \frac{x_s}{r} \frac{x_i}{r} d\Omega. \tag{47}$$

$\Omega$ stands for the solid angle, and we must extend the integration
over the full solid angle. The result of the integration will depend
on whether the two indices $s$ and $i$ are equal or different. Without
much computation, we can assert immediately that the integral
must vanish if $i \neq s$.

For different indices $i$ and $s$, for every point $P$ on the sphere
where $x_i$ and $x_s$ have certain values, there exists exactly one corresponding point $P^*$ at which $x_i^* = x_i$, $x_s^* = -x_s$, and where the
third coordinate has the same value for $p$ and $P^*$. The neighbor-

hoods of the two points $P$ and
$P^*$ will make exactly opposite
contributions to the integral (47);
since we can pair off all points on
the sphere in the same manner,
the integral extended over the
whole sphere (or over the whole
solid angle) will vanish.

If $i$ and $s$ are equal, the construction just indicated is, of
course, impossible. The integral
will not vanish, but it can be
evaluated easily enough. $x_i/r$ is
the cosine of the angle which the
radius through a point on the
sphere makes with the $x_i$-axis

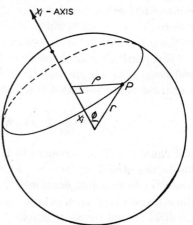

FIG. 12.   Integration of (47).

(Fig. 12). We shall call that angle $\phi$. With its introduction, we can reduce the integral (47) to

$$I_i = 3p_i \int_\Omega \cos^2 \phi \, d\Omega. \tag{48}$$

The increment of the solid angle can also be expressed in terms of the angle $\phi$. If $\phi$ increases by an amount $d\phi$, then we cover on the spherical surface an area that equals

$$dA = 2\pi \, \rho \, r \, d\phi = 2\pi \, r^2 \sin \phi \, d\phi. \tag{49}$$

This area subtends a solid angle at the origin

$$d\Omega = \frac{dA}{r^2} = 2\pi \sin \phi \, d\phi. \tag{50}$$

With this substitution, the integral (48) turns into

$$\begin{aligned}
I_i &= 6\pi \, p_i \int_{\phi=0}^\pi \cos^2 \phi \sin \phi \, d\phi \\
&= 6\pi \, p_i \int_{\cos\phi=-1}^1 \cos^2 \phi \, d\cos \phi = 4\pi \, p_i,
\end{aligned} \tag{51}$$

the final result of our integration of eq. (42).

Because of eq. (41), the value of the integral (42) will not change if we deform the closed surface $S$ in any arbitrary fashion, as long as the dipole at the origin remains inside $S$ and as long as no other charges (poles, dipoles, and the like) get inside $S$. Charge distributions outside the closed surface $S$ will make an additive contribution to the potential $\Phi$, but this addition to $\Phi$ will contribute nothing to the integral (42), again because of eq. (41).

If the surface $S$ encloses several dipoles, then each of the dipoles will contribute an amount to the integral (42) given by eq. (51), and these contributions will add. That is, the integral

$$\frac{1}{4\pi} I_i \equiv \frac{1}{4\pi} \oint_S (\delta_{is} \Phi - x_i \Phi_{,s}) \, n_s \, dS = p_i \tag{52}$$

will equal the $i$th component of the total dipole moment contained inside the closed surface $S$. For instance, we can determine the total dipole moment contained in a piece of matter by means of the integral (52), taken over its material surface, without examining the field caused by these dipoles "at infinity."

The integral (52) enables us to determine the total dipole moment inside $S$ if $S$ contains nothing but dipoles, and in particular no poles. How do single charges contribute to the integral (52)?

Since we know explicitly the contribution of a single point charge to the electric potential, we can first evaluate the contribution of a single charge to the integral (52), carried out over a spherical surface with the charge at the center, then deform the surface, and finally add together the contributions of several charges. This computation requires no special techniques and will be left to the reader. Its result is that the contribution of point charges inside $S$ to the integral (52) is

$$p_i = \sum_n e_n x_{i \atop n}. \tag{53}$$

The expression $e_n \cdot x_{i \atop n}$ is called the *moment* of the $n$th charge with respect to the origin of the coordinate system, in analogy with a similar terminology in mechanics with respect to mass.

If the total charge in the interior of $S$ vanishes (the positive charges canceling the negative charges), then the sum of these moments equals the total dipole moment which would be obtained if all the charges were to be composed of pairs and their individual dipole moments computed and added. In that case, the value of the vector **p** for the whole distribution will be independent of the choice of coordinate origin. We can appropriately add the contribution of the point charges to the dipole moment contributed by the dipole singularities and then consider this procedure as an extension of the concept of dipole moment.

We can justify this interpretation further by considering the potential field of our assembly of singularities (which is wholly located in the interior of $S$) outside and at very great distances from $S$. If we expand the potential field there into a power series in $1/r$, where $r$ is the distance from some interior point of $S$, then the terms dropping off as $1/r$ will vanish if the total charge of our collection of singularities is zero. There will, however, be a non-vanishing term dropping off as $(1/r)^2$, and this term will have the form of the field of a dipole, of precisely the magnitude and direction given by the integrals $I_i$ of eq. (52).

If the total charge inside $S$ does not vanish, then the values of the three integrals $I_i$ depend on the choice of the coordinate origin. To examine this dependence, let us compare the values obtained with two different choices of coordinate origin. If the coordinates of any particular point with respect to one system (the "unprimed" system) are $x_i$, the coordinates of the same point in the other (the "primed") system are

$$x_i' = x_i + c_i. \tag{54}$$

Now we shall determine the difference between $p_i$ and $p_i'$, both computed according to eq. (52). We find that this difference is determined by the total charge $e$ inside $S$:

$$p_i' - p_i = -\frac{1}{4\pi} \oint_S c_i \, \Phi_{,s} \, n_s \, dS = \frac{c_i}{4\pi} \oint_S E_s \, n_s \, dS \tag{55}$$
$$= e \, c_i,$$

according to eq. (18). The constants $c_i$ represent the (negative) displacement of the coordinate origin from $O$ to $O'$. The expression $e\, c_i$ is, therefore, the change in the moment of the total charge with respect to the coordinate origin. If we expand the potential at great distance again into a power series in $1/r$, where $r$ is now the distance from the origin, and if there is a term linear in $1/r$, then a displacement of the origin will leave the $1/r$ term unchanged, but the terms with $1/r^2$ will have their coefficients changed precisely in accordance with eq. (55).

In summary, the three integrals (52) measure the total dipole moment inside $S$, that is, the coefficient of the $(1/r^2)$ term of the potential "at infinity." This dipole moment is a true vector in the absence of a net charge inside $S$. If the net charge does not vanish, then the dipole moment will obey a transformation law of the form (55), which is similar to the transformation law of coordinates with respect to translations. It can be shown, incidentally, that all other types of possible singularities of the field make zero contributions to the integral (52).

**Higher poles.** Point charges and dipoles represent only the first two types in an infinite sequence of singularities which a field may possess if its potential obeys Laplace's equation outside the singularities. The next type in this sequence is the so-called *quadrupole*. We may think of a quadrupole as the combination of two dipoles which are equal in magnitude and opposite in direction and which are placed a short distance apart. In other words, a quadrupole has the same relationship to the two constituent dipoles that a dipole has to its two constituent point charges. If a quadrupole is to be built up of point charges, we require four point charges of which two are positive and two negative, and all four, except for the sign, of equal magnitude. If these four point charges are placed at the four corners of a parallelogram, so that equal charges are at opposite corners, we have a quadrupole. Ordinarily, we call a quadrupole the limiting case which is obtained if the parallelogram is contracted and the charges are increased so that the product of charge magnitude and parallelogram area remains constant.

We shall obtain the potential field of a quadrupole by methods similar to those which led to eq. (35), the potential field of a dipole. Equation (36) can be written as

$$\Phi = -\frac{\partial}{\partial x_s}\left(\frac{1}{r}\right) \cdot p_s. \tag{56}$$

This form indicates the derivation of the expression (36) from (33) by means of Taylor's theorem. If we proceed in a similar manner to obtain the potential of two dipoles with moments $\mathbf{p}$ and $-\mathbf{p}$, which are separated a distance $\mathbf{q}$, then we get for the potential of such a quadrupole the expression

$$\Phi = p_r\, q_s\, \frac{\partial^2\left(\frac{1}{r}\right)}{\partial x_r\, \partial x_s}. \tag{57}$$

The two vectors $\mathbf{p}$ and $\mathbf{q}$ enter into the expression for the potential of a quadrupole symmetrically. The potential drops off with the distance as $(1/r)^3$. If we add several quadrupoles to obtain the most general potential with this dependence on $r$, we find that $\Phi$ can be represented by the expression

$$\Phi = q_{ik}\, \frac{\partial^2\left(\frac{1}{r}\right)}{\partial x_i\, \partial x_k} \qquad q_{ik} = q_{ki}, \quad q_{ss} = 0. \tag{58}$$

The $q_{ik}$ are the components of a constant tensor. The tensor is symmetric, because an antisymmetric part would contribute nothing to the potential once we multiply it by the (symmetric) second derivatives of $(1/r)$. Likewise, a nonzero trace of the tensor $q_{ik}$ would vanish when multiplied by $(1/r)_{,ik}$. Thus, the most general

expression for a quadrupole potential can be composed linearly of
five fixed independent quadrupole moments, just as there are three
linearly independent dipole moment potentials.

Quadrupoles inside a closed surface $S$ can be determined by
means of a closed surface integral of the type (42), with the right
choice of the function $v$.  We shall not go through the details, but
it is not at all difficult to show that expressions of the form

$$v_{ik} = x_i x_k - \tfrac{1}{3} \delta_{ik} r^2 \tag{59}$$

will lead to integrals that measure the individual components of the
total quadrupole moment inside $S$.   On the other hand, quadrupoles
inside $S$ will contribute nothing to the surface integral (52), which
serves for a determination of the total dipole moment.

If we place two opposite quadrupoles close to each other, we
obtain a potential which drops off with the fourth power of $(1/r)$
and which is called an *octupole potential*.   Continued composition
of multipoles of opposite sign will lead to ever more complex potentials; these higher multipoles form a systematic sequence.   Each
member of the sequence has a $(1/r)^n$ dependence on the distance,
and $n$ increases by one when we pass from one multipole to the
next.   The angular dependence of all these multipoles is represented
by a class of functions which are known as *Legendre polynomials*
and *associated Legendre polynomials*.   The total multipole moment
inside a closed surface can always be determined by means of
integrals of the form (42); for each component of a higher multipole, there exists an appropriate function $v$ that must be used in
the integral.   We shall not carry out this whole theory, but we
shall return to the dipoles inside polarized matter.

**Polarization.**   If matter is subjected to an external electric field,
the constituent charged particles are displaced from their normal
positions; as a result, we induce a certain dipole moment density
or *polarization*.   The new equilibrium positions will be determined
by the requirement that the total electric field inside matter should
exert on each charged particle a force that is just balanced by the
restoring force.   The total field is composed of the external applied
field and the field caused by the displacement of the internal charges.
If some of the charged particles in the interior are not bound to
any particular equilibrium position, they will continue to move
until they have achieved a constellation where the net electric

force on any one of them vanishes. Materials in which electrons (the most easily displaced particles) possess that freedom of motion are called *electric conductors*. Metals belong to this type of matter. If, on the other hand, there are restoring forces acting even on the most motile charged particles, the particles will be displaced only until there is equilibrium between the electric and the restoring forces, with the result that the electric forces in the interior will not vanish, though they are smaller there than outside the piece of matter. Such materials are called *dielectrics*.

The result of a charge displacement will be the accumulation of charges on the surfaces of the piece of matter and possibly even in its interior. Naturally, displacement cannot change the total amount of charge in the material present, but it is possible to start with a distribution which is initially everywhere zero and to end up with one in which regions with positive charge accumulation are compensated by regions with negative charge accumulation, the total charge present still being zero.

We can describe the contribution of the displaced charges to the electric field in two different ways. If we place the emphasis on the resulting charge density in the interior and on the surface charge density, then the contribution of these charges to the electric field may be computed by means of eq. (12) or some similar equation. On the other hand, since the total charge vanishes, we may also characterize the displacement of charged particles with the help of the resulting *dipole moment per volume unit*. The latter quantity is directly proportional to the mean displacement of the charged particles from their normal positions (the positions they occupy in the absence of an electric field); thus, it is reasonable to expect that it will have a more direct relationship to the applied field than has the charge density. Furthermore, we shall see that the charge density may be obtained from the dipole moment per unit volume uniquely, but the reverse is not the case. We shall, therefore, base our description of the conditions inside the dielectric on the dipole moment per unit volume, called the *polarization*.

The existence of polarization gives rise both to a charge density (both volume and surface, in general) and to an electric field. This electric field must be added to the applied external field if we are to obtain the total electric field. It is clear that the electric field will be modified not only in the interior of the dielectric but also in its surroundings; the charge density, on the other hand, will be changed only in the interior of the dielectric.

To obtain the charge density $\sigma'$ that results from the polarization **P**, we shall again, as usual, consider a volume $V$ in the interior of the dielectric that is bounded by a closed surface $S$. Assuming that **P** is a function of the coordinates, we shall find the total charge carried into $V$ as a result of the polarization. By definition, the dipole moment resulting from the displacement of a single charge $e$ through a distance **s** is the product $e\,\mathbf{s}$ [compare eq. (35)]. If the dipole moment in a unit volume is **P**, then **P** is the sum of all the products of the form (35) arising from the displacement of charges inside the unit volume considered. If we now consider an arbitrary surface element $dS$ at a given location and with a certain orientation, a number of electrically charged particles will have been displaced across that surface element as a result of polarization. We shall now show that the total amount of charge carried across $dS$ equals the dot product of **P** by the unit surface normal, multiplied by $dS$. For the proof, let us refer to Fig. 6 in Chapter 3.

In terms of the notation for averages developed in that chapter, the polarization **P** is determined by the expression

$$\mathbf{P} = \langle e\mathbf{s} \rangle. \tag{60}$$

Now consider the charge carried across a surface element $dS$ by the charge displacements **s**. If the displacement suffered by a particular particle equals **s**, then it will carry its charge across $dS$ if it is initially inside a prism with the base $dS$ and the height $\mathbf{s} \cdot \mathbf{n}$. If the particle has been picked at random, though inside $\Delta V$, then the probability that it will be located initially inside the prism must be equal to the ratio of the volumes, $\mathbf{n} \cdot \mathbf{s}\, dS/\Delta V$. On the average, then, our particle will carry across a charge

$$d\epsilon = e\,\frac{\mathbf{n} \cdot \mathbf{s}}{\Delta V}\, dS; \tag{61}$$

and if we sum this expression over all the particles initially inside $\Delta V$, then we get for the charge carried across $dS$ as a result of polarization the expression

$$dq = \langle e\,\mathbf{s} \rangle \cdot \mathbf{n}\, dS = \mathbf{P} \cdot \mathbf{n}\, dS. \tag{62}$$

For a finite volume $V$, then, the charge brought in as a result of polarization equals

$$Q = - \oint_S \mathbf{P} \cdot \mathbf{n} \, dS. \tag{63}$$

If we convert this surface integral into a volume integral by means of Gauss's theorem, we find

$$Q = - \int_V \text{div } \mathbf{P} \, dV = - \int_V \frac{\partial P_i}{\partial x_i} dV, \tag{64}$$

and, therefore, for the volume charge density as a result of polarization:

$$\sigma' = - \text{div } \mathbf{P} = - \frac{\partial P_i}{\partial x_i}. \tag{65}$$

If the dielectric is bounded by empty space, there will be found a surface charge density $\tau'$, which is given by the integrand of eq. (63). If the normal is pointing out of the dielectric, the surface charge density will be

$$\tau' = + \mathbf{P} \cdot \mathbf{n}, \tag{66}$$

including the sign.

Our next job is to discover the laws obeyed by the electric field in a polarized dielectric. If we call the charge density which is present independently of the polarization the "real charge density" $\sigma$, and the additional charge density which is caused by polarization the "polarization charge density" $\sigma'$, then eq. (21), Gauss's law, must be changed into

$$\text{div } \mathbf{E} = 4\pi(\sigma + \sigma'), \tag{67}$$

since the effective total charge density is the sum of $\sigma$ and $\sigma'$. In this equation we can separate the "real charge density" from the remainder, with the help of eq. (65). We shift the term $4\pi \sigma'$ to the left-hand side and substitute from eq. (65), whereupon we find the relationship

$$\text{div } \mathbf{E} + 4\pi \text{ div } \mathbf{P} = 4\pi \sigma. \tag{68}$$

We call the sum $(\mathbf{E} + 4\pi \mathbf{P})$ the *electric displacement* and designate it by the symbol $\mathbf{D}$. The equation

$$\text{div } \mathbf{D} = 4\pi \sigma, \tag{69}$$

according to which the real charge density equals $4\pi$ times the divergence of the electric displacement, is the most general formulation of Gauss's law.   Equation (69) is more useful than (21) in the presence of dielectrics because the real charge density is independent of the polarization of the dielectric whereas the total charge density is not, and because the polarization, in turn, will depend on external circumstances (the applied electric field).   In empty space the polarization vanishes, and $\mathbf{D}$ and $\mathbf{E}$ are identical.

## 5.4. Dielectrics

Together, eqs. (69) and (24) express the most general differential laws obeyed by the field quantities $\mathbf{E}$ and $\mathbf{D}$ (eq. (24) expressing the fact that the field strength can be derived from the electric potential and that the electric field is, therefore, conservative).   However, since these two relationships deal with two different field quantities, they do not determine the electric field completely unless further relationships connect the electric field strength with the displacement.   Such a third relationship is, of course, nothing but some condition on the polarization.   Its form will depend on the nature of the dielectric and the type of internal forces that tend to hold the charged particles to their normal positions.   In empty space, as mentioned above, the polarization must vanish, and $\mathbf{E}$ and $\mathbf{D}$ are identical.   In many dielectrics, the restoring forces are proportional and parallel to the displacement (*harmonic isotropic forces*).   (Any property dependent on the direction, as in crystals, is called *anisotropic*).   In the isotropic case, the polarization will be proportional and parallel to the field strength, and the factor of proportionality is called the *electric susceptibility* $\epsilon$,

$$\mathbf{P} = \epsilon\,\mathbf{E}. \tag{70}$$

It follows that, again in the isotropic case, the electric displacement is also proportional to the electric field strength,

$$\mathbf{D} = \mathbf{E} + 4\pi\,\mathbf{P} = (1 + 4\pi\,\epsilon)\,\mathbf{P}. \tag{71}$$

The factor of proportionality, $(1 + 4\pi\,\epsilon)$, is called the *dielectric constant* and is usually designated by the symbol $\kappa$.   The dielectric constant of empty space equals unity; in a dielectric $\kappa$ is always greater than one.

Before we go on to the anisotropic case, a word about the system of units is in order.   In our discussion, we have uniformly used *electrostatic units* (esu), in which **E, P,** and **D** are all quantities of the same dimension, so that the dielectric constant is a dimensionless quantity.   In so-called *practical units*, potential is measured in volts and charge in coulombs.   Because of eq. (7), the dimension of the electric field strength must be volts/cm.   On the other hand, the most important property of the electric displacement is that its divergence equals $4\pi$ times the real charge density [see eq. (69)]. It follows that the dimension of **D** must be coulombs/cm$^2$.   The ratio of **D** and **E** is then a quantity with the dimension coulombs/ (volt-cm).   A further modification of units is provided by the so-called *rationalized systems of units*, in which the unit of electric displacement is redefined so that the factor $4\pi$ in eq. (69) is absorbed into the unit of electric displacement.   In such a system of units, the factor $4\pi$ appears nowhere in the basic differential equations. This advantage is offset by the necessity of retaining factors of proportionality (which are not dimensionless quantities) in the basic laws of the electrostatic field even in empty space.   The choice of system of units is, thus, governed largely by personal taste and convenience of application.   Although the confusion in the literature may bewilder the uninitiated, all systems are serviceable for the formulation of the laws of nature, and transition from one to the other is facilitated by tables put out by the prophets of new systems.   The author has yet to discover an adequate basis for the emotional fervor exhibited occasionally in discussions whether the dielectric constant is "in truth" dimensionless or not, and similar issues.

Even when the polarization is proportional to the field strength, it may not be isotropic; that is, the restoring force per unit displacement acting on the charged particles need not be the same in all directions.   The generalization of eq. (70) is

$$P_i = \epsilon_{ik} E_k \qquad (\epsilon_{ik} = \epsilon_{ki}). \tag{72}$$

The tensor $\epsilon_{ik}$ must be symmetric in its subscripts if the restoring forces are to be conservative, for essentially the same reasons that led us to require symmetry for the stress tensor in Chapter 3.   In the anisotropic case, the polarization is not parallel to the field strength, except in three principal directions, which are mutually perpendicular to each other.   In these three principal directions, the ratios between the polarization and the applied field strength may be called the *principal values* of the electric susceptibility, in analogy with the terminology used in the case of the stress tensor.

By substituting eq. (72) into (68), we find for the relationship between $\mathbf{D}$ and $\mathbf{E}$ the law

$$D_i = \kappa_{ik} E_k \qquad (\kappa_{ik} = \delta_{ik} + 4\pi \, \epsilon_{ik}). \tag{73}$$

The dielectric constant, too, is a symmetric tensor, and its three principal values are each greater than 1.

If the electric field strength is sufficiently great, it is quite possible that the relationship between $\mathbf{E}$ and the resulting polarization is not linear but more involved. Furthermore, the reaction of the dielectric to the applied field will in general not be instantaneous but delayed, because of effects of inertia. If we apply periodic fields (a-c potentials), the polarization will be out of phase with the applied field, and its amplitude is frequency-dependent. Recently, substances have been discovered in which the relationship between field strength and polarization is so highly nonlinear that we can no longer define uniquely a dielectric constant even for a given frequency. Dielectrics of this type are called *ferroelectrics*. We shall not present a detailed discussion here; be it sufficient to establish the point that the linear relationship between electric field strength and electric displacement (71) or (73) is an approximate law, just like Hooke's law in the theory of elastic materials. This approximation is useful in a large variety of problems but does not possess the same universal character as Gauss's law [eq. (69)] or eq. (24).

## 5.5. Magnetostatics

It is well known that Coulomb's law holds not only for electric point charges but also for magnetic poles, with the important difference that single poles are unknown. All magnetic matter, when isolated, contains zero magnetic "charge," but dipoles are very well known. Thus, the construction of a "magnetostatic" theory, built in close analogy to electrostatics and based on the concept of single magnetic poles and their interaction, appears somewhat artificial; it is the magnetic dipole that appears to be the basic building stone of the magnetic field. We can, of course, formulate the interaction law between two pointlike magnetic dipoles. This force law is consistent with Newton's third law, concerning the equality of action and reaction, and we have conservation of momentum and angular momentum; but the force depends on the orientation of both dipoles and is not directed along the connecting straight line. Moreover, the multitude of interaction effects between electric and magnetic phenomena is disregarded in magnetostatics, rendering the results not only unsatisfactory from the point of Newtonian mechanics but also quite unrealistic.

We shall devote only a few paragraphs to a description of magnetostatics, since it requires no new physical concepts and will merely serve to introduce a number of terms. We can repeat every word of the previous four sections in this chapter, provided that at each stage we add the condition that there are no free (single) magnetic poles, and provided that we rename some of the quantities introduced. The field will again be described by the *magnetic field strength*, **H**, which may be considered as the gradient of a "magnetic potential" and which, therefore, satisfies the analogous equation (24),

$$H_{i,k} - H_{k,i} = 0. \tag{74}$$

This equation holds only for magnetostatics in the narrowest sense of the word; specifically, as long as we disregard the effect of electric currents on the magnetic field.

Since there are no magnetic poles, the divergence of **H** vanishes in empty space,

$$H_{s,s} = 0. \tag{75}$$

In the presence of matter, we again encounter the effect of polarization, which is here called *magnetization;* the symbol **M** denotes this magnetic dipole moment per unit volume. In the magnetic case, it is found that in some materials the magnetization induced by the magnetic field is directed against rather than parallel to the magnetic field strength. In other words, the magnetic susceptibility $\chi$ may be positive (as the electric susceptibility is always) or negative. Materials of the first type are called *paramagnetic*, those of the latter type *diamagnetic*.

In the presence of magnetized matter, the magnetic pole density is the sum of the "real pole density" and the "magnetization pole density." The real pole density vanishes everywhere, since the absence of single poles is a basic characteristic of the magnetic field, but the magnetization pole density need not vanish. However, if we introduce the analogue of the electric displacement, the *magnetic induction* **B**,

$$\mathbf{B} = \mathbf{H} + 4\pi \, \mathbf{M}, \tag{76}$$

then, as the relationship corresponding to (69), we find

$$\operatorname{div} \mathbf{B} = 0, \tag{77}$$

which replaces eq. (75) in the presence of magnetized matter.

If the magnetized material is isotropic and if the magnetization is proportional to the applied magnetic field, then **B** and **H** will be parallel and proportional to each other, and their ratio $\mu$ is called the *magnetic permeability*.

The nonlinear case, in which there is no simple relationship between **B** and **H**, is known as the *ferromagnetic state* and is of immense practical importance. In ferromagnetic materials, the magnetization in the presence of a weak applied field is usually several hundred times greater than the applied field **H**; when the applied field is raised, **M** approaches a maximum which is not exceeded (*saturation*). Then, when the applied field is gradually reduced, the magnetization does not return to zero together with the applied field but remains finite, because the strong applied field has produced a shift in the equilibrium structure of the ferromagnetic material. This feature is called *remanence*. To demagnetize the material, it is necessary to apply a magnetic field pointing in the direction opposite to that of the remaining magnetization. If this applied counterfield is stronger than sufficient to remove magnetization, magnetization in the direction opposite to the original one will be induced. If this counterfield is driven up to the saturation stage, then again reduced to zero and replaced by a field in the original direction, and so on, the magnetization vs. applied field curve will pass through a loop, which is called the *hysteresis loop*. Generally, any effect in which an applied stress (mechanical, magnetic, or otherwise) produces shifts in the equilibrium state of solids is called hysteresis. Hysteresis effects always go hand in hand with gross deviations of the response from linearity (Hooke's law).

Relatively early in the investigation of electric and magnetic phenomena, Oersted and other scientists discovered the fact that moving electric charges (electric currents) exert forces on magnetized pieces of steel. In Chapter 6, we shall carefully examine this type of interaction, and we shall find that it cannot be reconciled with Newton's mechanics.

## Problems

**5.1.** A condenser consists of two concentric spherical shells of radii $a$ and $b$; one plate carries the charge $q$, the other plate the charge $-q$. Determine the resulting electric field strength and the resulting potential throughout space, assuming that:

(a) The space is empty.

(b) The space between the two condenser plates is filled with a dielectric material.

**5.2.** Consider an electrostatic field part of which is caused by a point charge $e$. In the immediate vicinity of that point charge, we can split the total field into the "self-field" of the point charge (given by Coulomb's law), and the remainder, the "incident field." The latter must, of course, satisfy Gauss's law for empty space. Now obtain an expression for the stress tensor in the vicinity of the point charge $e$, taking the whole field into account. Find the force this stress will exert on a small spherical volume which has the point charge as its center.

**5.3.** If the surface integral (42) is formed with the help of one of the functions $v_{ik}$, eq. (59), examine how single poles, dipoles, and quadrupoles inside $S$ contribute to the value of the integral.

**5.4.** Show that quadrupoles do not contribute to the integral (52).

**5.5.** With the help of spherical harmonics, set up a classification of all multipoles.

**5.6.** Show that on an interface which separates two dielectrics with different values of the dielectric constant:

(a) The normal component of the electric displacement has the same value on both sides.

(b) The tangential component of the electric field strength is the same on both sides.

(c) If the two dielectrics are both isotropic, with well-defined values of the dielectric constant, the ratio between the tangents of the angles formed by the field strengths with the interface normal equals the ratio between the dielectric constants.

**5.7.** Between the plates of a parallel-plate condenser with greatly extended plates (plate diameter large compared with plate distance) place an extended slab of dielectric material, the surfaces of which are plane and parallel to the condenser plates. Develop formulas showing:

(a) The decrease in voltage if the plate charge is kept constant.

(b) The increase in plate charge density if the voltage is fixed.

(c) The change in condenser capacity.

**5.8.** In general, a dielectric body placed into a homogeneous electric field ($E_i$ = constant) will become subject to inhomogeneous polarization, and the resulting field both inside and outside the dielectric body will no longer be homogeneous. However, if a sphere consisting of an isotropic dielectric is placed into such a field, it can be shown that:

(a) The field inside is homogeneous, and the field strength inside is related to the field strength at infinity ($\mathbf{E}_0$) by the formula

$$\mathbf{E} = \frac{\mathbf{E}_0}{1 + \frac{4}{3}\pi\epsilon}.$$

(b) The field outside consists of the original homogeneous part, $\mathbf{E}_0$, and the field of a dipole, the moment of which equals the product of the inside electric field strength, the volume of the sphere, and the electric susceptibility. These two expressions will together satisfy the requirements on the boundary surface formulated in Problem 5.6.

# Chapter 6

## Electromagnetic Interaction

In this chapter, we shall approach the forces between magnets and moving charges. There are three different types: the force by a current or moving charge on a magnet, the force that a magnet exerts on a moving charge, and the force that a moving magnet exerts on an electric charge at rest. The first of these three types of interaction has been known longest. It was discovered by Oersted in 1820 and is described by *Biot-Savart's law*. The second force, which is the necessary corollary to the first if we attempt to retain the validity of Newton's third law, is now known as the *Lorentz force*. The last effect, the action of a changing magnetic field on electric charges at rest, is called *electromagnetic induction*. To describe these various interactions between magnets and electric charges, we shall also develop vector and tensor calculus somewhat beyond the stage that so far has been sufficient for our purposes.

### 6.1. Biot-Savart's law

If we pass a steady current of electrons through a long straight piece of wire, by maintaining a steady potential difference between its two ends, then a magnetized steel rod in the vicinity will experience a *torque*, just as if there were another magnet near by. The magnitude of the torque of a magnetic needle of finite size depends on several factors—its position and orientation, and its length and state of magnetization as well. We can reduce the complexity of the observed effects if we make a very long uniform steel rod, magnetize it as uniformly as possible, so that effectively its two ends only carry "magnetization pole density," and then hold it so that only one end is close to the electric wire. With that arrangement, we can observe the force acting on one "single pole."

Our assumption that the observed forces are caused by the moving charges inside the wire and that they act on the magnetic dipoles inside our magnet needle is, of course, conjectural. The conjecture has, however, been confirmed by subsequent experiments. The magnitude of the force on the magnetic needle is independent of the chemical composition of the wire and independent of the potential drop between its end points. It depends, as far as the wire is concerned, exclusively on the shape of the wire and on the amount of current passing through it. With present techniques, we can dispense with the wire altogether and replace it by a stream of free electrons in an evacuated glass bulb. Likewise, the force on a magnetic "single pole" at a given location relative to the wire or electron stream is strictly proportional to the pole strength (which can be determined by magnetostatic experiments) but is found to be independent of all other accidental characteristics the magnetized rod may possess. Thus, we can express the observed facts adequately by claiming that a current or a moving stream of charges gives rise to a *magnetic field*.

This magnetic field can be described in terms of a magnetic field strength **H**. Its magnitude is given by Biot-Savart's law, which is usually formulated so that the equation describes the contribution of the charges in a piece of wire of length $dl$ to the magnetic field strength. By interpreting electric current as a flow of point charges, we can formulate Biot-Savart's law just as readily in terms of the contribution of individual moving charges to the magnetic field. In that formulation, the law has the form

$$|\mathbf{H}| = \frac{|\mathbf{v}|}{c} \frac{e}{r^2} \sin \theta. \tag{1}$$

Here $e$ is the magnitude of the moving point charge and **v** its velocity, $r$ is the distance of the space point considered from the present location of the charge, and $\theta$ is the angle that **r** makes with **v**. Finally, $c$ is a universal constant which possesses the dimension of a velocity and which has the value of approximately $3 \times 10^{10}$ cm-sec$^{-1}$. The fact that $c$ happens to equal the known velocity of light in vacuum appears here as an accident. That the electromagnetic theory explains "accidents" like these gave it the strength which eventually persuaded physicists to discard Newtonian mechanics as the foundation of physics.

The direction of the magnetic field strength caused by a moving charge in accordance with eq. (1) is at right angles both to the distance vector **r** and the velocity vector **v**. Ordinarily, the "positive" pole of the magnet is chosen so that the "right-hand rule" holds: If we look in the direction of the moving charge (assuming the charge to be positive), then the magnetic field tends to move a magnetic positive pole clockwise about the moving point charge.

Biot-Savart's law does not satisfy the usual postulates of Newtonian mechanics. Though it is quite easy to formulate the law in terms of the interaction of individual particles (the moving point charge and the single magnetic pole), the force between these two mass points depends on the velocity of at least one of them, and it is not in the direction of the connecting straight line but at right angles. Obviously, if Biot-Savart's law is valid, we shall have to modify the foundations of mechanics, but it is yet too early to foresee to what extent. At any rate, if eq. (1) is really valid, then the proofs for the conservation laws of energy and for angular momentum cannot be maintained in the form that was presented in Chapter 1.

Before we enter into a discussion of these questions, we shall consider the magnetic fields produced by specially shaped wires in which an electric current is flowing. First of all, let us note that in the presence of a steady electric current, we do not need to know the magnitude of the individual moving charges, their mean velocities, or the total number of moving charges per unit length of wire in order to compute the resulting magnetic field strength, but merely the product of these three quantities, that is, the *electric current*. As usual, we define the electric current as the amount of charge that crosses an arbitrary cross section of wire per unit time. That this amount of charge equals the volume-averaged product of charge and velocity can be shown by an argument that is similar to those employed in Chapters 3 and 5. Carrying out the transition from the "mass-point law" to the "bulk law" in our usual manner, we can obtain readily Biot-Savart's law in its usual form:

$$d|\mathbf{H}| = \frac{\sin \theta}{cr^2} I \, dl, \tag{2}$$

where $I$ is the magnitude of the current defined above. If the wire is curved in an arbitrary manner, the vector addition of these individual contributions, or rather their "vector integration," must be carried out with great care, because they are not all parallel to each other.　Since at this stage we do not yet possess the necessary mathematical tools to accomplish this integration conveniently, we shall restrict ourselves to a special case in which symmetry considerations facilitate the computational work.

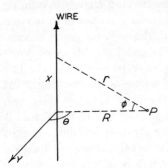

**The field of an infinite straight wire.** Consider a very long and completely straight wire (Fig. 13). We shall compute the magnetic field strength at a point $P$ that has a (perpendicular) distance $R$ from the wire. We shall designate the coordinate along the wire by $x$, setting $x = 0$ at the point closest to $P$. According to eq. (2), the contribution of an infinitesimal segment of wire of length $dx$ to the magnetic field strength at the point $P$ is

Fig. 13.　Magnetic field of an infinite straight electric wire.

$$dH = \frac{I}{cr^2} \cos \phi \, dx = \frac{I}{cR} \cos \phi \, d\phi. \tag{3}$$

The directions of all these contributions are the same, namely, at right angles to the plane of the paper (into the paper if the current is flowing upward).　Therefore, we can simply integrate all these contributions,

$$H = \frac{I}{cR} \int_{\phi = -\frac{\pi}{2}}^{\frac{\pi}{2}} \cos \phi \, d\phi = \frac{2I}{cR}. \tag{4}$$

This result is interesting for a number of reasons.　First of all, eq. (4) gives the approximate magnitude of the field in close proximity to a current-bearing wire, no matter what its shape.　This is because the principal contribution to the integral comes from those portions of the wire for which $\phi$ is appreciably different from $\pm \pi/2$. For instance, those portions of the wire for which $\phi$ lies between $-88°$ and $88°$ will contribute more than 99 per cent of the total magnetic field.　Now, obviously, no matter how great the curvature of the wire, we can get sufficiently close to the wire that the portion of the wire subtended by 176° of arc curves less than any specified angle.　Thus, for any wire of finite curvature the expression (4) will provide a good approximation sufficiently close to the wire.

The expression (4) shows also that the force acting on a magnetic pole cannot possibly be represented as the gradient of a "magnetic potential." Otherwise, if the test particle is moved through a closed-path trajectory, the net amount of work done would have to be zero, a result obviously not consistent with eq. (4). If the test pole is carried through a circular orbit in a plane at right angles to the wire, with the wire itself passing through the center of the circle, the displacement is everywhere parallel to the force, which is constant in magnitude. Thus, the total amount of work done in moving the pole once about this closed circle is

$$W = 2\pi \, R \, p \cdot \frac{2I}{cR} = \frac{4\pi}{c} \, I \, p, \tag{5}$$

independently of the radius. The symbol $p$ has been used here to denote the magnitude of the magnetic pole strength.

This result can be generalized quite easily for curves of arbitrary shape. We can show that the magnetic field strength of the wire is in fact the gradient of a "magnetic potential," but only *locally;* in any attempt to extend the potential function throughout space, the function will turn out to be multivalued. We have

$$H = -\text{grad} \, \psi,$$
$$\psi = -\frac{2}{c} I \, \text{arc tan} \left( \frac{z}{y} \right) = -\frac{2}{c} I \, \theta. \tag{6}$$

$\psi$ is the "magnetic potential," the work required to move a magnetic unit pole from the plane $z = 0$ to the point at which the potential is to be measured. $\theta$ is the angle which the perpendicular connecting line $R$ of Fig. 13 makes with the plane in which the "potential" has been set zero. This angle is not a single-valued function but increases by $2\pi$ every time we complete a closed path about the $x$-axis.

True, there are no single magnetic poles. But if we replace the electric wire by a stream of free electrons, we can move a long, uniformly magnetized rod (which bears opposite poles at its ends) through this stream in such a manner that one end of the rod passes once around the wire, the other not, and that the final and initial positions of the rod are the same. In other words, the force which a current exerts on magnetized material will apparently change the magnet's total energy under appropriate circumstances. We shall return to this question later.

## 6.2. Cross product and curl

We cannot treat other wire shapes conveniently until we have extended the vector and tensor methods at our disposal to include the cross product and the curl. For this reason we shall interrupt the discussion of electromagnetic interaction at this point by a purely mathematical section. The cross product is a product of two vectors of the same type that we encounter in the formulation of Biot-Savart's law, eq. (1). By multiplying the magnitudes of two vectors by each other and by the sine of the angle between them, we can obtain a new vector-like set of three components. This formation is not one of the covariant combinations we studied in Chapter 3, and closer examination will show us that its transformation law differs somewhat from that of a vector. To understand this difference, we shall return once more to the properties of orthogonal transformations, eqs. (3.16), (3.21).

From the theory of multiple integrals, it is well known that if we wish to express the integrand of a multiple integral in terms of a new set of variables of integration, we may do so, provided that we multiply the original integrand by the so-called *Jacobian*, the determinant of the partial derivatives of the original variables with respect to the new ones. The Jacobian may be interpreted as the ratio of the infinitesimal "volume" element $dx_1\, dx_2\, \cdots\, dx_n$ of the original variables and the "volume" element $dx_1'\, dx_2'\, \cdots\, dx_n'$ formed with the help of the new variables. We shall now examine the value of the Jacobian of an orthogonal transformation. We can obtain this value with the help of eq. (3.21); if we take the determinant on both sides, we get an expression

$$\det \begin{vmatrix} c_{1k}\,c_{1k}, & \cdots, & c_{1k}\,c_{3k} \\ c_{2k}\,c_{1k}, & \cdots, & c_{2k}\,c_{3k} \\ c_{3k}\,c_{1k}, & \cdots, & c_{3k}\,c_{3k} \end{vmatrix} = \det \begin{vmatrix} 1, & 0, & 0 \\ 0, & 1, & 0 \\ 0, & 0, & 1 \end{vmatrix}. \tag{7}$$

The right-hand side equals unity. The left-hand side can be simplified by means of the multiplication law for determinants, according to which that expression equals the product of the determinant det $|c_{ik}|$ by itself.[1]   It follows that the square of the Jacobian of the orthogonal transformation equals unity,

$$|c_{ik}|^2 = 1, \tag{8}$$

meaning that the Jacobian itself must be either 1 or $-1$.

Further investigation shows that all orthogonal transformations belong to one of two types.   First, we can go over from the original to the transformed coordinate system by merely rotating the original coordinate system about a suitable axis through some angle; such a transformation is called a *proper orthogonal transformation* or a *rotation*.   Or we can accomplish the transition by combining an *inversion* (a transformation that merely changes the sign of every coordinate) with a rotation; these transformations are known as *improper orthogonal transformations* or *perversions*.   We can convert any rotation into another rotation by changing *continuously* the values of the $c_{ik}$ in such a manner that every intermediate stage also represents a rotation.   Likewise, we can convert any perversion continuously into any other perversion.   In each of these two classifications, the value of the Jacobian (which is $\pm 1$ to begin with) can change only continuously and, therefore, not at all. Since the rotations include the "identity transformation," they all must have a Jacobian $+1$; whereas the perversions, which include the inversion, must have a Jacobian $-1$.

Hence there are two clearly separated classes of orthogonal transformations, and they possess different values of the Jacobian. Now consider some volume integral such as the integral over the mass density, which will yield the total mass in the volume.   As long as we restrict ourselves to rotations, the same integrand will lead to the same value of the integral.   But what if we carry out an improper transformation?   To keep the total mass positive, we usually reverse the direction of integration; that is, we integrate in the direction of increasing value of the new coordinates as well. This method is, however, somewhat ambiguous from a formal point of view; and if the integrand has no such obvious physical significance as a mass density, the method of changing the direction

---

[1] Readers who are not familiar with the multiplication law of determinants can convince themselves of this equality by straightforward computation of the left-hand side of eq. (7) and of the square of the determinant of the $c_{ik}$, but these computations are quite lengthy.

of integration may well lead to ambiguities. We can avoid the ambiguity if we introduce for the integrand a new law of transformation: we can decree that the integrand is to be multiplied by the Jacobian of the coordinate transformation. Although we should hardly wish to apply this new transformation law to mass densities (which would then have to be taken as negative whenever we used a left-handed coordinate system), it is, for instance, a very convenient transformation law for magnetization pole densities. At any rate, we shall introduce a new class of quantities besides tensors, the *tensor densities* or *pseudotensors*, and define them by the following transformation equation:

$$\mathfrak{T}'_{ik\ldots} = \det |c_{ab}| \, c_{im} \, c_{kn} \cdots \mathfrak{T}_{mn\ldots}. \tag{9}$$

This definition includes *pseudovectors* and *pseudoscalars*. In our applications, pseudovectors will occur quite frequently.

The difference between proper and improper transformations can be understood in terms of the screw sense of the coordinate systems to be transformed. Customarily, coordinate systems are chosen so that if in the $x_1$, $x_2$-plane a rotation is carried out leading from the positive $x_1$-axis to the positive $x_2$-axis, then an ordinary (right-handed) screw that is lined up along the $x_3$-axis will move in the direction of the positive $x_3$-axis. Naturally, we can choose the coordinate axes just as well in such a manner that a right-handed screw turned in the direction from the positive $x_1$-axis to the positive $x_2$-axis will move toward the negative $x_3$-axis. Coordinate systems of both kinds are illustrated in Fig. 14. The first kind is called a *right-handed coordinate system*, the second a *left-handed system*. Obviously, if we turn our whole coordinate system in space, its right- or left-handedness is not affected. But if we carry out a perversion, a right-handed system will go over into a left-handed system, and vice versa. Thus, we may characterize a rotation as a transformation that preserves the screw sense of the coordinate system, whereas a perversion reverses the screw sense.

Pseudovectors occur in many physical applications. The torque, the angular momentum, and the angular velocity in mechanics, and the magnetic field strength, the magnetic induction, and the magnetization in electromagnetic theory are among the principal examples. Instead of pseudovectors, they are also often called *axial vectors*, because all of them are associated with rotation.

Usually, their definition includes some "right-hand rule" or equivalent convention concerning the direction in which they are to face. Without such a rule, their direction would be subject to an ambiguity, because in comparison to an ordinary (or *polar*) vector they multiply by $-1$ if we change the screw sense of the coordinate system. All the usual right-hand rules are formulated

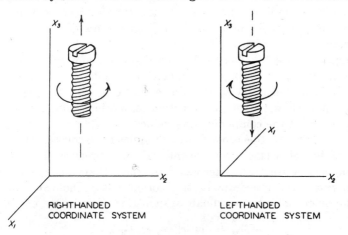

RIGHTHANDED
COORDINATE SYSTEM

LEFTHANDED
COORDINATE SYSTEM

Fig. 14. The screw sense of coordinate systems.

in accordance with the adoption of a right-handed coordinate system.

The algebraic rules for the combination of pseudotensors are very simple. We may add pseudotensors of the same rank, but not a pseudotensor and an ordinary tensor. In other words, all the terms in an equation, and both sides, must have precisely the same transformation properties. In no law of physics will an electric and a magnetic field strength ever be added together. But we can multiply pseudotensors by each other or by ordinary tensors. The transformation character of the product will be determined by the power of the Jacobian by which it must be multiplied in the event of a perversion. Thus, the product of a tensor by a pseudotensor will be a pseudotensor, but the product of two pseudotensors is an ordinary tensor. Differentiation does not change the power of the Jacobian by which the components must be mutliplied; the gradient of a pseudoscalar, for instance, will be a pseudovector. The details of the proofs will be left to the reader.

The actual combination of pseudotensors and tensors in physical laws is accomplished with the help of a very important peudotensor with constant coefficients, the so-called *pseudotensor of Levi-Civita*. In three-dimensional space this pseudotensor has the rank 3 (its rank in other spaces always equals the number of dimensions) and is defined as follows. The components $\delta_{ikl}$ are zero if any two of the three indices are equal. In the remaining components, the three indices must perforce be a permutation of (123). If the permutation is cyclic, (123), (231), or (312), the value of that component is $+1$. The remaining three index combinations, (213), (321), and (132), belong to components equal to $-1$. Thus, the Levi-Civita pseudotensor is antisymmetric in all its indices. We must now show that upon transition to another coordinate system the values of the components reproduce.

To carry out this proof, it will be sufficient to consider the transformation of a single component, say $\delta_{123}$, because all the other components are then determined by the antisymmetry, which is conserved under coordinate transformations. The value of this component in a new coordinate system $x_i'$ is given by the expression

$$\delta_{123}' = \det |c| \cdot c_{1i} \, c_{2k} \, c_{3l} \, \delta_{ikl}. \tag{10}$$

Because of the antisymmetry of the Levi-Civita pseudotensor, only those terms contribute to the triple sum in which the three dummy indices, $i$, $k$, and $l$ are all different, and they will be positive if $(ikl)$ is an even permutation of (123) but negative if it is odd. In other words, the expression on the right-hand side can be simplified by the relationship

$$c_{1i} \, c_{2k} \, c_{3l} \, \delta_{ikl} \equiv \det |c|, \tag{11}$$

to yield
$$\delta_{123}' = (\det |c|)^2 = 1. \tag{12}$$

This equation completes the proof.

It is with the help of the Levi-Civita pseudotensor that we can characterize the cross product as a covariant operation. We define as the cross product of two vectors **u** and **v** the pseudovector $\mathfrak{w}$

$$\mathfrak{w}_i = \delta_{ikl} \, u_k \, v_l. \tag{13}$$

We can easily show that the cross product is at right angles to each of the two factors. We multiply the defining eq. (13) by either $u_i$ or $v_i$ and make $i$ a dummy index. The right-hand side will vanish in either case because of the antisymmetry of the Levi-Civita pseudotensor. By either of two methods, we can show that the magnitude of the pseudovector $\mathfrak{w}$ equals the product of the magnitudes of the two factors, multiplied by the sine of the angle between them. First, we can choose a special coordinate system in which the vector $\mathbf{u}$ is parallel to the $x_1$-axis and the pseudovector $\mathfrak{w}$ (which is at right angles to $\mathbf{u}$, anyway) is parallel to the $x_3$-axis. In this coordinate system, $\mathfrak{w}_3$ equals the product of $u_1$ and $v_2$, and the latter component equals the magnitude of $\mathbf{v}$, multiplied by the sine of the angle which $\mathbf{v}$ forms with the $x_1$-axis.

The second and more elegant proof makes use of the relationship

$$\delta_{ijs}\,\delta_{kls} \equiv \delta_{ik}\,\delta_{jl} - \delta_{il}\,\delta_{jk}. \tag{14}$$

This relationship between the Levi-Civita pseudotensor and the Kronecker tensor is frequently useful in derivations of vector-algebraic relations. Of the four indices $i,j,\ k,l$, the second pair must be identical with the first if the expression is to be different from zero; then, provided that $i \neq j$, the product on the left will equal $+1$ if $(i,j)$ is the same sequence as $(k,l)$, and $-1$ if the two pairs are in opposite sequence. If we now square the defining eq. (3), we get the expression

$$\begin{aligned}
|\mathfrak{w}|^2 = \mathfrak{w}_i\,\mathfrak{w}_i &= \delta_{ikl}\,\delta_{imn}\,u_k\,u_m\,v_l\,v_n \\
&= (\delta_{km}\,\delta_{ln} - \delta_{kn}\,\delta_{lm})\,u_k\,u_m\,v_l\,v_n \\
&= |\mathbf{u}^2||\mathbf{v}^2| - |\mathbf{u}\cdot\mathbf{v}|^2 = |\mathbf{u}^2||\mathbf{v}^2|(1 - \cos^2\theta) \\
&= (\sin\theta\,|\mathbf{u}||\mathbf{v}|)^2.
\end{aligned} \tag{15}$$

The differential analogue to the algebraic operation of taking the cross product is the curl. The curl of a vector field $\mathbf{u}$ is defined as the pseudovector with the components

$$\mathfrak{v}_i = \delta_{ikl}\,u_{l,k} \equiv (\text{curl } \mathbf{u})_i \equiv (\nabla \times \mathbf{u})_i. \tag{16}$$

Applied to a pseudovector, the curl operation leads to an ordinary vector field.

By this time, the reader has probably noticed that with the help of the cross product we can formulate Biot-Savart's law in covariant notation and that, since the velocity $\mathbf{v}$ and the distance $\mathbf{r}$ are ordinary vectors, **H** must be a pseudovector if $e$ is to be considered an ordinary scalar.

We shall find later that Biot-Savart's law can be transformed into a differential relationship, just as we were able to derive Gauss's law from Coulomb's law. For this derivation, we shall require an integral theorem, similar to Gauss's theorem, involving the curl. Accordingly, we shall conclude this section with the derivation of *Stokes's theorem.*

**Stokes's theorem.** Stokes's theorem states in effect that a closed-path integral of the dot product of a vector field **u** and the infinitesimal displacement along the path of integration equals a surface integral over an arbitrary open surface (also called *cap*), bounded by the original path of integration, of the dot product of the curl of the vector field **u** and the local unit vector normal to the cap, multiplied by the magnitude of the surface element $dS$. In terms of an equation:

$$\oint \mathbf{u} \cdot \mathbf{dl} \equiv \int_S \text{curl } \mathbf{u} \cdot \mathbf{n} \, dS. \tag{17}$$

The unit normal vector of a surface element is not uniquely defined. In the case of closed surfaces (the type involved in the formulation of Gauss's theorem), we have followed custom by agreeing that the normal is to point into the exterior of the closed surface. This convention is useless for a cap. We shall fix the direction of the normal by requiring that it is to have the same relationship to the sense in which we run about the path integration as the $x_3$-axis of the chosen coordinate system has to the sense of rotation leading from the positive $x_1$-direction to the positive $x_2$-direction (compare Fig. 15). In other words, we are tying the direction of the normal of a cap both to the direction in which we carry out the integration on the left-hand side of eq. (17) and to the screw sense of the chosen coordinate system. With respect to coordinate transformations, the thus defined unit normal vector is, therefore, not an ordinary vector but a pseudovector.

In order to derive eq. (17), we shall consider the closed-path integral on the left-hand side term by term, starting with the term $\oint u_2 \, dx_2$. If we cut up the cap into a number of strips parallel to the $x_1$, $x_3$-plane (as indicated in the figure), we can bring this particular term into the form

$$\oint u_2 \, dx_2 = + \int_{x_2} \left( \int_{x_1} \frac{\partial u_2}{\partial x_1} \, dx_1 + \int_{x_3} \frac{\partial u_2}{\partial x_3} \, dx_3 \right) dx_2. \qquad (18)$$

If we repeat this procedure with the term $\oint u_1 \, dx_1$, this time cutting

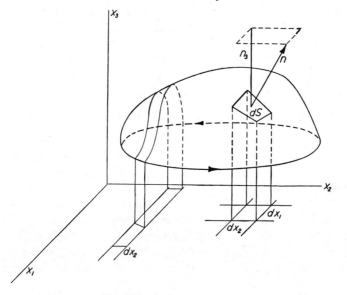

FIG. 15. Stokes's theorem.

up $S$ into strips that are parallel to the $x_2$, $x_3$-plane, we obtain

$$\oint u_1 \, dx_1 = - \int_{x_1} \left( \int_{x_2} \frac{\partial u_1}{\partial x_2} \, dx_2 + \int_{x_3} \frac{\partial u_1}{\partial x_3} \, dx_3 \right) dx_1. \qquad (19)$$

The signs on the right-hand sides of eqs. (18) and (19) are different because in both cases we wish to integrate in the direction of increasing values of $x_1$ and $x_2$ (at least if the cap has the position indicated in Fig. 15). $x_3$ will not change monotonically (without changing direction) throughout the range of integration.

If we combine the two terms multiplied by $dx_1 \, dx_2$ into a single surface integral, as a preliminary result we get

$$\oint \mathbf{u} \cdot \mathbf{dl} = \int \int_S \left( \frac{\partial u_2}{\partial x_1} - \frac{\partial u_1}{\partial x_2} \right) dx_1 \, dx_2 + \cdots. \qquad (20)$$

We have now collected *all* terms containing just those two differentials, since the third term in (17) does not contribute such a product of differentials. The expression (20) can be improved somewhat. If we consider the two strip systems leading to (18) and (19) simultaneously, we obtain a grating on the cap $S$. One cell of this grating is shown in Fig. 15, and also its projection on the $x_1, x_2$-plane. The magnitude of the grating cell is $dS$; the magnitude of its projection, $dx_1\, dx_2$. The ratio between these two areas must be the same as the ratio in the magnitudes of $\mathbf{n}$ and $n_3$; but $|\mathbf{n}|$ equals 1, by definition. We can, therefore, give eq. (20) the form

$$\oint \mathbf{u} \cdot d\mathbf{l} = \int\int_S \left( \frac{\partial u_2}{\partial x_1} - \frac{\partial u_1}{\partial x_2} \right) n_3\, dS + \cdots . \tag{21}$$

In the part of the derivation just concluded, the determination of the signs of the two terms under the integral is the most delicate step. This sign was determined. under the assumption, realized in Fig. 15, that $n_3$ is positive everywhere on the cap. If at any point the cap should be bent over so that one of the differentials $dx_1, dx_2$ is negative, then in that region the normal would also be tipped over so that $n_3$ becomes negative. In other words, the validity of eq. (21) does not depend on the accidental position of the path of integration and the cap relative to the chosen coordinate system.

The remaining terms, which were omitted in eqs. (20) and (21), can be found simply by permutating cyclically the three indices (1,2,3). Once these terms are added in eq. (21), the complete right-hand side takes the form

$$\oint u_i\, dx_i = \int\int_S \delta_{ikl} \frac{\partial u_l}{\partial x_k}\, n_i\, dS. \tag{22}$$

This equation is identical with (17), the theorem we set out to prove.

### 6.3. The magnetic field of a stationary current distribution

We are now ready to tackle the problem of finding general integral and differential expressions for the magnetic field produced by a steady current distribution. To do so, we shall first rewrite Biot-Savart's law in a covariant form with the help of the cross product. We shall begin with the case in which magnetizable materials are absent.

Equation (1) assumes the form

$$H_i = \frac{e}{c} \delta_{ikl} \frac{v_k \, r_l}{|r|^3}, \tag{23}$$

where, as usual, the vector $r_i$ is composed of the coordinate differences between the point at which we wish to determine the magnetic field and the location of the moving charge. Likewise, eq. (2) can be given the form

$$dH_i = \frac{I}{c} \delta_{ikl} \frac{dx_k \, r_l}{|r|^3}. \tag{24}$$

These two equations show that **H** cannot be an ordinary vector if all the quantities on the right-hand side are to have the usual transformation properties. Since coordinate differences and velocity vectors cannot be pseudovectors, the only quantities of which we could modify the transformation properties are the electrical quantities $e$ and $I$. In other words, with respect to improper rotations, we have this choice: either the magnetic field is a pseudovector and will change its direction under an improper transformation, or the electric charge (and with it the electric current) is a pseudoscalar and will change its sign under improper transformations. This alternative is purely formal and implies no difference in the physical significance of our laws, since it is, after all, purely arbitrary which kind of electric charge we wish to call positive or which end of a magnetized bar we shall call positive. However, custom decrees that we consider the electric charge a true scalar, so that electrons are negatively charged and positrons positively charged regardless of the choice of coordinate system; we are then forced to call the magnetic north pole the positive pole in a right-handed coordinate system but the negative pole in a left-handed system.

We shall now use Stokes's theorem to derive an integral formula for the field of a current loop of arbitrary shape, starting out with eq. (24). Suppose that we are connecting the two terminals of a battery with a wire having a finite resistance; then current will indeed flow in a closed loop, since inside the battery a current of the same magnitude $I$ as in the exterior circuit is being created by the migration of ions toward the two electrodes. If we just integrate the expression (24), we obtain a closed-path integral,

$$H_i = \frac{I}{c} \oint \delta_{ikl} \frac{r_l}{|r|^3} \, dx_k, \tag{25}$$

in which the variables of integration are the coordinates of the closed loop; the integration has to be carried out by going in the direction of the positive current exactly once around the loop. In order to apply Stokes's theorem, we shall now construct a cap, arbitrary except that it is to be bounded by the loop of current. We can then convert the closed-path integral of eq. (25) into a surface integral over the cap,

$$H_i = \frac{I}{c} \int \int_S \delta_{smn} \, \delta_{inl} \frac{\partial}{\partial x_m} \left( \frac{r_l}{|r|^3} \right) n_s \, dS. \tag{26}$$

This formidable-looking expression can be reduced without difficulty. First, we can eliminate the product of two Levi-Civita tensor densities by applying eq. (14), having first permutated indices so that they occur in the same sequence as in that formula. The result of this operation is

$$
\begin{aligned}
H_i &= \frac{I}{c} \int \int_S (\delta_{sl} \, \delta_{mi} - \delta_{si} \, \delta_{ml}) \frac{\partial}{\partial x_m} \left( \frac{r_l}{r^3} \right) n_s \, dS \\
&= \int \int_S \left[ \frac{\partial}{\partial x_i} \left( \frac{r_s}{r^3} \right) n_s - \frac{\partial}{\partial x_s} \left( \frac{r_s}{r^3} \right) n_i \right] dS.
\end{aligned}
\tag{27}
$$

The second term in this expression can be shown to vanish by straightforward computation, making use of the two formulas

$$\frac{\partial r_s}{\partial x_i} = -\delta_{si}, \qquad \frac{\partial r}{\partial x_i} = -\frac{x_i}{r}. \tag{28}$$

We are, therefore, left with the expression

$$H_i = \frac{I}{c} \int \int_S \frac{\partial}{\partial x_i} \left( \frac{r_s}{r^3} \right) n_s \, dS. \tag{29}$$

If we introduce the coordinates $\xi_i$ of the point $P$ at which $H_i$ is to be determined, eq. (29) can be transformed into

$$H_i(\xi) = -\frac{I}{c} \int \int_S \frac{\partial}{\partial \xi_i} \left( \frac{r_s}{r^3} \right) n_s \, dS = -\frac{I}{c} \frac{\partial}{\partial \xi_i} \int \int_S \frac{r_s n_s}{r^3} \, dS. \tag{30}$$

We can give the last equation a very interesting interpretation. We find that (locally) the magnetic field strength can be expressed as the negative gradient of a "magnetic potential," which is given by the expression

$$\psi(\xi) = + \frac{I}{c} \int \int_S \frac{r_s \, n_s}{r^3} \, dS. \tag{31}$$

The integrand of this expression, however, is exactly the potential that would be produced if the cap $S$ were covered evenly with dipoles having the direction of the normal at each point of the cap and the magnitude $(I/c)$ per unit area. In other words, the magnetic field strength produced by a closed loop of current is the same as that of a magnetic double layer or "shell" magnetized uniformly so as to have a dipole strength per unit area of $(I/c)$ at right angles to the double layer.

We had found previously that in the case of a straight wire it is not possible to introduce a magnetic potential which is unique and continuous throughout space, because a closed-path integral over $\mathbf{H} \cdot \mathbf{dl}$, looped about the wire, did not vanish. Since our present eq. (31) covers a much more general class of cases, it is of interest to see whether or not we can obtain results similar to eq. (5). The expression (31) suffers a discontinuity if we pass through the cap. Since the choice of the cap is arbitrary within wide limits, it stands to reason that the physically significant quantity, $\mathbf{H}$, remains continuous even though the potential $\psi$ may jump when we cross the magnetic double layer. The question remains how the choice of cap affects the value of the potential at any one point. This question can be answered by a very illuminating geometrical consideration. If we look at the integrand of eq. (31), we find that its value equals the solid angle under which the surface element $dS$ appears when viewed from the point $P$. The solid angle, it will be recalled, is defined as the area that a given cone cuts out of the surface of the unit sphere about the apex. If the vector $\mathbf{r}$ were normal to $dS$, the solid angle would be $dS/r^2$. If $dS$ is not at right angles to the line of vision, the cone is flattened by a factor that equals the cosine between the line of vision $\mathbf{r}$ and the surface normal $\mathbf{n}$,

$$d\Omega = \frac{dS}{r^2} \cos \theta = \frac{dS}{r^2} \frac{\mathbf{r} \cdot \mathbf{n}}{|\mathbf{r}|}. \tag{32}$$

But this is precisely the value of the integrand of eq. (31), and it follows that the magnetic potential $\psi$ equals $(I/c)$ times the (finite) solid angle under which the current loop appears when viewed from the point $P$.

Now this solid angle is not uniquely determined; if we approach the current loop from opposite sides until we reach some one point $P$, then the solid angle subtended by the loop reaches two different values. As far as their absolute magnitudes are concerned, their sum amounts to one full solid angle, which is $4\pi$. In computing the resulting magnetic potential, however, we must consider that the current when viewed from one side possesses the opposite sense of circulation to that it has when viewed from the other side (clockwise and counterclockwise, respectively). Therefore, if the solid angle equals $\Omega_1$ if the approach is made from the one side and equals $\Omega_2$ from the other side, with

$$\Omega_1 + \Omega_2 = 4\pi, \tag{33}$$

then the resulting values of the magnetic potential at the same point will be

$$\psi_1 = + \frac{I}{c}\, \Omega_1,$$
$$\psi_2 = - \frac{I}{c}\, \Omega_2 = - \frac{I}{c}\, (4\pi - \Omega_1) = \frac{I}{c}\, \Omega_1 - \frac{4\pi}{c}\, I. \tag{34}$$

We conclude that the ambiguity in magnetic potential is expressed by the equation

$$\psi_1 - \psi_2 = \frac{4\pi}{c}\, I. \tag{35}$$

If the "potential" is multivalued, then the work required to carry a unit pole once about the electric wire can be determined. Suppose that we move a unit magnetic pole about a closed path intertwined with the current loop in the manner shown in Fig. 16. This closed path will cross the cap (the magnetic double layer) exactly once, irrespective of the detailed shape of both the current loop and the closed path described by the unit pole, provided only that in any deformation of either of these two closed curves they do not cross each other. Since the jump in potential upon crossing the double layer is equal to the ambiguity expressed in eq. (35) and since this

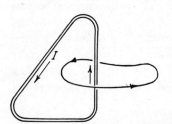

FIG. 16. Path of integration for **H** circling the electric wire.

jump must equal the value of the path integral $\oint \mathbf{H} \cdot \mathbf{dl}$, which would vanish if the potential were continuous and single-valued, we conclude that for a closed path of integration circling the electric wire once in the direction indicated, we shall always have

$$\oint \mathbf{H} \cdot \mathbf{dl} = \frac{4\pi}{c} I. \qquad (36)$$

This result is in agreement with the more restricted answer we obtained in eq. (5).

We shall return to the physical significance of our "magnetic shell" construction later. First, we shall generalize the result (36) by considering a "continuous" current distribution. We call a current distribution continuous if the moving charges are not confined to thin electric wires but are permitted to fill a whole region of space. The distribution is then continuous in the sense in which a mass density $\rho$ is "continuous." We describe the current distribution conveniently with the help of a vector field, the "current density" $\mathbf{j}$. The vector field $\mathbf{j}$ is defined in analogy to the momentum density, by means of the equation

$$\mathbf{j} = \langle e\, \mathbf{V} \rangle. \qquad (37)$$

Its dot product by a unit vector $\mathbf{n}$ normal to a surface $S$ measures the amount of current (charge per unit time) passing through a unit area of $S$. If the surface is not plane and the current density not uniform, then the total amount of current through $S$ is given by the integral

$$I = \iint_S \mathbf{j} \cdot \mathbf{n}\, dS. \qquad (38)$$

Charges cannot be created or destroyed. Therefore, the charge density $\sigma$ and the current density $\mathbf{j}$ must together satisfy an equation of continuity similar to eq. (3.76).

$$\frac{\partial \sigma}{\partial t} + \operatorname{div} \mathbf{j} \equiv \frac{\partial \sigma}{\partial t} + j_{s,s} = 0. \qquad (39)$$

If the current distribution is stationary, that is, if neither $\sigma$ nor $\mathbf{j}$ change with time (though both be functions of the coordinates $x_i$), then we can introduce "current tubes" throughout space. A current tube has walls that are everywhere parallel to $\mathbf{j}$, so that no charges are carried either into or out of the tube. These tubes either are closed on themselves or else reach from infinity to infinity. Because with a stationary current distribution, div **j** must vanish, each tube carries a constant amount of current throughout its length. With this picture, we may apply the results of eq. (36) to the present situation. An artibrary closed path of integration will circle a certain number of current tubes (which we have previously called loops); since at each point the total finite magnetic field strength **H** is the linear superposition of the contributions of all the tubes in space, the integral $\oint \mathbf{H} \cdot \mathbf{dl}$, too, must be the sum of all the contributions of those tubes which have been circled,

$$\oint \mathbf{H} \cdot \mathbf{dl} = \frac{4\pi}{c} I = \frac{4\pi}{c} \int \int_S \mathbf{j} \cdot \mathbf{n} \, dS. \tag{40}$$

With the help of Stokes's theorem, (17), we can convert the closed-path integral on the left-hand side into a surface integral,

$$\oint \mathbf{H} \cdot \mathbf{dl} \equiv \int \int_S \text{curl } \mathbf{H} \cdot \mathbf{n} \, dS. \tag{41}$$

Since the resulting equality between two surface integrals will hold for any surface that can be constructed in the region of space containing the continuous current distribution, we may conclude that generally, for a stationary current distribution, we have

$$\delta_{ikl} H_{l,k} = \frac{4\pi}{c} j_i, \qquad \text{curl } \mathbf{H} = \frac{4\pi}{c} \mathbf{j}. \tag{42}$$

This relationship goes over into eq. (5.76) of magnetostatics in the absence of electric currents. The derivation given here restricts eq. (42) to stationary current distributions; and we shall see later, in fact, that it needs to be modified in the nonstationary, time-dependent case. According to eq. (42), a current distribution appears to generate a magnetic field somewhat as an electric charge distribution generates an electric field in accordance with eq. (5.71).

The validity of eq. (42) is not affected by the presence of magnetized bodies, since the contribution of such bodies to the magnetic field can be represented as the field of a collection of magnetic dipoles. Such a field is conservative and is the gradient of a continuous and unique potential; its contribution to the antisymmetric derivatives of **H**, $(H_{i,k} - H_{k,i})$ must vanish.

We shall now return to our representation of the magnetic field caused by a current loop as the field caused by a uniformly magnetized shell. "At infinity," the field of the shell is approximated by the field of a single dipole, representing the total magnetic dipole moment of the shell. Conversely, we must be able to represent the field of a magnetic dipole also as the field caused by a small loop of current, where the area bounded by the loop, multiplied by the current, must equal $c$ times the magnetic dipole moment. Ampère was the first to realize that this equivalence between current loops and magnetic dipoles, as far as the resulting magnetic field is concerned, might serve to explain the nonexistence of magnetic poles in nature. We should have to assume that neither elementary magnetic poles nor dipoles exist, but that the observed magnetic fields are produced by moving electric charges. If the orbits of the moving charges are sufficiently small, then the resulting magnetic fields should be indistinguishable from fields produced by magnetic dipoles, suitably distributed.

On the whole, Ampère's hypothesis concerning the origin of magnetic fields has been borne out by our increasing knowledge of the structure of matter. Atoms consist of positively charged nuclei, surrounded by orbital electrons. The observed magnetization of matter in bulk is contributed in part by the circulating electrons, constituting miniature loops of electric current. As for the remainder of the magnetization of matter, it has become known recently that both electrons and atomic nuclei possess "intrinsic" magnetic dipole moments, irrespective of orbital motion. These magnetic dipole moments are always connected with an intrinsic "rotation," or intrinsic angular momentum of these particles.

Now for the quantitative aspects of Ampère's hypothesis. Suppose we have a current loop and wish to compute the equivalent magnetic dipole moment. In that case we must first construct a cap, then distribute dipoles over it so that the local dipole moment per unit area equals $(I/c)$ in magnitude and is normal to the cap, and finally add all the dipole moments together. The resulting dipole will determine that portion of the field at a great distance which drops off with the inverse third power of the distance; all other terms will drop off with higher negative powers of $r$. The total dipole moment $\mathbf{M}$ will then be

$$\mathbf{M} = \frac{I}{c} \int \int_S \mathbf{n} \, dS. \tag{43}$$

For a circular loop in the $x_1, x_2$-plane of radius $R$, for instance, the total magnetic dipole moment will be

$$M = \frac{\pi}{c} R^2 I \tag{44}$$

and will be directed parallel to the $x_3$-axis.

The expression (43) makes it possible to find a law for the dipole moment of an electron which is moving about an atomic nucleus in a planetary orbit, an expression which is of great significance in the theory of atomic spectra. Since an electron moves under the influence of attractive forces pulling it toward the atomic nucleus, its orbit lies wholly in a plane, as was shown in Chapter 1 for the special case of gravitational forces. If we call the plane area bounded by the orbit $A$ and the period of its orbit $T$, it follows from eq. (43) that the magnetic dipole moment (which will be perpendicular to the plane of the orbit) must be

$$|\mathbf{M}| = -\frac{e}{c} \frac{A}{T}, \tag{45}$$

in which $-e$ is the electronic charge and $-e/T$ is the total charge passing through a suitably chosen cross section per unit time. Neither $A$ nor $T$ will in general be known accurately, but these two quantities are connected with the angular momentum $p_\theta$ of the orbit through Kepler's second law. (In Chapter 1, this angular momentum was designated $I_{12}$, but we shall here use the designation $p_\theta$ in order to avoid confusion with the electric current $I$.) In polar coordinates, the angular momentum is

$$p_\theta = m r^2 \dot{\theta}, \tag{46}$$

where $m$ is the mass of the electron, $r$ the distance from the nucleus to the electron, and $\dot{\theta}$ the angular velocity. This expression is, however, equal to $2m$ times the area swept out by the radius vector per unit time, by straight geometry. If the angular momentum is constant along the orbit, as it must be in planetary motion, it follows that

$$\frac{A}{T} = \frac{p_\theta}{2m}. \tag{47}$$

Combining this expression with eq. (45), we find that for all electronic orbits the ratio between the magnetic dipole moment and the angular momentum is the same,

$$\frac{M}{p_\theta} = - \frac{e}{2m\,c}. \qquad (48)$$

This equation has assumed even increased importance since the advent of quantum mechanics, which predicts that the angular momentum can assume only discrete values, namely, integral multiples of $h/2\pi$. It follows that the orbital magnetic dipole moment of an electron is always an integral multiple of $-(e\,h/4\pi m\,c)$, a result that has been fully confirmed by spectroscopic evidence.

## 6.4. The Lorentz force

So far, we have devoted our attention to the force that a moving electric charge exerts on a magnetic pole. In this section, we shall tackle the counterforce.

It is true that the force described by Biot-Savart's law violates some of the tenets of Newtonian mechanics. Its direction is at right angles to the connecting straight line between moving charge and magnetic pole, and its magnitude depends on the velocity of the charge as well as on the distance between the two interacting particles. Nevertheless, it is not unreasonable to attempt to retain as much as possible of the original structure of mechanics. We shall, therefore, try to obtain an expression for the counterforce simply by applying Newton's third law, requiring that the sum of force and counterforce vanish. Naturally, the result will have to be tested by experiment. If our assumption is correct, then the force that a "single magnetic pole" of strength $p$ exerts on a moving charge $e$ must equal

$$\mathbf{f} = \frac{e}{c}\,p\,\frac{\mathbf{v} \times \mathbf{r}}{r^3}. \qquad (49)$$

The vector $\mathbf{r}$ here points from the pole to the moving electric charge. Since single poles do not occur in nature and since the action of the several poles that make up an actual piece of magnetic material is the vector sum of their individual contributions, we shall describe the total force $\mathbf{f}$ experienced by our moving charge $e$ in terms of the total magnetic field produced by all the magnetic poles (or rather dipoles) present. Since the expression $(pr/r^3)$ is the contribution of a single magnetic pole $p$ to the magnetic induction $\mathbf{B}$ ($\mathbf{B}$ rather than $\mathbf{H}$ if space is filled with magnetizable material), it follows that the total force on the moving charge $e$ will be

$$f = \frac{e}{c} \mathbf{v} \times \mathbf{B}. \tag{50}$$

If we add to this magnetic force the electric force with which we are familiar from electrostatics, we obtain an expression for the total force acting on a moving electric point charge:

$$f_i = e \left( E_i + \delta_{ikl} \frac{v_k}{c} B_l \right),$$
$$\mathbf{f} = e \left( \mathbf{E} + \frac{\mathbf{v}}{c} \times \mathbf{B} \right). \tag{51}$$

This expression was formulated first by H. A. Lorentz and is named after him.   Naturally, both $\mathbf{E}$ and $\mathbf{B}$ in this equation represent the "incident" field, the field that is independent of the presence of the particle subject to the force.   This particle makes contributions of its own to both the electric and magnetic field which at the location of the particle are infinite.

Equation (51) is the result of the application of Newton's third law.   Since we have already discovered that electromagnetic interaction cannot be wholly integrated in the Newtonian scheme, this "derivation" must be considered speculative and requires experimental verification.   This verification has been amply forthcoming, particularly in recent times.   The cyclotron, the mass spectrograph, the cloud chamber (with magnetic field), and a host of other modern instruments utilize the action of the magnetic field on moving charges, both electrons and ions, and almost any one of them permits a quantitative check of eqs. (51).   Since none of these instruments incorporate single magnetic poles (there being none) but other sources of magnetic fields, mostly electromagnets, it is eq. (51) rather than eq. (49) that is being tested.   Because of the absence of free magnetic poles in nature, eq. (49) has no experimental significance.

## 6.5. Electromagnetic induction

The third effect to be considered in this chapter is the electromagnetic induction.   In a circular loop of wire we observe an electromotive force whenever the magnetic flux through the loop is changed.   In order to describe this effect in terms of ordinary electric and magnetic field quantities we must define the terms

"*electromotive force*" (emf) and magnetic flux.   By emf the engineer
means a voltage (in addition to any others that may be present)
produced between the terminals of his coiled wire, a force which
will cause additional current to flow against electric resistance.
Since the electromagnetically induced emf is independent of current
that may already be flowing in the wire and, therefore, apparently
independent of the motion of the electrons, this force must be
described in terms of an additional *electric* field strength.   Since the
emf is measured in volts (units of potential), it follows that it must
be the *integral of an electric field strength*, taken along the electric
wire.   We shall, therefore, set the emf equal to the integral

$$\mathcal{E} = \int E_s \, dx_s = \int \mathbf{E} \cdot d\mathbf{l}, \tag{52}$$

and since the law of induction above is formulated in terms of loops
of wire, we shall further take it for granted that in its mathematical
formulation we shall have to deal with closed-path integrals.   In
other words, the induced emf will be correctly described by an
expression

$$\mathcal{E}_{(i)} = \oint \mathbf{E} \cdot d\mathbf{l}. \tag{53}$$

In accepting this formulation, we admit right away that this electric
field cannot be conservative; that is, it is not the negative gradient
field of a potential function.   The reason is that any field which
leads to a nonvanishing closed path integral of the kind (53) must
have a nonvanishing curl, because of Stokes's theorem; but the
curl of a gradient field vanishes identically [compare eq. (5.24) and
Problem 6.2].   However, if we are to do justice to the experimental
fact that the observed emf does not depend on the material of which
the wire is made or on the presence of dielectrics or magnetic materials, we must conclude that the electric field strength is there, irrespective of the presence of the wire, and that the wire serves merely
the purpose of making the electric field observable, through the
appearance of additional current.   And since this emf will apparently make itself felt in *loops* of current and since it can be easily
multiplied by an integer $n$, merely by replacing the single loop of
wire by a coil of $n$ turns, there is at least a strong suggestion that
the description (53), though running counter to the spirit of Newtonian mechanics, is actually appropriate for the description of the
observed facts.

The induced emf is now supposed to be proportional to the time rate of change of the *magnetic flux* through the loop. The magnetic flux is defined as the number of *"lines of force"* through the loop. The lines of force, the reader will recall, are a way of representing a vector field graphically. We draw them as curves which everywhere represent the direction of the vector field **v**; its magnitude $v$ is represented by the density of these curves. The number of lines of force through a surface $S$ is the product of their density, the sine of the angle at which they intersect the surface, and the area element $dS$, all integrated over the finite surface,

$$N = \int \int_S |\mathbf{v}| \sin \phi \, dS = \int \int_S \mathbf{v} \cdot \mathbf{n} \, dS. \tag{54}$$

Now, in general, lines of force will start at certain points and end in others. In fact, if we consider a *closed* surface and take a balance of the lines of force, subtracting those which enter into the interior from those which leave, then the net number of lines leaving the interior of the closed surface and, therefore, having originated there, must equal the expression on the right-hand side of eq. (54). But this closed surface integral can be transformed into a volume integral with the help of Gauss's theorem, and we find that the number of lines of force originating in a unit volume equals the divergence of the vector field **v**.

Returning to our law of induction, we must define the flux in terms of a field in which the number of lines passing through a closed curve is the same for all caps bounded by that closed curve. This condition will be satisfied by a system of lines of force in which no lines originate or terminate anywhere or, in other words, by a field which has a zero divergence. The magnetic field strength does not possess this property, but the magnetic induction does, eq. (5.77), because of the nonexistence of free magnetic poles. We can, therefore, define the magnetic flux so that our law of induction does not suffer from internal inconsistencies, by the equation

$$\Phi = \int \int_S \mathbf{B} \cdot \mathbf{n} \, dS, \tag{55}$$

and our law of induction takes the form

$$\oint \mathbf{E} \cdot d\mathbf{l} \propto \frac{d}{dt} \int \int_S \mathbf{B} \cdot \mathbf{n} \, dS = \int \int_S \frac{\partial \mathbf{B}}{\partial t} \cdot \mathbf{n} \, dS. \tag{56}$$

Naturally, we shall not let this relationship stand without converting the integral on the left into a surface integral. By applying Stokes's theorem to the closed-path integral, we obtain the proportionality

$$\int\int_S \text{curl } \mathbf{E} \cdot \mathbf{n} \, dS \propto \int\int_S \frac{\partial \mathbf{B}}{\partial t} \cdot \mathbf{n} \, dS. \tag{57}$$

Observation tells us that the emf induced is clockwise if the magnetic flux is increased toward the observer and counterclockwise if it is increased away from the observer; therefore, the sign in the proportionality must be negative. As for the constant of proportionality, a comparison of the dimensions on both sides shows that the constant must have the dimension of a reciprocal velocity; and so we shall not be greatly surprised if measurements show that its magnitude is $c^{-1}$,

$$\int\int_S \text{curl } \mathbf{E} \cdot \mathbf{n} \, dS = -\frac{1}{c} \int\int_S \frac{\partial \mathbf{B}}{\partial t} \cdot \mathbf{n} \, dS. \tag{58}$$

Since the equation (58) holds for any cap, we may omit the integral and conclude that everywhere we shall have

$$\text{curl } \mathbf{E} + \frac{1}{c}\frac{\partial \mathbf{B}}{\partial t} = 0. \tag{59}$$

This is a most remarkable law. The mere change of the magnetic field in the course of time is to induce in space an electric field strength, even in the absence of any electric charges that might be considered the source of this field strength. On second thought, though, this law is not unrelated to the velocity-dependent effects we studied in the preceding sections. Let us return once more to the force experienced by a moving electric particle in the presence of a magnetic field. We found that this force is velocity-dependent and that it obeys the equation (50) if no electric field is present. In the discussion leading up to that equation, we assumed, without stressing that point, that the magnetic field is time-independent. If we go back one step further and consider the magnetic field as the force exerted by magnetic poles or, since they do not exist, magnetic dipoles, it is then assumed that the sources of the magnetic field are at rest while the electric charges are not. This is, obviously, a somewhat restricted point of view. We ought to attempt to consider the case in which both the electric and the magnetic particles are moving. Now it is reasonable to expect that the force a magnetized particle and an electric particle exert on each other should depend only on their *relative* motion rather than on the *absolute* motion of the electric particles alone—reasonable because it is consistent with the sum total of our physical experience. Since this argument is of great historical importance, we shall devote some space to it, even though it may appear a digression.

In Newtonian mechanics, the concept of inertial coordinate system is basic, because it defines the frame of reference with respect to which nature is to be described. We introduced the inertial systems in Chapter 1 as those coordinate systems with respect to which the law of inertia is valid. Now given an inertial system, any other coordinate system that moves with respect to the inertial system in a straight-line, uniform motion and without any rotation of the axes is itself an inertial system; any body which is unaccelerated with respect to system number 1 will also be unaccelerated with respect to the second system. Thus, on the basis of the first law alone, there is an infinity of coordinate systems, the inertial systems, which are all equivalent as far as force-free motion is concerned. If we now go over the other two laws of Newton, we notice that they formulate conditions for accelerations rather than for velocities. But accelerations of bodies are the same no matter what inertial system they are referred to, a property not possessed by the velocities. Finally, in Newtonian mechanics proper the forces between two particles are functions of their distance only, and the distance is again the same in all inertial systems. In other words, the laws of nature, including the force law, must be the same in all inertial systems; and if Newton's mechanics were to embrace all of physics, then it would be impossible to single out, by observation and experiment, one particular inertial frame of reference and say: "This is the frame representing *absolute* rest; all the others are in absolute motion." This equivalence of all inertial systems in the theoretical structure of Newton's mechanics is known as the (*classical*) *principle of relativity*.

Experience has shown us that general principles of invariance (in this case invariance with respect to a certain class of coordinate transformations involving the time) or conservation laws which form part of a successful theory rarely, if ever, need to be discarded together with the underlying theory. They may require modification, to be sure, and we shall encounter instances of such modification shortly; but a negative statement such as the nonexistence of an absolute frame defining rest hardly admits of any modification short of its discard. If we now return to the interaction of magnetic and electric particles, we find that the law of force appears to embody the velocity of the electric particles; and if this were the general form of the law, then accurate measurement of the observed force of interaction should reveal the *absolute* mode of motion of the electric particles and, thus, reveal the frame of reference representing absolute rest. To avoid this contingency, we are certainly justified in attempting to generalize eq. (49) by assuming that the vector **v** represents the motion of the electric particle *relative to the source of the magnetic field.*

Let us follow up this hypothesis. If we consider the presence of more than one electric pole (the actual dipoles can be considered mathematically as pairs of poles), we can describe the total force acting on our electric particle by the expression

$$\mathbf{f} = \frac{e}{c} \sum_n p_n \frac{\mathbf{v}_n \times \mathbf{r}_n}{|\mathbf{r}_n|^3} = \frac{e}{c} \sum_n p_n \frac{(\dot{\mathbf{x}} - \dot{\mathbf{x}}_n) \times (\mathbf{x} - \mathbf{x}_n)}{|\mathbf{r}_n|^3}. \quad (60)$$

The coordinates of the electric particle are here designated by **x** (without a subscript), and the poles and their coordinates and pole strengths have been numbered by means of the subscript $n$. $\mathbf{r}_n$ is the vector drawn from the $n$th pole to the electric particle. This force can now be split up into two contributions, those terms depending on the velocity of the electric particle and those depending on the velocities of the magnetic poles (all velocities relative to the chosen coordinate system). These two contributions have the form

$$\mathbf{f} = \frac{e}{c} \dot{\mathbf{x}} \times \sum_n p_n \frac{\mathbf{r}_n}{|\mathbf{r}_n|^3} - \frac{e}{c} \sum_n p_n \frac{\dot{\mathbf{x}}_n \times \mathbf{r}_n}{|\mathbf{r}_n|^3}. \quad (61)$$

The first term, which represents the force proportional to the motion of the electric particle, has the expected form. The second term is the one of interest now. It represents the action of moving magnetic particles on an electric particle irrespective of the latter's motion. It is, therefore, the direct counterpart of the magnetic action of moving electric particles, which is described by Biot-

Savart's law.   The action must be interpreted as an induced electric field strength, leading to the equation

$$\mathbf{E} = -\frac{1}{c} \sum_n p_n \frac{\dot{\mathbf{x}}_n \times \mathbf{r}_n}{|\mathbf{r}_n|^3}. \tag{62}$$

This formula differs from Biot-Savart's law only by the interchange of electric and magnetic quantities and by the sign.

In the case of Biot-Savart's law, we were able to produce a "local" law, that is a set of partial differential equations, for the special case that the moving electric particles form a steady (time-independent) current distribution.   In the magnetic case, there can be no current density because there is no (free) pole density. However, we can still obtain a "local" law by a somewhat different procedure.   First, we might see whether this kind of electric field strength possesses a divergence, so that a moving magnetic particle is equivalent to an electric charge.   But the divergence vanishes: The "lines of force" of this electric field are all closed curves, namely, circles symmetric about the instantaneous tangent of the pole's path.   Thus, we are led to examine the curl of this field, and it turns out that the curl does not vanish.   We can obtain the curl most conveniently by making use of a formula that follows directly from the defining equations of the cross product and the curl and from eq. (14).   This formula is

$$[\text{curl } (\mathbf{u} \times \mathbf{v})]_i = \frac{\partial}{\partial x_s} (u_i v_s - u_s v_i). \tag{63}$$

If we now rewrite eq. (62) in the form

$$\mathbf{E} = +\frac{1}{c} \sum_n p_n \dot{\mathbf{x}}_n \times \nabla \left(\frac{1}{|\mathbf{r}_n|}\right), \tag{64}$$

where the del-symbol denotes partial differentiation with respect to the coordinates of the electric particle, and if we consider that $\dot{\mathbf{x}}_n$ does not depend on those coordinates, we get for curl $\mathbf{E}$ the expression

$$\begin{aligned}
(\text{curl } \mathbf{E})_i &= \frac{1}{c} \sum_n p_n \left[ \dot{x}_i \left(\frac{1}{r_n}\right)_{,ss} - \dot{x}_s \left(\frac{1}{r_n}\right)_{,si} \right] \\
&= 0 + \frac{1}{c} \sum_n p_n \dot{x}_s \frac{\partial}{\partial x_s} \left[ \left(\frac{1}{r_n}\right)_{,i} \right].
\end{aligned} \tag{65}$$

The first term vanishes, simply because the Laplacian of the function $1/r$ vanishes everywhere except where $r = 0$. In the second term, use has been made of the defining equation

$$\mathbf{r}_n = \mathbf{x} - \mathbf{x}_n, \tag{66}$$

and one differentiation with respect to $\mathbf{x}$ has been replaced by differentiation with respect to $-\mathbf{x}_n$. This change in the second term enables us to interpret the factor

$$\dot{x}_{s\atop n} \frac{\partial}{\partial x_{s\atop n}} \left[ \left( \frac{1}{r_n} \right)_{,i} \right]$$

as the rate of change of the value of the function in the bracket at the point with the fixed coordinates $x_i$,

$$\operatorname{curl} \mathbf{E} = \frac{1}{c} \sum_n p_n \frac{\partial}{\partial t} \left[ \nabla \left( \frac{1}{r_n} \right) \right] = \frac{1}{c} \frac{\partial}{\partial t} \left[ \nabla \sum_n \frac{p_n}{r_n} \right] = -\frac{1}{c} \frac{\partial \mathbf{B}}{\partial t}. \tag{67}$$

In this equation, we finally encounter the partial derivative of the field $\mathbf{B}$ with respect to the time $t$, and our final result is eq. (59).

One point is worth mentioning in this derivation. When we set the first term in eq. (65), upper line, equal to zero, we assumed that even in a smeared, "continuous" distribution of magnetic material, the free pole density would always vanish. Otherwise, this first term should have led to the insertion of a "magnetic current density" term in eq. (59).

Conversely, our derivation enables us now to generalize the results obtained in Section 6.3. In that section, we restricted ourselves to the case of steady current. But the similarity of eq. (62) with Biot-Savart's law indicates what needs to be done to generalize for the time-dependent case. We must add to eq. (42) a term which contains the time derivative of $\mathbf{D}$ but which has the opposite sign as the corresponding term in eq. (59). The amended eq. (42) will then read

$$\operatorname{curl} \mathbf{H} - \frac{1}{c} \frac{\partial \mathbf{D}}{\partial t} = \frac{4\pi}{c} \mathbf{j}. \tag{68}$$

## 6.6. Summary

The basic dynamical idea of Newtonian mechanics is the action at a distance of discrete mass points. It is possible to extend this concept to certain aspects of the interaction of electric and magnetic particles, and we have carried out this extension in the last two chapters. First of all, it is possible to describe the interaction of electric particles at rest with electric particles at rest or near-rest completely in Newtonian terms; the same holds for magnetic particles, except for the circumstance that the elementary magnetic particle envisaged by Coulomb's (magnetic) law, the free pole, does not occur in nature. The description of these purely electric and purely magnetic interactions was the subject of Chapter 5. In Chapter 6, we attempted the description of electromagnetic interactions proper; that is the action of electric on magnetic particles, and vice versa. We found that the laws of interaction differ from purely Newtonian laws: they are velocity-dependent, and the forces are not in the connecting straight line but at right angles to it. At this stage, the abandonment of the conservation laws of energy and angular momentum appears inevitable, but we did succeed in maintaining the third law of Newton, which in turn implies the conservation of linear momentum, and so far we have not been forced to give up the (classical) principle of relativity.

For later convenience, we shall here summarize those partial differential equations obtained through the two chapters 5 and 6 which describe the laws discussed:

$$\operatorname{div} \mathbf{D} = 4\pi\sigma, \qquad \operatorname{curl} \mathbf{E} + \frac{1}{c}\frac{\partial \mathbf{B}}{\partial t} = 0,$$
$$\operatorname{div} \mathbf{B} = 0, \qquad \operatorname{curl} \mathbf{H} - \frac{1}{c}\frac{\partial \mathbf{D}}{\partial t} = \frac{4\pi}{c}\mathbf{j}. \tag{69}$$

Added to these must be the expression for the force acting on an electric particle,

$$\mathbf{f} = e\left(\mathbf{E} + \frac{\mathbf{v}}{c} \times \mathbf{B}\right). \tag{70}$$

We shall not attempt to write down an amended force law for magnetic poles, since free poles do not exist and since free dipoles, according to Ampère's hypothesis, are in reality tiny circular currents, in other words, rapidly moving charges. Instead, in the next chapter we shall take up this problem by reexamining the interaction between two electric charges of which at least one is moving so rapidly that it gives rise to a magnetic field. The successful completion of this task will actually tell us what forces are experienced by the only "magnetic" particles that occur in nature.

## Problems

**6.1.** In the derivation of Stokes's theorem, vary the location and orientation of the cap relative to the chosen coordinate system and vary the direction of the line integral several times, in order to show in detail that the theorem holds regardless of the choice of coordinate system or the position of the closed path of integration and the cap.

**6.2.** Show that the divergence of a curl vanishes identically. Show that the curl of a gradient field vanishes identically.

**6.3.** Show that a vector field whose curl vanishes everywhere can always be represented as the gradient of a scalar field, and that the scalar field is uniquely determined except for a single additive constant.

**6.4.** Show likewise that a vector field whose divergence vanishes can always be represented as the curl of a pseudovector field, the latter being determined except for the addition of an arbitrary gradient field.

**6.5.** The magnetic induction exerts on each piece of a wire that carries an electric current a force $\mathbf{f}$ equal to $-I\mathbf{B} \times d\mathbf{l}/c$, in accordance with eq. (50). The net force exerted on a closed loop of current by a *uniform* magnetic field is zero, because the integral $\oint d\mathbf{l}$ vanishes. However, the total torque does not vanish. Show that it is exactly the torque that would be experienced by the equivalent magnetic dipole. To avoid complications, it is suggested that this proof be carried out only for the case in which the magnetic permeability is 1, although a general proof is possible.

**6.6.** Compute the magnetic field in the interior of a long solenoid on the assumption that outside the coil the field is negligible. Consider a ring made of ferromagnetic material with a short air gap on which is wound a coil. Determine the field in the air gap as well as inside the electromagnetic material.

**6.7.** Consider the problem of planetary motion of an electron about an atomic nucleus in the presence of a uniform, constant magnetic field at right angles to the plane of motion. Because of the presence of the magnetic field, the quantity $mr^2\dot{\theta}$ is not conserved. It is, however, possible to find a similar quantity that is conserved. Find that quantity. In this connection, what can be said about the conservation law of energy?

**6.8.** Designating, for the sake of convenience, the new quantity that satisfies the law of conservation formerly obeyed by the angular momentum by $p_\theta$, find out whether in terms of this quantity the magnetic dipole moment of the electronic orbit is greater or smaller than required by eq. (48). The answer will, of course, depend on whether the dipole moment is parallel or antiparallel to the applied external magnetic field. This consideration leads to a (classical) theory of the diamagnetism of many substances.

**6.9.** Consider a uniform magnetic field of induction **B** along the $x_3$-axis and compute the orbits of free electrons in the $x_1, x_2$-plane, assuming that their initial speed $v_0$ is given. If now the magnetic field is changed in magnitude at a constant rate $\dot{B} = -a$, what will happen to the electronic orbits? (This is the underlying idea of the betatron; the theory that the reader can develop on the basis of the formulas of this chapter is non-relativistic and therefore fails for electronic kinetic energies from about $10^5$ electron volts upwards.)

# Chapter 7
## The Electromagnetic Field

### 7.1. Two moving charges

Up to now, we have formulated the interactions between electric charges and magnetic particles on the assumption that at least one of them is in motion. We succeeded in describing these interactions in terms of two different mathematical languages. One mode of representation describes the forces as *interactions between pairs of particles*, interactions that take place across empty space. Another mode of representation focuses attention on the force on a single particle and gathers the effect of all other particles up into the *field quantities*, the electric and magnetic field strengths, the electric displacement, and the magnetic induction. So far, the field quantities have appeared as auxiliary concepts serving primarily to formulate the effect of large numbers of (moving) charges that cannot be treated individually. Although for many purposes it is *convenient* to describe the force acting on an electric point charge in terms of the incident electromagnetic field, the description of the same force in terms of the actions of individual particles is more *fundamental*, corresponding more closely to the mechanical concept of the fundamental laws of nature.

It is true that the electromagnetic forces do not possess all the properties that are usually ascribed to mechanical forces. The effect of a magnetic field on a moving electric charge and the force that a moving charge exerts on a magnetic particle are not potential forces; that is, they cannot be represented as the negative partial derivatives of a potential energy function which depends only on the relative locations of the particles involved. But this deviation from the standard mechanical features does not appear too serious. We have so far been able to maintain the third law and thus to retain the conservation law of linear momentum for isolated systems. Also, the magnetic field (which is that part of the force which is not derivable from a potential) does not change the kinetic energy of an electrically charged particle, since the force caused by the magnetic field is always at right angles to the instantaneous particle velocity and, thus, does not contribute to its change of speed.

We have refrained from formulating a law of force on a moving magnetic pole, because there are no poles in nature and because Ampère's hypothesis on the nature of magnetic dipoles suggests that neither magnetic poles nor magnetic dipoles are "elementary" particles. We should be able to obtain the acceleration that a dipole will suffer in an electromagnetic field by replacing it by an equivalent loop of current or a rapidly circulating electric charge and by computing the total force acting on such a loop. Now we already know the force that acts on a magnetic dipole at rest in a stationary field. What we are interested in is the effect of a changing field on a moving dipole, and we must, therefore, derive an expression for the interaction between two electric charges *both of which* possess high velocities. The first moving charge will cause a magnetic field (in addition to an electric field), because of Biot-Savart's law, and this magnetic field will act on the second moving charge in accordance with our expression for the Lorentz force. Thus, it would appear that all we have to do to obtain the desired law is to combine two laws already available. We shall discover that the result of this operation will lead to a law of interaction that destroys the validity of Newton's third law and with it the law of conservation of linear momentum.

Consider two particles with charges $e_1$, $e_2$ and velocities $\mathbf{v}_1$, $\mathbf{v}_2$. Designate the distance between them by the symbol $r$ and their respective coordinate triplets by $\mathbf{x}_1$, $\mathbf{x}_2$. Consider the space otherwise empty, so that we may not be bothered by the need of considering dielectric and diamagnetic properties of the surrounding medium. Now the first particle will cause electric and magnetic fields at the location of the second particle given by the expressions

$$\mathbf{E} = \frac{e_1}{r^3} (\mathbf{x}_2 - \mathbf{x}_1), \qquad \mathbf{B} = \frac{e_1}{r^3} \frac{\dot{\mathbf{x}}_1}{c} \times (\mathbf{x}_2 - \mathbf{x}_1). \tag{1}$$

The force acting on the second particle is then given by the Lorentz force, which the reader will find listed in the summary section of Chapter 6, eq. (6.70). Substituting the above expressions, we get

for the force that the first particle exerts on the second particle,
the expression

$$\mathbf{f}_{12} = \frac{e_1 e_2}{r^3} \left\{ (\mathbf{x}_2 - \mathbf{x}_1) + \frac{1}{c^2} \dot{\mathbf{x}}_2 \times [\dot{\mathbf{x}}_1 \times (\mathbf{x}_2 - \mathbf{x}_1)] \right\}. \tag{2}$$

Of the two terms, the first is simply the Coulomb force and at present
is of no further interest. The second term represents an interaction via the magnetic field. It can be transformed with the help
of eq. (6.14) and has then the form

$$\mathbf{f}_{12}^{(m)} = \frac{e_1 e_2}{c^2 r^3} \left\{ \dot{\mathbf{x}}_1 [\dot{\mathbf{x}}_2 \cdot (\mathbf{x}_2 - \mathbf{x}_1)] - (\mathbf{x}_2 - \mathbf{x}_1)(\dot{\mathbf{x}}_1 \cdot \dot{\mathbf{x}}_2) \right\}. \tag{3}$$

This law, which supposedly describes the magnetic part of the
interaction of two moving electric charges, is remarkable in that it
differs in two respects from all laws we have met with previously.
This law of interaction does not obey Newton's third law, since the
force of the first on the second charge does not equal the negative
force of the second particle on the first. Furthermore, this law does
not depend on the *relative* velocities of the two particles but on
their velocities with respect to the coordinate system; it cannot hold
simultaneously with respect to all inertial frames of reference.
We shall discuss both of these aspects.

Equation (2) gives the force which the first charge exerts on the
second. The force of the second on the first charge can be obtained
simply if we switch all indices 1 and 2. If we add these two forces
vectorially, the purely electric contributions (that is, the velocity-
independent terms) will cancel, and we retain

$$\mathbf{f}_{12} + \mathbf{f}_{21} = \frac{e_1 e_2}{c^2 r^3} \left\{ \dot{\mathbf{x}}_1 [\dot{\mathbf{x}}_2 \cdot (\mathbf{x}_2 - \mathbf{x}_1)] - \dot{\mathbf{x}}_2 [\dot{\mathbf{x}}_1 \cdot (\mathbf{x}_2 - \mathbf{x}_1)] \right\}. \tag{4}$$

We can simplify this expression with the help of eq. (6.14) and
rewrite it in the form

$$\mathbf{f}_{12} + \mathbf{f}_{21} = \frac{e_1 e_2}{c^2 r^3} (\mathbf{x}_2 - \mathbf{x}_1) \times (\dot{\mathbf{x}}_1 \times \dot{\mathbf{x}}_2). \tag{5}$$

This expression gives us the deviation of the interaction of two
moving electric charges from Newton's third law. Equation (5)
represents the net rate of change of the total linear momentum of

an isolated system consisting only of two moving point charges. Very obviously, this rate of change is not in general zero. If, for instance, one of the two particle velocities is in the connecting straight line, the other at right angles to that line, then the magnetic force on the second particle vanishes, whereas the magnetic force on the first particle does not.

As long as the velocities of the two charges involved are small compared with $c$, the ratio of magnetic to electric interaction will be small, and thus the deviation from Newton's third law possibly not conspicuous. But that is scant comfort. First of all, even small deviations can be discovered and measured, for instance if the electric interaction is masked by the presence of compensating charges at rest and if the magnetic effect alone is left. Thus, two neutral atoms at rest will exert primarily magnetic forces on each other if the net angular momenta of their electronic orbits are both nonzero. It stands to reason that in a large piece of matter the internal forces, which according to Newton's third law cancel, will not cancel if there is even one type of force which violates that law, and that we should then be able to observe self-acceleration of the piece as a whole. Thus, a clear-cut violation of Newton's law, even though small, is disturbing and difficult to reconcile with our everyday physical experience. But there is another consideration: modern experimental techniques permit acceleration of electrons and even of ions to velocities which are not very small compared to $c$. Thus, the argument of smallness of the deviation, though realistic in the nineteenth century, would no longer carry weight today.

That the magnetic force which two moving charges exert on each other is not the same in each frame of reference follows directly from an inspection of eq. (3) or (2). In fact, if we were to choose a frame in which one of the two particles is momentarily at rest, this interaction will apparently vanish, whereas in another frame it does not. Thus, it would appear that eq. (3) requires us to drop the principle of relativity, which was discussed in Chapter 6, and to designate one particular frame of reference as the frame representing absolute rest, because in that frame alone does eq. (3) correctly describe magnetic interaction between moving charges.

Historically, the two problems sketched were to be solved by two different modifications of the mechanical interpretation of nature.

First, Faraday and Maxwell found that electromagnetic phenomena cannot be fully described in terms of action at a distance but require a "field theory." The development of that theory will be traced in the present chapter. This theory, generally known as *Maxwell's theory of the electromagnetic field*, does effectively restore the conservation laws of classical mechanics. This new theory requires that a certain amount of linear momentum, angular momentum, and even energy be ascribed to the electromagnetic field in empty space, in addition to those amounts carried by the particles in the usual manner. Maxwell's theory by itself, however, does not restore the principle of relativity to electromagnetic phenomena. Only Einstein's *special theory of relativity* accomplishes that task

## 7.2. The structure of a field theory

Maxwell's is the earliest example of a classical field theory. In this section, we shall attempt to describe the concepts which set field theories apart from mechanical theories. In a mechanical theory, the building stones of the physical universe are the mass points, and their motions are determined by the force laws which describe the interactions between them. These forces act directly between any two mass points, clear across the empty space between them. The forces of a mechanical theory are, therefore, often referred to by the descriptive name "action at a distance." The laws of motion have the mathematical form of *ordinary differential equations* of the second order, in which the one independent variable is the time, the dependent variables being the coordinates of the individual mass points. In the canonical form (Chapter 2, Section 2.2), the differential equations are of the first order and the dependent variables not only space coordinates but also momenta, but the equations are still *ordinary* differential equations.

The decisive physical idea behind a field theory is that the interaction between the individual mass points is not direct but indirect, with an intermediary, the field. The basic laws of nature fall, therefore, into two classes: the *field equations* describe the internal laws of the field as well as its dependence on the presence of matter, whereas the *equations of motion* describe the action of the field on material particles.

Let us take the field equations first. The field may be a scalar field, a vector field, a tensor field, or a pseudoscalar, pseudovector, pseudotensor field.  The field may be restricted by two types of differential equations.  At a given instant of time, the spatial distribution of the field quantities may be restricted.  An example of such an equation is

$$\text{div } \mathbf{B} = 0.$$

Furthermore, in a complete field theory we shall always find a set of equations which, with a given spatial distribution, determine the change of the field quantities with time, such as

$$\text{curl } \mathbf{E} + \frac{1}{c} \frac{\partial \mathbf{B}}{\partial t} = 0.$$

Finally, both types of equations may contain terms indicating the effect of the distribution of matter on the field·

$$\text{div } \mathbf{D} = 4\pi\sigma$$

and                 $$\text{curl } \mathbf{H} - \frac{1}{c} \frac{\partial \mathbf{D}}{\partial t} = \frac{4\pi}{c} \mathbf{j}.$$

All these equations have one property in common.  The independent variables are four in number, not one; they are $x_1$, $x_2$, $x_3$, and $t$. Consequently, the field equations are *partial differential equations*, containing both spatial and time derivatives.  The four equations just written down are the field equations of the electromagnetic field, summarized as eqs. (69) at the end of Chapter 6.  Matter appears in these equations as continuously distributed.  However, by a simple formal trick their form can still be maintained if matter is represented by individual, discrete point charges.  This trick consists of the introduction of the so-called *Dirac delta function*, which is not an actual function but rather the limiting case of a function with a very sharp maximum at one point and negligible magnitude elsewhere.  The function $\delta(x)$ is defined so that it vanishes for all values of the argument $x \neq 0$ but becomes infinite at zero, in such a manner that an integral of the function extended over any interval including the point $x = 0$ will have the value 1. With the help of the delta function, we can write the charge distribution of a single charged mass point with the coordinates $X_i$ and the charge $e$ as

$$\sigma(x_1, x_2, x_3) = e \cdot \delta(X_1 - x_1) \cdot \delta(X_2 - x_2) \cdot \delta(X_3 - x_3)$$
$$\equiv e \cdot \delta_3(\mathbf{X} - \mathbf{x}), \quad (6)$$

and its current distribution, if its velocity is **v**, as

$$\mathbf{j}(\mathbf{x}) = e \, \mathbf{v} \, \delta_3(\mathbf{X} - \mathbf{x}). \quad (7)$$

The combination of $N$ point charges will then lead to the charge and current distributions

$$\sigma(\mathbf{x}) = \sum_{n=1}^{N} e_n \cdot \delta_3(\mathbf{X}_n - \mathbf{x}),$$

$$\mathbf{j}(\mathbf{x}) = \sum_{n=1}^{N} e_n \cdot \mathbf{v}_n \cdot \delta_3(\mathbf{X}_n - \mathbf{x}). \quad (8)$$

The expressions (8), when substituted into the appropriate Maxwell equations (6.69), will serve to determine the fields created by a number of discrete point charges in motion. We shall see later that the expressions for these fields given by Coulomb's and Biot-Savart's laws are only approximate solutions of the field equations, satisfactory if the particles move with velocities small compared with the velocity of light and if their accelerations are small compared to $c^2$, divided by a length of the order of the distances between the particles of the system.

It is well known that the solutions of differential equations are not uniquely determined (at least in the absence of some restrictions) but contain "constants of integration" in the case of ordinary differential equations, and arbitrary functions in the case of partial differential equations. The equations of motion of mechanics, for instance, admit a totality of solutions that must be restricted further by a statement of initial positions and momenta in order to reduce the solutions to one. Likewise, the partial differential equations which we know as the field equations (or, in electrodynamics in particular, as Maxwell's equations), even with given current and charge distribution, admit a variety of solutions which must be further restricted by additional conditions if the solution is to be unique. Ordinarily, we require that the solutions, for all finite times, shall not lead to increasing values of any one field variable with increasing (spatial) distance from the system of charges considered. Even though this condition, known as a *boundary condition*, removes the great majority of mathematically possible solutions from further consideration, there is still more than one solution left, and we shall see later what kinds of physical arguments are used to make the solution of the field equations unique.

We shall now turn to the equations of motion, which describe the effect of the field on the particles. The equations of motion must again be *ordinary* differential equations which determine the accelerations suffered by the particles. These accelerations are, however, not determined directly by the positions of the other particles, as they are in a mechanical theory, but by the values of the field variables in the vicinity of the particle in question. The equations of motion in electrodynamics are eqs. (6.70). Here a peculiar difficulty arises, common to all field theories. The particle under consideration makes itself a contribution to the field, and this contribution is infinite at the location of the particle. Obviously, the equations of motion would be meaningless if they had to be solved precisely where the determining field quantities become infinite. Besides, consideration of these infinite fields, even if feasible mathematically, would physically amount to an action of the particle on itself, in contradiction to Newton's first law, that a particle left alone will not accelerate.

To avoid this mathematical and physical difficulty, we shall always interpret the equations of motion of point charges in the sense that the field responsible for the acceleration of a point charge is the field that would be present if we could temporarily remove the particle and its contribution to the field. For this purpose, we divide the total field in the vicinity of the particle into two parts, the "*self-field*," contributed by the particle, and the remainder, the "*incident field*." The incident field has no singularity at the location of our particle, and it alone is responsible for the accelerations predicted by the law of motion.

Of course, we were careful to consider only the incident field (rather than the total field) when we set up the law of motion of electrostatics in Chapter 5. There the distinction was relatively trivial, since at that time the "field" was no more than a convenient tool for describing action at a distance. At our present stage, we propose to accord the field the status of a fundamental physical concept, and the distinction between self-field and incident field is decisive.  Unfortunately, we shall discover later that the self-field, the field connected with a single particle, is by no means uniquely determined by the field equations.  The modification required in Coulomb's and Biot-Savart's laws is not uniquely determined by the field equations alone, but we shall find later that we can pick up a single self-field solution by establishing additional rules.  With these additional rules, which we shall formulate after we have examined in greater detail the solutions of the field equations, we shall be able to subtract a unique self-field solution from the total field and, thus, obtain the incident field which determines the force acting on a point charge.

It is much easier to treat continuously distributed charges and currents, although this case, according to our knowledge of the structure of the physical universe, can never have a significance beyond that of a "wholesale" treatment of a system involving large numbers of individual particles.  In the continuous case, we require the *force per unit volume* rather than the force per particle, and since the contribution of any one particle to the whole field is considered negligible, the splitting of the field into incident and self-field is unnecessary.  Equation (6.70) can be modified easily enough to fit this situation, becoming

$$\mathbf{f} = \sigma\,\mathbf{E} + \frac{\mathbf{j}}{c} \times \mathbf{B}, \tag{9}$$

where the field variables on the right-hand side stand for the total field.

To summarize this rather preliminary section: In order to formulate a field theory completely, we require field equations and equations of motion.  These equations need to be supplemented by restrictions on the solutions of the field equations and also by a rule that makes the determination of the incident field unique.  The prime characteristic of a field theory (in contrast to the preceding mechanical theories) is the *local* character of all laws; that is to say, both the field equations and the equations of motion make the change of the field or of the motion depend solely on the field and its derivatives at the same location.  There is no direct effect of the happenings at one location on the events at a distant location.  Such remote effects can be transmitted only through the intermediate action of the field that is spreading throughout space.

We shall see later that such effects also travel with a finite velocity that never exceeds the velocity of light.

### 7.3. The conservation laws

We found that the forces which two moving electric particles exert on each other in accordance with Biot-Savart's law do not obey Newton's third law and that, as a result, if this law (5) were to hold rigorously, a system containing electrically charged particles might accelerate its center of mass. We then replaced our mechanical system by one in which the field plays an integral role. We shall now see whether this proposed modification of the laws of nature accomplishes what we demand, namely, the recovery of the conservation laws. We shall carry out this examination with the help of our matter-in-bulk formalism, which was developed in Chapter 3, because this formalism is better adapted to the nature of a field theory. The results obtained will, however, also hold for discrete charge-current distributions, since such distributions may be considered as limits of continuous distributions which are sharply peaked.

We shall start with a piece of matter whose internal forces are given partly by a mechanical stress tensor $t_{ik}$ and partly by the electromagnetic forces of eq. (9) of this chapter, so that the total force per unit volume is given by the expression

$$f_i = \sigma E_i + \delta_{irs} \frac{j_r}{c} B_s - t_{is,s}. \tag{10}$$

We shall now examine whether this equation can be given a form like that of eq. (3.70). If this should be possible, then there is a conservation law. For if we integrate such an equation over a portion of space sufficiently large that the components of the stress tensor are negligibly small at the boundary, then the integral over the divergence will vanish (because of Gauss's law), while the integral over the first term will give the rate of change of the linear momentum of the system as a whole. To the extent that the integral over the second term vanishes, the total linear momentum remains constant in the course of time.

To transform eq. (10), we shall first repeat the steps traversed in previous chapters, to arrive at the equation

$$\frac{\partial}{\partial t}\,(\rho u_i) + \frac{\partial}{\partial x_s}\,(\rho u_i\,u_s + t_{is}) = \sigma\,E_i + \delta_{irs}\frac{j_r}{c}\,B_s. \qquad (11)$$

Next we shall transform the specifically electromagnetic terms. The first step in this transformation consists of the substitution of $\sigma$ and $\mathbf{j}$ from Maxwell's equations. The purpose of this substitution is to retain only $\mathbf{E}$, $\mathbf{D}$, $\mathbf{H}$, and $\mathbf{B}$ as the quantities representing electromagnetic interaction and, at the same time, to introduce derivatives which may ultimately lead to complete divergences and to complete time derivatives. The result of this first step is the equation

$$\frac{\partial}{\partial t}\,(\rho u_i) + \frac{\partial}{\partial x_s}\,(\rho u_i\,u_s - t_{is})$$
$$= \frac{1}{4\pi}\left[ D_{s,s}\,E_i + \delta_{irs}\,B_s\left(\delta_{rmn}\,H_{n,m} - \frac{1}{c}\frac{\partial D_r}{\partial t}\right)\right]. \qquad (12)$$

We can make further progress by applying repeatedly the product rule of differentiation, replacing, for instance $D_{s,s}\,E_i$ by $(D_s\,E_i)_{,s} - D_s\,E_{i,s}$. We obtain as an intermediate form for the right-hand side

$$\frac{1}{4\pi}\left[ D_{s,s}\,E_i + \delta_{irs}\,B_s\left(\delta_{rmn}\,H_{n,m} - \frac{1}{c}\frac{\partial D_r}{\partial t}\right)\right]$$
$$= \frac{1}{4\pi}\left[ D_{s,s}\,E_i + B_s(H_{i,s} - H_{s,i}) - \frac{1}{c}\,\delta_{irs}\,B_s\frac{\partial D_r}{\partial t}\right]$$
$$= \frac{1}{4\pi}\left[ (D_s\,E_i + B_s\,H_i)_{,s} - B_s\,H_{s,i} - \frac{1}{c}\frac{\partial}{\partial t}\,(\delta_{irs}\,D_r\,B_s)\right.$$
$$\left. + \frac{1}{c}\,\delta_{irs}\,D_r\frac{\partial B_s}{\partial t} - D_s\,E_{i,s} - H_i\,B_{s,s}\right]. \qquad (13)$$

Obviously, the last term in the bracket vanishes, because the divergence of $\mathbf{B}$ always vanishes. Furthermore, we can substitute for the partial time derivative of $B_s$ from another Maxwell equation, so that

$$\frac{1}{c}\,\delta_{irs}\,D_r\frac{\partial B_s}{\partial t} = D_s(E_{i,s} - E_{s,i}). \qquad (14)$$

If we insert this expression into eq. (13), we get for the electromagnetic force density

$$\frac{1}{4\pi}\left[(D_s\,E_i + B_s\,H_i)_{,s} - B_s\,H_{s,i} - \frac{1}{c}\frac{\partial}{\partial t}(\delta_{irs}\,D_r\,B_s)\right.$$
$$+ \frac{1}{c}\delta_{irs}\,D_r\frac{\partial B_s}{\partial t} - D_s\,E_{i,s} - H_i\,B_{s,s}\bigg]$$
$$= \frac{1}{4\pi}\left[(D_s\,E_i + B_s\,H_i)_{,s} - \frac{1}{c}\frac{\partial}{\partial t}(\delta_{irs}\,D_r\,B_s)\right.$$
$$\left. - (B_s\,H_{s,i} + D_s\,E_{s,i})\right]. \tag{15}$$

Only the last two terms are not complete partial derivatives. They can be brought into the desired form directly only if the dielectric and magnetic properties of the continuously distributed matter satisfy certain conditions. The simplest procedure is, of course, to count all charges present as "free charges," because then we may drop the distinction between **E** and **H** on the one hand and **D** and **B** on the other. In that case, these last terms turn into derivatives of squares, and we get

$$\frac{\partial}{\partial t}(\rho u_i) + \frac{\partial}{\partial x_s}(\rho u_i\,u_s + t_{is})$$
$$= \frac{1}{4\pi}\left\{\frac{\partial}{\partial x_s}\left[E_s\,E_i + B_s\,B_i - \frac{1}{2}\delta_{is}(E^2 + B^2)\right]\right. \tag{16}$$
$$\left. - \frac{1}{c}\frac{\partial}{\partial t}(\delta_{irs}\,E_r\,B_s)\right\}.$$

Now we can combine the terms on the left-hand side with those on the right, and the final result is

$$\frac{\partial}{\partial t}\left[\rho u_i + \frac{1}{4\pi c}\delta_{irs}\,E_r\,B_s\right] + \frac{\partial}{\partial x_s}\left[\rho u_i\,u_s + t_{is}\right.$$
$$+ \frac{1}{4\pi}\left(\frac{1}{2}\delta_{is}\,E^2 - E_i\,E_s\right) + \frac{1}{4\pi}\left(\frac{1}{2}\delta_{is}\,B^2 - B_i\,B_s\right)\bigg] = 0. \tag{17}$$

This result is remarkable on two counts. It shows that the total stress is composed additively of the mechanical stress, the electric stress, and the magnetic stress. Each one of these three contributions is a symmetric tensor. More important is the result that the electromagnetic field makes a contribution to the linear momentum density, and this contribution is proportional to the cross product of electric displacement and magnetic induction. In the presence of an electromagnetic field, the total linear momentum of an isolated system will be conserved only if this specifically electromagnetic term is included with the mechanical momentum. Otherwise, this conservation law is not different from the one we obtained in eq. (3.70) of Chapter 3.

In the derivation of eq. (17), we included *all* charges with the "free" charges, and thus we were able to disregard the dielectric and diamagnetic properties of the material filling space. Lorentz followed essentially this procedure, and he explained the polarization and magnetization of matter in terms of changed electron configurations and changed electronic orbits. If we do not wish to follow his procedure, then we cannot write down a simple, ever-valid expression for the electromagnetic stress tensor. We can carry the procedure completely through, however, when the polarization and magnetization laws of a substance assume a specially simple form. If the dielectric constant and the magnetic permeability are constant scalars throughout the region of space we consider, then there is no difficulty; the conservation law (17) then requires as the only changes the multiplication of each term quadratic in the **E**-components by the dielectric constant, the division of each term quadratic in the **B**-components by the permeability, and the replacement of $E_r$ in the time-differentiated term by $D_r$. A few other cases can be treated completely in similar fashion. However, in the most general case imaginable, in which **D** depends on **E** nonlinearly and exhibits hysteresis, the derivation breaks down, because it fails to take into account the microscopic stresses set up by the dislocation of the charged particles from their normal positions. If it were possible to consider them explicitly, then the conservation law could undoubtedly be formulated in every case.

We shall now proceed to establish the conservation law of energy. The work done by the electromagnetic forces per unit volume and per unit time equals the product of electric field strength and current density, since the magnetic forces act always at right angles to the instantaneous motion and, thus, do no work. If we take eq. (3.119) as our point of departure, an equation which represents the conservation law of energy for a perfect fluid, then the increase in energy as a result of the work done by the electromagnetic fields is

$$\frac{\partial}{\partial t}\left(\frac{\rho}{2}v^2 + P\right) + \frac{\partial}{\partial x_s}\left(\frac{\rho}{2}v^2 v_s + P v_s + p v_s\right) = E_s j_s. \quad (18)$$

Again, we shall substitute the current density **j** from the field equations. If we apply once more the product rule of differentiation, we obtain the successive steps:

$$E_s j_s \equiv \mathbf{E} \cdot \mathbf{j} = \mathbf{E} \cdot \left(\frac{c}{4\pi}\operatorname{curl}\mathbf{H} - \frac{1}{4\pi}\frac{\partial\mathbf{D}}{\partial t}\right)$$

$$= \frac{c}{4\pi}\operatorname{div}(\mathbf{H}\times\mathbf{E}) + \frac{c}{4\pi}\mathbf{H}\cdot\operatorname{curl}\mathbf{E} - \frac{1}{4\pi}\mathbf{E}\cdot\frac{\partial\mathbf{D}}{\partial t} \quad (19)$$

$$= -\frac{c}{4\pi}\operatorname{div}(\mathbf{E}\times\mathbf{H}) - \frac{1}{4\pi}\left(\mathbf{H}\cdot\frac{\partial\mathbf{B}}{\partial t} + \mathbf{E}\cdot\frac{\partial\mathbf{D}}{\partial t}\right).$$

In further transforming this expression, we are again confronted by a similar difficulty as in the derivation of the conservation law of linear momentum. If we drop the distinction between **E** and **D** and between **H** and **B**, we find immediately that

$$\frac{\partial}{\partial t}\left[\frac{\rho}{2}v^2 + P + \frac{1}{8\pi}(E^2 + B^2)\right]$$
$$+ \operatorname{div}\left(\frac{\rho}{2}v^2\mathbf{v} + P\mathbf{v} + p\mathbf{v} + \frac{c}{4\pi}\mathbf{E}\times\mathbf{H}\right) = 0. \quad (20)$$

If we wish to consider the most general case, we have, at least,

$$\frac{\partial}{\partial t}\left(\frac{\rho}{2}v^2 + P\right) + \frac{1}{4\pi}\left(\mathbf{E}\cdot\frac{\partial\mathbf{D}}{\partial t} + \mathbf{H}\cdot\frac{\partial\mathbf{B}}{\partial t}\right)$$
$$+ \operatorname{div}\left(\frac{\rho}{2}v^2\mathbf{v} + P\mathbf{v} + p\mathbf{v} + \frac{c}{4\pi}\mathbf{E}\times\mathbf{H}\right) = 0. \quad (21)$$

If we can make the assumption that **B** is parallel to **H** and its magnitude a function of $|\mathbf{H}|$ only (in other words, that there is no hysteresis), then there exists a function $U_m(H)$ so that

$$\frac{dU_m}{dH} = \frac{1}{4\pi}H\frac{dB}{dH}, \quad (22)$$

and, with the analogous assumptions for the electric quantities, there exists a function $U_e(E)$ with the property

$$\frac{dU_e}{dE} = \frac{1}{4\pi} E \frac{dD}{dE}. \tag{23}$$

If we introduce these two functions, we get the energy-conservation law

$$\frac{\partial}{\partial t} \left( \frac{\rho}{2} v^2 + P + U_m + U_e \right)$$
$$+ \operatorname{div} \left( \frac{\rho}{2} v^2 \mathbf{v} + P\mathbf{v} + p\mathbf{v} + \frac{c}{4\pi} \mathbf{E} \times \mathbf{H} \right) = 0. \tag{24}$$

In the presence of hysteresis effects, the law of conservation of energy cannot be formulated in closed form, for the simple reason that in this case the energy stored in the material depends on other variables in addition to those taken into account in these formulas. The situation is similar to that encountered in Chapter 3, Section 3.7. There we introduced the mechanical energy density $P$, by means of the integral expression (3.115). This integral leads to a unique function $P(\rho)$ only if the pressure $p$ is a function of the density $\rho$ only. Otherwise, for instance if there is partial conduction of heat and if the local temperature has to be taken into consideration explicitly, there is no simple function $P$ of the kind introduced but only a function $P$ that depends on both density and temperature. In that case, energy transfer will take place by means of transport of matter, by means of work done across boundary surfaces, and also by means of the conduction of heat. As a result, the law of conservation of energy then requires additional terms to be valid. In the present electromagnetic case, too, the formulation of a relatively simple conservation law depends on a simple expression for the electromagnetic energy stored in the material. Naturally, if the dielectric constant and the permeability are appreciably one, then eq. (20) represents the correct formulation of the conservation law.

In the simple case of eq. (19) as well as in the somewhat more general case covered by eq. (24), the energy density is composed of the mechanical contributions known to us from Chapter 3 and of an electric and a magnetic term. To the energy flux there must be added a vector that is the cross product of electric and magnetic field strength, multiplied by $c/4\pi$. In other words, the electromagnetic field not only possesses a certain energy density but also gives rise to a flow of energy through space. This flow vector, $c/4\pi \cdot (\mathbf{E} \times \mathbf{H})$, is known as *Poynting's vector*.

### 7.4. The electromagnetic potentials.  The field of a particle

The field concept, we have found, enables us to reinstitute the conservation laws of linear momentum and energy, provided that we are willing to assign to the electromagnetic field, even in empty space, the properties of stress, momentum density, energy density, and energy flux density.  We shall now begin to examine the specific aspects of Maxwell's theory of the electromagnetic field; that is to say, we shall discuss solutions of the field equations.

The first and obvious task is to find solutions of the field equations that may properly be regarded as the field of a single electric point charge.  Even that task requires some preparation.  The field equations are not only partial differential equations; they are not even "separated," because in each one of them several components of the field appear side by side.  Thus it appears that we cannot solve the field equations one at a time but that we must tackle them all at once.  Fortunately, we shall find that we can introduce a set of "potentials," functions to which the field quantities are related by differentiation processes.  With the help of the potentials, we shall be able to separate the equations partially, and we shall obtain solutions (at least in the absence of dielectrics) by means of straightforward integrations.

We start with the equation

$$\operatorname{div} \mathbf{B} = 0. \tag{25}$$

There is a theorem to the effect that any vector (or pseudovector) field whose divergence vanishes can be represented as the curl of another pseudovector (or vector) field,

$$\mathbf{B} = \operatorname{curl} \mathbf{A} \tag{26}$$

(cf. Problems 6.2 and 6.4).  A proof of this theorem will be given below.  First, however, we shall follow the line of the physical argument through.  Granting for the moment that a vector field $\mathbf{A}$ does in fact exist of which $\mathbf{B}$ is the curl, we can substitute the expression (25) into the field equation containing the curl of $\mathbf{E}$, to get

$$\text{curl } \mathbf{E} + \frac{1}{c} \frac{\partial}{\partial t} (\text{curl } \mathbf{A}) = \text{curl} \left( \mathbf{E} + \frac{1}{c} \frac{\partial \mathbf{A}}{\partial t} \right) = 0. \qquad (27)$$

Now any vector field with vanishing curl can be represented as the gradient of a scalar field,

$$\mathbf{E} + \frac{1}{c} \frac{\partial \mathbf{A}}{\partial t} = - \text{grad } \Phi, \qquad (28)$$

so that we get for $\mathbf{E}$ the expression

$$\mathbf{E} = - \text{grad } \Phi - \frac{1}{c} \frac{\partial \mathbf{A}}{\partial t}. \qquad (29)$$

Equations (26) and (29) together show that $\mathbf{E}$ and $\mathbf{B}$ can be represented as partial derivatives of a scalar field $\Phi$ and a vector field $\mathbf{A}$. The scalar $\Phi$ is known as the *scalar* or *electric potential*, and $\mathbf{A}$ is called the *vector* or *magnetic potential*. In stationary fields, $\Phi$ has the same significance as in electrostatics.

Now to the proof of eq. (26). We shall construct explicitly a solution of eq. (26), with a given field $\mathbf{B}$, which, moreover, satisfies the additional condition that the divergence of $\mathbf{A}$ vanishes. We shall see later that, once we have obtained one field $\mathbf{A}$ that satisfies eq. (25), we can readily construct additional solutions. We proceed by first taking the curl on both sides of eq. (26) and then applying eq. (6.14),

$$\text{curl } \mathbf{B} = \text{curl curl } \mathbf{A} = \text{grad div } \mathbf{A} - \nabla^2 \mathbf{A}. \qquad (30)$$

Next, we shall construct a solution of this equation with the additional property

$$\text{div } \mathbf{A} = 0. \qquad (31)$$

Naturally, once we have obtained such a solution, we shall have to prove that it really satisfies eq. (26). If div $\mathbf{A}$ vanishes, the last term in eq. (30) can be dropped, with the result that the three component equations in (30) are separated; each contains only one component of the vector field $\mathbf{A}$. But then each component equation separately has the form of (5.21) and it is reasonable to attempt a solution of the form of the integral (5.12). In other words, we shall try for the field $\mathbf{A}$ the expression

$$\mathbf{A}(\mathbf{x}) = \frac{1}{4\pi} \int_{\xi} \frac{1}{r} \text{curl } \mathbf{B}(\boldsymbol{\xi}) \, d\xi_1 \, d\xi_2 \, d\xi_3 \qquad [r^2 \equiv (x_s - \xi_s)^2]. \quad (32)$$

This trial turns out to be successful. First we shall show, by means of integration by parts, that the divergence of this integral vanishes identically. We have

$$
\begin{aligned}
4\pi \frac{\partial A_s}{\partial x_s} &= \int_\xi \frac{\partial}{\partial x_s}\left(\frac{1}{r}\right)(\operatorname{curl}\mathbf{B})_s \, d\xi_1 \, d\xi_2 \, d\xi_3 \\
&= -\int_\xi \frac{\partial}{\partial \xi_s}\left(\frac{1}{r}\right)\delta_{smn}\frac{\partial B_n}{\partial \xi_m} \, d\xi_1 \, d\xi_2 \, d\xi_3 \\
&= -\int_\xi \frac{\partial}{\partial \xi_s}\left[\frac{1}{r}\,\delta_{smn}\frac{\partial B_n}{\partial \xi_m}\right] d\xi_1 \, d\xi_2 \, d\xi_3 \\
&\qquad + \int_\xi \frac{1}{r}\,\delta_{smn}\frac{\partial^2 B_n}{\partial \xi_m \, \partial \xi_s} \, d\xi_1 \, d\xi_2 \, d\xi_3.
\end{aligned}
\tag{33}
$$

The second integral obviously vanishes identically. The first is a divergence, to be integrated over all space. If we convert it into a surface integral in accordance with Gauss's theorem, the integrand will vanish on the surface (which is located "at infinity"), and the contribution of that integral will likewise be zero. It follows that the divergence of the expression (32) vanishes.

Now we shall proceed to determine the curl of **A**. We have

$$
\begin{aligned}
\operatorname{curl}\mathbf{A} &= \frac{1}{4\pi}\int_\xi \nabla_x\left(\frac{1}{r}\right) \times \operatorname{curl}\mathbf{B} \, d\xi_1 \, d\xi_2 \, d\xi_3 \\
&= -\frac{1}{4\pi}\int_\xi \nabla_\xi\left(\frac{1}{r}\right) \times \operatorname{curl}\mathbf{B} \, d\xi_1 \, d\xi_2 \, d\xi_3,
\end{aligned}
\tag{34}
$$

$$
\delta_{imn} A_{n,m} = -\frac{1}{4\pi}\int_\xi \left(\frac{1}{r}\right)_{,s}(B_{s,i} - B_{i,s}) \, d\xi_1 \, d\xi_2 \, d\xi_3.
$$

In this integral, we shall carry out integrations by part separately in each term. Omitting immediately the complete divergences, which vanish automatically, we may write

$$
\begin{aligned}
\delta_{imn} A_{n,m} &= -\frac{1}{4\pi}\int_\xi \left[B_i\left(\frac{1}{r}\right)_{,ss} - \frac{1}{r}B_{s,si}\right] d\xi_1 \, d\xi_2 \, d\xi_3 \\
&= \int_\xi B_i(\xi)\delta_3(\mathbf{x} - \xi) \, d\xi_1 \, d\xi_2 \, d\xi_3 = B_i(\mathbf{x}).
\end{aligned}
\tag{35}
$$

The last line is to be justified as follows. The second term of the integral in the first line vanishes because the divergence of **B** vanishes. In the first term there appears the Laplacian of the function $(1/r)$, which, multiplied by the factor $-(1/4\pi)$, equals the three-dimensional Dirac delta function. Finally, the integral of the delta function, multiplied by any factor function, equals that factor at the point where the delta function becomes infinite. Herewith, we have completed the existence proof of eq. (26).

Now we shall show that the integral (31) is only one of many possible solutions of eq. (26). Given some one solution, we can always obtain another solution *which belongs to the same field* **B** by adding to **A** the gradient of a completely arbitrary scalar field $\Psi$,

$$\mathbf{A}^* = \mathbf{A} + \operatorname{grad} \Psi. \tag{36}$$

If the curl is taken on both sides of this equation, the second term on the right-hand side drops out, because the curl of a gradient vanishes identically. Naturally, if we add to our prototype solution (32) an arbitrary gradient, the new **A**-field will no longer satisfy the special restrictive condition (31). We introduced this "divergence condition" only in order to obtain the particular solution (32) and, thus, to prove the existence of a vector potential.

The principal reason for introducing the electromagnetic potentials here is to make possible the partial separation and the solution of the field equations, at least in empty space. In fact, right now we are interested in obtaining solutions that can rightly be called the electromagnetic field of a single particle. Two of the four sets of Maxwell equations are already satisfied identically by the introduction of the potentials; they are

$$\operatorname{div} \mathbf{B} = 0, \qquad \operatorname{curl} \mathbf{E} + \frac{1}{c}\frac{\partial \mathbf{B}}{\partial t} = 0.$$

If we restrict ourselves to empty space and substitute the potentials in the remaining equations, we get

$$\operatorname{curl} \mathbf{B} - \frac{1}{c}\frac{\partial \mathbf{E}}{\partial t} = \operatorname{curl} \operatorname{curl} \mathbf{A} + \frac{1}{c}\frac{\partial}{\partial t}\left(\nabla\Phi + \frac{1}{c}\frac{\partial \mathbf{A}}{\partial t}\right)$$

$$= \operatorname{grad}\left(\operatorname{div} \mathbf{A} + \frac{1}{c}\frac{\partial \Phi}{\partial t}\right) + \frac{1}{c^2}\frac{\partial^2 \mathbf{A}}{\partial t^2} - \nabla^2 \mathbf{A} = \frac{4\pi}{c}\,\mathbf{j},$$

$$\operatorname{div} \mathbf{E} = -\operatorname{div}\left(\operatorname{grad}\Phi + \frac{1}{c}\frac{\partial \mathbf{A}}{\partial t}\right) \tag{37}$$

$$= -\frac{1}{c}\frac{\partial}{\partial t}\left(\operatorname{div} \mathbf{A} + \frac{1}{c}\frac{\partial \Phi}{\partial t}\right) + \frac{1}{c^2}\frac{\partial^2 \Phi}{\partial t^2} - \nabla^2\Phi = 4\pi\,\sigma.$$

The last versions of these equations show that the variables can be separated if it is possible to find solutions that satisfy the special restriction

$$\nabla \cdot \mathbf{A} + \frac{1}{c}\frac{\partial \Phi}{\partial t} = 0. \tag{38}$$

In that case, the second-order partial differential equations take the form

$$\frac{1}{c^2}\frac{\partial^2 \mathbf{A}}{\partial t^2} - \nabla^2 \mathbf{A} = \frac{4\pi}{c}\,\mathbf{j},$$

$$\frac{1}{c^2}\frac{\partial^2 \Phi}{\partial t^2} - \nabla^2 \Phi = 4\pi\,\sigma. \tag{39}$$

These equations are now separated, except for the restrictive condition (38). But this condition is of a lower differential order, the first, whereas the equations (39) are of the second order. We shall find that it is possible to construct solutions in terms of certain integrals that satisfy both (39) and (38). Were it not for the second-order time derivative, we should be able to solve the equations by means of integrals similar to (32) or (5.12); as a matter of fact, the equation (39) differs from (5.21) only by that second-order time derivative. We shall, therefore, attempt to solve eqs. (39) by integrals that somehow resemble the integral (5.12). Because of the time derivatives on the left, the equations (39) are called *wave equations;* they possess a structure very similar to that of equations for acoustic waves, such as eqs. (3.147) of Chapter 3. Such equations describe disturbances that propagate with a certain, finite velocity ("waves"). In our case, the equations plainly suggest that this velocity should be $c$. Thus we are led to try to solve the equation (39) by the integral

$$\Phi(\mathbf{x}, t) = \int\int\int_\xi \frac{1}{r}\,\sigma\left(\xi, t - \frac{r}{c}\right)d\xi_1\,d\xi_2\,d\xi_3 \quad [r^2 = (x_s - \xi_s)^2], \tag{40}$$

and the remaining three component equations by the analogous integrals

$$\mathbf{A}(\mathbf{x}, t) = \frac{1}{c}\int\int\int_\xi \frac{1}{r}\,\mathbf{j}\left(\xi, t - \frac{r}{c}\right)d\xi_1\,d\xi_2\,d\xi_3. \tag{41}$$

In setting up these integrals, we are applying, in a certain sense, Coulomb's law; but in sampling a given space point we do not use the present charge density but the density of a certain instant in the past, the one from which a disturbance traveling with the velocity $c$ would arrive at just the right moment.   Let us see whether the proposed integrals are solutions of the equations (39).   If they are, we shall still have to show that eq. (38) is satisfied as well. In carrying out the differentiations required for the test of the solutions, we shall, as before, make use of the fact that differentiation of $r$ with respect to $x_s$ leads to the same result as differentiation with respect to the variable of integration $\xi_s$, except for the sign, which needs to be reversed.   Thus, differentiation of the integral (40) with respect to $x_s$ leads to

$$
\begin{aligned}
\frac{\partial \Phi}{\partial x_s} &= \int \int \int_\xi \left\{ \frac{\partial}{\partial x_s} \left( \frac{1}{r} \right) \cdot \sigma \left( \xi, t - \frac{r}{c} \right) \right. \\
&\qquad \left. - \frac{1}{rc} \frac{\partial}{\partial t} \left[ \sigma \left( \xi, t - \frac{r}{c} \right) \right] \cdot \frac{\partial r}{\partial x_s} \right\} d\xi_1 \, d\xi_2 \, d\xi_3 \\
&= - \int \int \int_\xi \left\{ \frac{\partial}{\partial \xi_s} \left( \frac{1}{r} \right) \cdot \sigma - \frac{1}{rc} \frac{\partial r}{\partial \xi_s} \frac{\partial \sigma}{\partial t} \right\} d\xi_1 \, d\xi_2 \, d\xi_3 \qquad (42) \\
&= - \int \int \int_\xi \frac{\partial \left( \frac{1}{r} \right)}{\partial \xi_s} \left( \sigma + \frac{r}{c} \frac{\partial \sigma}{\partial t} \right) d\xi_1 \, d\xi_2 \, d\xi_3.
\end{aligned}
$$

If we repeat the differentiation, we obtain the following expression:

$$
\begin{aligned}
\frac{\partial^2 \Phi}{\partial x_s^2} &= + \int \int \int_\xi \left\{ \frac{\partial^2 \left( \frac{1}{r} \right)}{\partial \xi_s^2} \left( \sigma + \frac{r}{c} \frac{\partial \sigma}{\partial t} \right) \right. \\
&\qquad \left. - \frac{\partial \left( \frac{1}{r} \right)}{\partial \xi_s} \frac{\partial r}{\partial \xi_s} \frac{r}{c^2} \frac{\partial^2 \sigma}{\partial t^2} \right\} d\xi_1 \, d\xi_2 \, d\xi_3 \\
&= - 4\pi \int \int \int_\xi \delta_3(\mathbf{x} - \xi) \, \sigma \left( \xi, t - \frac{r}{c} \right) d\xi_1 \, d\xi_2 \, d\xi_3 \qquad (43) \\
&\qquad + \int \int \int_\xi \frac{\partial^2 \sigma \left( \xi, t - \frac{r}{c} \right)}{\partial t^2} \frac{d\xi_1 \, d\xi_2 \, d\xi_3}{c^2 \, r} \\
&= - 4\pi \, \sigma(\mathbf{x}, t) + \frac{1}{c^2} \int \int \int_\xi \frac{\partial^2 \sigma \left( \xi, t - \frac{r}{c} \right)}{r \, \partial t^2} d\xi_1 \, d\xi_2 \, d\xi_3.
\end{aligned}
$$

By comparison, the time derivative of $\Phi$ is easy to evaluate. We find that

$$\frac{\partial^2\Phi}{\partial t^2} = \int\int\int_\xi \frac{1}{r}\frac{\partial^2\sigma}{\partial t^2}\,d\xi_1\,d\xi_2\,d\xi_3. \tag{44}$$

If we substitute the expressions (43) and (44) into the last eq. (39), we find that that equation is satisfied. Identical computations can be carried out to confirm that the integral (41) is a solution of the remaining eqs. (39). We shall now turn our attention to the first-order equation (38), without which the wave equations (39) would not be equivalent to Maxwell's equations. For $\partial\Phi/\partial t$, we find that

$$\frac{\partial\Phi}{\partial t} = \int\int\int_\xi \frac{1}{r}\frac{\partial\sigma}{\partial t}\,d\xi_1\,d\xi_2\,d\xi_3. \tag{45}$$

To compute the divergence of **A**, we shall proceed as before, integrating by parts and discarding divergences:

$$\begin{aligned}
\frac{\partial A_s}{\partial x_s} &= \frac{1}{c}\int\int\int_\xi\left[\frac{\partial\left(\frac{1}{r}\right)}{\partial x_s}j_s + \frac{1}{r}\frac{\partial r}{\partial x_s}\frac{\partial j_s}{\partial r}\right]d\xi_1\,d\xi_2\,d\xi_3\\
&= -\frac{1}{c}\int\int\int_\xi\left[\frac{\partial\left(\frac{1}{r}\right)}{\partial\xi_s}j_s + \frac{1}{r}\frac{\partial r}{\partial\xi_s}\frac{\partial j_s}{\partial r}\right]d\xi_1\,d\xi_2\,d\xi_3\\
&= -\frac{1}{c}\int\int\int_\xi\frac{\partial}{\partial\xi_s}\left(\frac{j_s}{r}\right)d\xi_1\,d\xi_2\,d\xi_3\\
&\quad + \frac{1}{c}\int\int\int_\xi\frac{1}{r}\frac{\partial}{\partial\xi_s}j_s\left(\boldsymbol\xi, t - \frac{r}{c}\right)d\xi_1\,d\xi_2\,d\xi_3\\
&= \frac{1}{c}\int\int\int_\xi\frac{1}{r}\operatorname{div}\mathbf{j}\left(\boldsymbol\xi, t - \frac{r}{c}\right)d\xi_1\,d\xi_2\,d\xi_3.
\end{aligned} \tag{46}$$

If we combine the expressions (45) and (46), we find for the left-hand side of eq. (38) the integral

$$\frac{\partial A_s}{\partial x_s} + \frac{1}{c}\frac{\partial\Phi}{\partial t} = \frac{1}{c}\int\int\int_\xi\frac{1}{r}\left(\operatorname{div}\mathbf{j} + \frac{\partial\sigma}{\partial t}\right)d\xi_1\,d\xi_2\,d\xi_3. \tag{47}$$

The partial derivatives of $j_s$ with respect to $\xi_s$ in these equations do **not** have all the same significance: in the second line of eq. (46),

$j_s$ is to be differentiated only through the argument $(t - r/c)$; in the third line, $j_s$ is to be differentiated with respect to $\xi_s$ both directly and through the argument $(t - r/c)$; whereas in the fourth and last lines, and in eq. (47), partial differentiation with respect to a coordinate refers to the direct dependence of the current distribution (at a given time) on that space coordinate and does not involve the spatial dependence of the argument $(t - r/c)$.

The integrand of (47), that is, the parenthesis, will vanish because of the conservation law of charge, eq. (6.39). The integrals (40) and (41) are thereby shown to satisfy eqs. (38) and (39) and, therefore, the field equations. If we are provided with some electric charge and current distribution which satisfies the conservation law of charge, then we can always find a corresponding electromagnetic field by evaluating the integrals (40) and (41).

Our next step is to apply this general solution to the case of a single point charge moving in an arbitrary manner, and thus to discover the modifications that Coulomb's and Biot-Savart's laws suffer in Maxwell's theory. The necessary calculations are, however, rather involved, as the reader may have guessed from the complicated form of the integrals (40) and (41). For the charge-current distribution we have to substitute the expressions (6) and (7). To find the potentials at a point $P$ with the coordinates $x_s$ at a time $t$, we shall have to determine that point on the trajectory of the particle from which a disturbance traveling with the speed $c$ could just reach $P$ at the time $t$. If we designate the coordinates of the particle again with $X_s(t)$, and if that certain point in the past is $\overset{0}{x_s}$, then its coordinates must satisfy the equations

$$\overset{0}{x_s} = X_s\left(t - \frac{\overset{0}{r}}{c}\right), \tag{48}$$

where $\overset{0}{r}$ is the distance of that past location from the point where we wish to determine the field at the time $t$,

$$\overset{0}{r^2} = (\overset{0}{x_s} - x_s)(\overset{0}{x_s} - x_s). \tag{49}$$

Naturally, the three coordinates $\overset{0}{x_s}$ can be determined in principle if the functions $X_s(t)$ are given (that is, the motion of the particle in the course of time), and they are then functions of the four space-time coordinates $x_s$, $t$. However, unless the motion of the particle is specially simple, for instance unaccelerated, the equations (48) have no closed-form solution, though the $\overset{0}{x}_s$ can be determined approximately, for instance as a power series in ascending powers of $(\dot{X}_s/c)$. With the help of the quantities introduced above, the results of the integration (the details of which are omitted here) can be represented in the form

$$\Phi(x_s, t) = \frac{e}{r_0\Delta},$$

$$A_n(x_s, t) = \frac{e}{cr_0\Delta}\, \dot{X}_n\left(t - \frac{\overset{0}{r}}{c}\right),$$

$$\Delta = 1 - \frac{x_s - \overset{0}{x}_s}{\overset{0}{r}} \cdot \frac{\dot{X}_s\left(t - \frac{\overset{0}{r}}{c}\right)}{c}.$$

(50)

In other words, the instantaneous field depends not on the present position of the point charge but on the past position and velocity at the time it passed through the point with the coordinates $\overset{0}{x}_s$. Moreover, the scalar potential equals not simply the fraction $(e/\overset{0}{r})$, as might be expected; we must insert a correcting factor, the magnitude of which depends on the rate at which the particle at that past instant was approaching (or receding from) the point $x_s$. The potentials (50) can be differentiated, and the electric and magnetic field strength thus determined, by a straightforward but lengthy calculation, which we shall not reproduce here. An important result is that the field strengths depend not only on the particle velocity but on its acceleration as well. If Poynting's vector, the energy flux, is integrated over a small sphere surrounding the charged particle, then the net energy passing through that envelope does not vanish but is positive and proportional to the square of the acceleration. This effect, which is the foundation of the classical theory of the production of X rays on the target in the X-ray tube which stops a stream of fast electrons, is called *bremsstrahlung*, a German word meaning "brake radiation."

### 7.5. Gauge transformations.   Retarded and advanced potentials

In Section 7.4 we obtained solutions of the field equations from a given charge-current distribution in the form of the integrals (40), (41). The question arises whether this solution is unique or, if it is not, what other solutions exist. As a matter of fact, the variety of possible solutions is so large that we shall need to organize their discussion into three stages. We shall show that more than one set of electromagnetic potentials belongs to a given field of electric and magnetic field strengths. These solutions are physically equivalent, because the field strengths, not the potentials, are the physically significant quantities. Then, for every given charge-current distribution there are solutions which are physically different but satisfy the boundary condition to drop off with increasing distance from the material system. Finally, there are solutions of the "homogeneous" problem, that is, solutions belonging to a zero charge-current distribution, which fill all space evenly. These last solutions will be discussed in later chapters.

For the first part of this discussion, we shall return to the indefiniteness of the vector potential, which was expressed in eq. (36). Suppose we consider two vector potentials which differ only by a gradient and which, therefore, belong to the same magnetic field. If the electric field is given also, then eq. (29) shows that the addition of a gradient to the vector potential requires a modification of the scalar potential as well, and the required change turns out to be

$$\Phi^* = \Phi - \frac{1}{c} \frac{\partial \Psi}{\partial t}. \tag{51}$$

If we substitute $\Phi^*$ and $\mathbf{A}^*$ into eq. (29), the influence of the arbitrary function $\Psi$ simply drops out. We conclude: if we add to the electromagnetic potentials certain partial derivatives of an arbitrary scalar field in accordance with eqs. (36) and (51), the field strengths remain unchanged. Such an operation is called a *gauge transformation;* and since the field strengths, like the charge and current densities, remain unchanged, all these quantities are said to be *gauge-invariant.* This strange name, gauge transformation, has its historical explanation in a theory by H. Weyl, which is now considered obsolete.

Suppose we possess a set of potential functions that satisfy the

field equations (37).   If we carry out a gauge transformation, then
the transformed potentials will again satisfy that same set of equations.   The equations (37) are, therefore, said to be gauge-invariant.
Now we have been able to simplify these equations in the event
that the restrictive condition (38) is satisfied.   In that case, the
field equations separate and turn into (39).   If we start with such
a special solution and then carry out a gauge transformation, will
eq. (38) remain satisfied?   The answer is no.   Because if we substitute for the transformed potentials the expressions (36) and (51),
we find

$$\nabla \cdot \mathbf{A}^* + \frac{1}{c}\frac{\partial \Phi^*}{\partial t} = \nabla \cdot \mathbf{A} + \frac{1}{c}\frac{\partial \Phi}{\partial t} + \nabla^2 \Psi - \frac{1}{c^2}\frac{\partial^2 \Psi}{\partial t^2}. \qquad (52)$$

Equation (38) is, therefore, by no means gauge-invariant.   Quite
the contrary: the relation (51) gives us a very important piece of
information.   Given a set of potentials that do not satisfy eq. (38),
we can always carry out a gauge transformation and obtain a set
of potentials that do so, by determining the "generating function"
$\Psi$ from the equation

$$\frac{1}{c^2}\frac{\partial^2 \Psi}{\partial t^2} - \nabla^2 \Psi = \nabla \cdot \mathbf{A} + \frac{1}{c}\frac{\partial \Phi}{\partial t}. \qquad (53)$$

It is clear that this equation for $\Psi$, with a given right-hand side,
always has a solution.   The structure of eq. (53) is exactly the same
as that of eqs. (38), and at least one solution can be obtained in the
form of the integral

$$\Psi(\mathbf{x}, t) = \frac{1}{4\pi} \int \int \int_\xi \left[ \nabla \cdot \mathbf{A}\left(\xi, t - \frac{r}{c}\right) + \frac{1}{c}\frac{\partial}{\partial t}\Phi\left(\xi, t - \frac{r}{c}\right) \right] \\ d\xi_1 \cdots d\xi_3. \qquad (54)$$

In other words, the condition (38) does not restrict the variety of
*physically different* solutions of Maxwell's equations but merely
requires a certain choice of potentials to represent a given physical
field.   The condition (38), if imposed, restricts the variety of possible gauge transformations; it is called a *gauge condition*.

   We can now proceed to the second step of our discussion of the
variety of solutions: Are there several physically different solutions

belonging to the same charge-current distribution? The answer is yes. One important alternative solution is that in which the potentials depend not on the *past* but on the *future* charge-current distribution. The integrals for the potentials take the form

$$\Phi(\mathbf{x},\ t) = \int\int\int_{\xi} \frac{1}{r}\ \sigma\left(\xi,\ t + \frac{r}{c}\right) d\xi_1\ d\xi_2\ d\xi_?,$$

$$\mathbf{A}(\mathbf{x},\ t) = \int\int\int_{\xi} \frac{1}{r}\ \frac{\mathbf{j}\left(\xi,\ t + \frac{r}{c}\right)}{c}\ d\xi_1\ d\xi_2\ d\xi_3, \tag{55}$$

$$r^2 = (x_s - \xi_s)(x_s - \xi_s).$$

The solution (55) is mathematically just as valid as (40), (41). If it has always been discarded until recently, it was because this type of solution appears to "anticipate" the future behavior of the charged particles and thus seems to contradict the principle of causality. On closer examination, this argument against the solution (55) loses its apparent validity. Although nature quite obviously obeys some order of cause and effect, the precise significance of causality has changed and developed throughout the history of the natural sciences. As far as we can tell, causality in physics means no more and no less than that nature should be fully comprehended in terms of the laws of physics and that we should be able to discover these laws and thus predict the behavior of physical systems. As our knowledge of the laws of physics develops, so does our "philosophical" requirement of causality.

In mechanics, the starting point of our description of nature is the mass point, the material particle. Naturally, the forces observed in a system should be the *effect* that is *caused* by the particle. Surely, no force can anticipate the future behavior of its source. But whether this point of view can be maintained in a field theory is at least questionable. In a field theory, the particles are at least as much affected by the field as is the field by the particles, and we should not be too certain that fields and potentials of the form (55) are to be excluded from consideration. At any rate, Dirac and others have recently begun to examine the contribution that solutions of the type (55) could make to problems of radiation. The two types of solution, (40), (41) on the one hand, (55) on the other, are called *retarded* and *advanced potentials*, respectively. It can be shown that with advanced potentials, the energy flow of the self-field is toward an accelerated particle, not away from it as with retarded potentials.

In addition to these two solutions, Dirac has called attention to a solution which we can obtain by adding half of the retarded and half of the advanced potentials together. Since the field equations are linear with respect to the potentials, we can apply the basic theorems applying to linear differential equations. Given a certain linear differential equation, we call the "corresponding homogeneous equation" that equation which is obtained by the discard of the inhomogeneous terms (terms free of the dependent variables). Now the theorem on solutions states that we obtain the most general solution of the inhomogeneous equation by adding to any one particular solution (of the inhomogeneous equation) all the solutions of the homogeneous problem. The latter have the property that any linear combination of homogeneous solutions is again a homogeneous solution. The difference of two inhomogeneous solutions, by the same token, must be a homogeneous solution. If we now subtract the advanced from the retarded potentials, we get a homogeneous solution (a solution of the field equations that corresponds to zero charge-current density). Half of this solution, added to the advanced potentials, gives the above-mentioned "half-and-half" solution.

Since the solution which belongs to any given charge-current distribution is not completely determined, the self-field of a single particle is not unambiguous either, except in the special case that the particle is in uniform, unaccelerated motion. Unfortunately, we cannot separate the incident field, which determines the force on the particle, out of the total field unless we possess a clear-cut rule for the determination of the self-field. Therefore it is necessary to make a choice between retarded and advanced potential, or some other integral formula for the self-field of a particle, before the force law for an electric point charge assumes a precise meaning.

## Problems

**7.1.** Derive expressions for the linear momentum carried by the electromagnetic field and for the stress tensor, the energy density, and the energy flux, for the case that the dielectric constant and the magnetic permeability are different from 1 but are constant symmetric tensors throughout space.

**7.2.** Derive the conservation law for angular momentum, starting with the expression for the mechanical (nonelectric) angular momentum density $\rho(x_i v_k - x_k v_i)$.

**7.3.** Derive an expression for $U_m$ for a material in which the magnetization increases at first linearly with the magnetic field strength up to a certain saturation value $I^*$ and then remains constant at that value, no matter how high $H$ is raised.

**7.4.** Supposing that a magnetic material with pronounced hysteresis loop is subjected to a magnetization cycle, give a simple graphical picture of the net work per unit volume required to go once around the cycle. What will happen to the energy thus expanded?

**7.5.** Carry out the calculations leading to eq. (50) and go on to obtain expressions for the electric and magnetic field strengths of a moving point charge.

**7.6.** From the foregoing problem, determine Poynting's vector and integrate the energy flux through a small spherical surface about the point with the coordinates $x_s^0$.

# Chapter 8

## Waves

We have now obtained some of the solutions of the field equations that belong to given charge-current distributions. Of at least equal importance are solutions belonging to zero charge-current distributions and extending from infinity to infinity. They are called *electromagnetic waves*. Maxwell was the first to recognize the possibility of wave solutions. Hertz constructed solutions with a definite center of excitation, and he was the first to produce electromagnetic waves in the laboratory and to prove the superiority of Maxwell's field theory over the old mechanical theories by experiment. In very recent time, microwave techniques have introduced yet another type of wave, the *guided wave*.

### 8.1. Plane waves

We call a disturbance a *plane wave* if at each instant of time $t$ the wave variables are constant on whole planes or, in other words, if all gradients of the wave variables throughout space point in the same direction. We call the planes *wave fronts*. Mathematically, plane waves are described by functions of the time $t$ and *one* linear combination of the coordinates, $\mathbf{n} \cdot \mathbf{x}$, where the three constants $n_s$ are the components of the unit normal to the wave fronts.

We shall now construct solutions of Maxwell's field equations with zero charge and current densities. We shall require that the electromagnetic disturbance travel only in one direction. Since the coefficients of the field equations (in empty space) are constants, the velocity of propagation of the wave will be independent of space and time. We shall, therefore, set up our field variables as functions of the single argument $s$,

$$
\begin{aligned}
s &= n_k x_k - c_0 t \qquad (n_k n_k = 1), \\
s &= \mathbf{n} \cdot \mathbf{x} - c_0 t \qquad (|\mathbf{n}| = 1).
\end{aligned}
\tag{1}
$$

The constant $c_0$ is the velocity of propagation of the plane waves.

In what follows, we shall denote differentiation of any field variable with respect to the single argument $s$ by a prime. With this notation, Maxwell's equations in empty space take the form

$$\mathbf{n} \cdot \mathbf{E}' = 0, \qquad \mathbf{n} \cdot \mathbf{B}' = 0,$$
$$\mathbf{n} \times \mathbf{B}' \times \frac{c_0}{c} \mathbf{E}' = 0, \qquad \mathbf{n} \times \mathbf{E}' - \frac{c_0}{c} \mathbf{B}' = 0. \tag{2}$$

These equations are quite easy to solve. First, it is obvious that the two vectors $\mathbf{E}'$ and $\mathbf{B}'$, which are, of course, again functions of $s$, are everywhere normal to the direction of propagation $\mathbf{n}$. The remaining equations show that they must be at right angles to each other as well. If we substitute the last two equations into each other, we get

$$\mathbf{n} \times (\mathbf{n} \times \mathbf{B}') + \left(\frac{c_0}{c}\right)^2 \mathbf{B}' = (\mathbf{n} \cdot \mathbf{B}')\mathbf{n} - \mathbf{B}' + \left(\frac{c_0}{c}\right)^2 \mathbf{B}' = 0,$$
$$\mathbf{n} \times (\mathbf{n} \times \mathbf{E}') + \left(\frac{c_0}{c}\right)^2 \mathbf{E}' = (\mathbf{n} \cdot \mathbf{E}')\mathbf{n} - \mathbf{E}' + \left(\frac{c_0}{c}\right)^2 \mathbf{E}' = 0. \tag{3}$$

Because $(\mathbf{n} \cdot \mathbf{E}')$ and $(\mathbf{n} \cdot \mathbf{B}')$ both vanish, it follows that

$$c_0 = c. \tag{4}$$

Furthermore, when we go back to eqs. (2), we get the result

$$|\mathbf{E}'| = |\mathbf{B}'| \tag{5}$$

and therefore (except possibly for constant uniform fields that do not form part of the progressive wave),

$$|\mathbf{E}| = |\mathbf{B}|. \tag{6}$$

Having satisfied all eqs. (2), we find that $\mathbf{E}$ and $\mathbf{B}$ are at right angles to each other and to the direction of propagation of the wave, and that their magnitudes are everywhere equal. The functional dependence of this joint magnitude on the argument $s$ is, however, in no way determined. In fact, any wave "profile" whatsoever will be compatible with the field equations in empty space.

A plane wave in empty space can then be characterized as a disturbance with an arbitrary profile that travels at the uniform speed $c$ and without any gradual change of shape. The electric

and magnetic field strengths will always be in the plane of the
wave fronts, equal and at right angles to each other, but otherwise
arbitrary. Of course it is possible to decompose such a very
general plane wave into two components characterized by the
orientation of the electric field strength. If we choose arbitrarily
some one plane that contains the direction of propagation, then for
each value of the argument $s$ the electric field strength can be
decomposed into one component which lies in that plane and one
which is perpendicular to that plane. We have, by this construction, decomposed the electromagnetic wave into two *plane-polarized*
components.

In empty space, the decomposition of a general plane wave into
two perpendicular polarized components is purely arbitrary, but
in an anisotropic medium, such as a crystal, the two polarized components may possess different velocities of propagation. Let us
consider a homogeneous but anisotropic dielectric; both the
dielectric constant and the magnetic permeability are to be constant,
symmetric tensors. Now let us write down the Maxwell equations,
again restricted to the plane-wave case:

$$\operatorname{div} \mathbf{D} \equiv \kappa_{ik}\, n_i\, E_k' = 0, \qquad \left(\operatorname{curl} \mathbf{E} + \frac{1}{c}\frac{\partial \mathbf{B}}{\partial t}\right)_i \equiv \delta_{ikl}\, n_k\, E_l'$$

$$- \frac{c_0}{c}\, \mu_{ik}\, H_k' = 0,$$

$$\operatorname{div} \mathbf{B} \equiv \mu_{ik}\, n_i\, H_k' = 0, \qquad \left(\operatorname{curl} \mathbf{H} - \frac{1}{c}\frac{\partial \mathbf{D}}{\partial t}\right)_i \equiv \delta_{ikl}\, n_k\, H_l'$$

$$+ \frac{c_0}{c}\, \kappa_{ik}\, E_k' = 0.$$

(7)

The two divergence equations are identical in the remaining two
sets of equations (provided, again, that we disregard the possibility
of constant, nonwave solutions), since taking the divergences of
these remaining equations leads to the result that the divergence of
$(\partial \mathbf{B}/\partial t)$ as well as the divergence of $(\partial \mathbf{D}/\partial t)$ vanish. In other words,
we have six equations for the six unknowns, the components of $\mathbf{E}'$
and $\mathbf{H}'$. For our further discussion, it is desirable to separate
them into two sets of three each, one set for $\mathbf{E}'$, the other for $\mathbf{H}'$.
But to do so, we need to be able to "divide through" the dielectric
constant and the magnetic permeability. If they are scalars, then

the division is trivial. If they are symmetric tensors, we can still divide through (though, of course, in a somewhat modified sense), because in any physically reasonable case the three principal values of these symmetric tensors are positive and different from zero.

We shall introduce two constant tensors, called the "inverse" or "reciprocal" dielectric constant or permeability, respectively; these are the tensors that permit the transition from **D** to **E** and from **B** to **H**. We shall define them by means of the equations

$$E_i = \hat{\kappa}_{ik} D_k, \qquad H_i = \hat{\mu}_{ik} B_k, \tag{8}$$

or, which is the same thing,

$$\hat{\kappa}_{ik} \kappa_{kl} = \delta_{il}, \qquad \hat{\mu}_{ik} \mu_{kl} = \delta_{il}. \tag{9}$$

In a coordinate system that diagonalizes the dielectric constant,

$$\kappa_{ik} = \begin{Bmatrix} \kappa_1, & 0, & 0 \\ 0, & \kappa_2, & 0 \\ 0, & 0, & \kappa_3 \end{Bmatrix}, \tag{10}$$

the components of the reciprocal tensor are simply

$$\hat{\kappa}_{ik} = \begin{Bmatrix} \dfrac{1}{\kappa_1}, & 0, & 0 \\ 0, & \dfrac{1}{\kappa_2}, & 0 \\ 0, & 0, & \dfrac{1}{\kappa_3} \end{Bmatrix}. \tag{11}$$

Obviously, this tensor will be defined only if none of the principal values of the dielectric constant vanishes.

With the help of these reciprocal tensors, we can solve the field equations in the form (7) with respect to the variables appearing in the second terms:

$$\hat{\kappa}_{ik} \, \delta_{krs} \, n_r \, H'_s + \frac{c_0}{c} \, E'_i = 0,$$
$$\hat{\mu}_{ik} \, \delta_{krs} \, n_r \, E'_s - \frac{c_0}{c} \, H'_i = 0. \tag{12}$$

These equations can then be substituted into each other, yielding the partially separated equations

$$\delta_{imn} \, n_m \, \hat{k}_{nk} \, \delta_{krs} \, n_r \, H'_s + \left(\frac{c_0}{c}\right)^2 \mu_{ik} \, H'_k = 0,$$

$$\delta_{imn} \, n_m \, \hat{\mu}_{nk} \, \delta_{krs} \, n_r \, E'_s + \left(\frac{c_0}{c}\right)^2 \kappa_{ik} \, E'_k = 0.$$

(13)

Each system (13) consists of linear homogeneous equations, which will possess nonzero solutions only if the determinant of the coefficients vanishes. Obviously, with a given direction **n**, there remains the adjustable parameter $c_0$. To simplify matters, we shall introduce the expression $(c_0/c)^2$ as the characteristic parameter $\lambda$. The chief difference between eqs. (13) and eqs. (3.90), for instance, is that in the present case the characteristic parameter is multiplied by a symmetric tensor that need not be the Kronecker tensor. (Actually, in almost all substances except the ferromagnetics the permeability is very close to 1, but right now we are interested in the most general linear case.) We can achieve complete analogy if we are willing to introduce new variables.

In what follows, we shall concentrate on the first set of eqs. (13); the other set can be treated in exactly the same manner. We shall introduce a coordinate system whose axes are parallel to the three principal directions of the magnetic permeability. The three equations then take the form

$$\delta_{imn} \, n_m \, \hat{k}_{nk} \, \delta_{krs} \, n_r \, H'_s + \lambda \, \mu_{\underline{i}} \, H'_{\underline{i}} = 0. \tag{14}$$

The underscored index $i$ in the second term is not to be treated as a dummy. There will be several more deviations from the usual summation rule; we shall note these exceptions wherever they arise. We shall now introduce new field variables, *only in this special coordinate system*, as follows:

$$\sqrt{\mu_i} \, H'_i = Y_i. \tag{15}$$

(None of the indices $i$ in this set of equations is to be a dummy!) If we introduce these new field variables, we get the first equation (13) in the form

$$\Lambda_{ik} \, Y_k - \lambda \, Y_i = 0,$$

$$\Lambda_{ik} = \frac{1}{\sqrt{\mu_i \, \mu_k}} \, \delta_{imn} \, \delta_{krs} \, n_m \, n_r \, \hat{k}_{ns}. \tag{16}$$

(In the second equation, do not sum over $i$ or $k$ on the right-hand side!) We have now achieved complete analogy to eq. (3.90). The form $\Lambda_{ik}$ is no tensor, to be sure, but it is a symmetric form,

$$\Lambda_{ik} = \Lambda_{ki}. \tag{17}$$

From our previous proofs, we know, therefore, that there are three different solutions which belong to three values of the characteristic parameter $\lambda$. These three solutions are not perpendicular to each other in the geometric sense, but they satisfy the relationship

$$\overset{(i)}{Y_s}\,\overset{(k)}{Y_s} = 0, \qquad (i \neq k), \tag{18}$$

if the form is not degenerate. If $\Lambda_{ik}$ is degenerate, we can always pick linear combinations which are solutions and which satisfy (18). If, as is usually the case, the three principal permeabilities are all very nearly unity, then eq. (18) implies orthogonality of the three characteristic magnetic vectors even in the geometric sense.

We can draw one further conclusion, also without laborious calculations: One of these three solutions does not correspond to a progressive wave. If we multiply the form $\Lambda_{ik}$ by a "vector" with the components

$$\overset{0}{Y_i} = \sqrt{\mu_i}\, n_i, \qquad \overset{0}{H_i'} \propto n_i, \tag{19}$$

(do not sum over $i$!), then the product vanishes identically, because it contains the cross product $\mathbf{n} \times \mathbf{n}$. The components (19) represent a solution that belongs to the characteristic value zero. Only the other two characteristic solutions represent progressive waves.

There is not much point in developing our general calculations further, because further progress could be achieved only by very laborious calculations. Instead, we shall now treat two important special conditions. The one is that the permeability of the anisotropic material equals unity; this condition is satisfied in excellent approximation by all crystals except ferromagnetics, which do not transmit electromagnetic waves because they conduct too well. The other special condition is that the material be isotropic.

**Crystal optics.** We shall now set all principal values of the permeability equal to 1. The introduction of the quantities $Y_i$ is then unnecessary, and the first equation (13) reduces to

$$\delta_{imn}\, n_m\, \hat{k}_{nk}\, \delta_{krs}\, n_r\, H_s' + \left(\frac{c_0}{c}\right)^2 H_i' = 0. \tag{20}$$

We shall now introduce a special coordinate system in which the direction of propagation is parallel to the $x_3$-axis. In that case, the equations reduce to

$$\hat{k}_{22} H_1' - \hat{k}_{12} H_2' = \left(\frac{c_0}{c}\right)^2 H_1',$$

$$-\hat{k}_{12} H_1' + \hat{k}_{11} H_1' = \left(\frac{c_0}{c}\right)^2 H_2', \tag{21}$$

$$0 = \left(\frac{c_0}{c}\right) H_3'.$$

The last of these three equations represents again the nonwave case. It can be discarded, since substitution of that solution into the full Maxwell equations would show that they cannot be satisfied. As for the remaining equations, we recover first the previous result that the two solutions are perpendicular to **n** and to each other. We can, to simplify the equations further, turn the coordinate system about the $x_3$-axis until the two-rowed form

$$\left\{ \begin{array}{cc} \hat{k}_{22}, & -\hat{k}_{12} \\ -\hat{k}_{12}, & \hat{k}_{11} \end{array} \right\}$$

is diagonalized, and we shall then find that the velocities of propagation which correspond to the two possible solutions of eqs. (21) are, in that special coordinate system,

$$\begin{array}{cc} c_0 = \sqrt{\hat{k}_{22}} & \overset{(1)}{H_2'} = 0, \\ c_0 = \sqrt{\hat{k}_{11}} & \overset{(2)}{H_1'} = 0. \end{array} \tag{22}$$

These two different velocities of propagation correspond to two different directions of polarization. The magnetic vectors of these two plane-polarized solutions are at right angles to each other, but not the electric vectors. We must now substitute our solutions (22) into the first set of equations (12); the result is:

$$\begin{array}{ll} \overset{(1)}{E_1'} = 0, & \overset{(2)}{E_1'} = + \sqrt{\hat{k}_{11}}\, \overset{(2)}{H_2'}, \\ \overset{(1)}{E_2'} = - \sqrt{\hat{k}_{22}}\, \overset{(1)}{H_1'}, & \overset{(2)}{E_2'} = 0, \\ \overset{(1)}{E_3'} = - \dfrac{\hat{k}_{23}}{\sqrt{\hat{k}_{22}}}\, \overset{(1)}{H_1'}, & \overset{(2)}{E_3'} = + \dfrac{\hat{k}_{13}}{\sqrt{\hat{k}_{11}}}\, \overset{(2)}{H_2'}. \end{array} \tag{23}$$

In other words, the electric vector in an anisotropic material has a component in the direction of propagation. However, it is perpendicular to the magnetic vector, and the projections of the two solutions into the plane of the wave fronts are perpendicular to each other. That is, to each direction of propagation in a crystal or other anisotropic material there belong two plane-polarized solutions whose planes of polarization are at right angles to each other and which possess different velocities of propagation. This phenomenon is called *birefringence*. Quite generally, the ratio $(c/c_0)$ is called the *index of refraction*. We find that in an anisotropic material, the indices of refraction of the two plane-wave solutions associated with each direction of propagation are different.

**Isotropic materials.** Next, we shall consider plane-wave propagation in a material in which the *scalars* $\kappa$ and $\mu$ are both different from 1. In that case, the Maxwell equations (7) reduce to

$$\text{(a)} \ \ \text{div } \mathbf{E} = 0, \qquad \text{(b)} \ \ \text{curl } \mathbf{E} + \frac{\mu}{c} \frac{\partial \mathbf{H}}{\partial t} = 0,$$

$$\text{(c)} \ \ \text{div } \mathbf{H} = 0, \qquad \text{(d)} \ \ \text{curl } \mathbf{H} - \frac{\kappa}{c} \frac{\partial \mathbf{E}}{\partial t} = 0. \tag{24}$$

These equations can be separated without difficulty. For instance, taking the curl of eq. (b) and the time derivative of eq. (d), by linear combination we can eliminate $\mathbf{H}'$ and obtain equations for $\mathbf{E}''$ alone:

$$\text{curl curl } \mathbf{E} + \frac{\kappa \mu}{c^2} \frac{\partial^2 \mathbf{E}}{\partial t^2} = \frac{\kappa \mu}{c^2} \frac{\partial^2 \mathbf{E}}{\partial t^2} - \nabla^2 \mathbf{E}$$

$$= \left( \frac{c_0^2}{c^2} \kappa \mu - 1 \right) \mathbf{E}'' = 0. \tag{25}$$

Identical equations can be obtained for the components of $\mathbf{H}''$. The velocity of propagation is, therefore,

$$c_0 = \frac{c}{\sqrt{\kappa \mu}}, \tag{26}$$

irrespective of the direction of propagation and the plane of polarization. The value of the index of refraction is $\sqrt{\kappa \mu}$.

## 8.2. Spherical waves

Mathematically, plane waves are the least complex of all solutions of the homogeneous Maxwell equations. They are useful because of their relative simplicity and because many other types of solution can be constructed by the linear superposition of plane waves. Physically, however, a plane wave cannot be produced by any simple device. If radiation emanates from a narrow region of space, the resulting electromagnetic disturbance spreads with *spherical* or nearly spherical wave fronts. The plane wave can at best be considered an approximation to physical waves at great distances from the source, where the radii of curvature of the wave fronts are very large compared with the wave length. For practical purposes, light from distant fixed stars comes to us as a plane wave, and in the laboratory we can produce good approximations to plane waves by passing spherically spreading waves through optical lenses.

Physically, the basic process of radiation must lead to spherical waves or, if there are many radiators, to linear superpositions of spherical waves. Mathematical investigation has shown that spherical waves can also be represented in terms of elementary functions, and their treatment is not much more difficult than that of plane waves. To facilitate the construction and examination of spherical-wave solutions of Maxwell's field equations, we shall again resort to the representation of the electromagnetic field by the electromagnetic potentials. In the absence of charges, the partially separated equations (7.39), (7.40) take the form

$$\frac{1}{c^2}\frac{\partial^2 \mathbf{A}}{\partial t^2} - \nabla^2 \mathbf{A} = 0, \qquad \frac{1}{c^2}\frac{\partial^2 \Phi}{\partial t^2} - \nabla^2 \Phi = 0,$$

$$\nabla \cdot \mathbf{A} + \frac{1}{c}\frac{\partial \Phi}{\partial t} = 0. \tag{27}$$

We shall now endeavor to find spherical functions which satisfy both the second-order *wave equations* and the first-order *gauge condition*.

If we had only one wave equation, for a single scalar-wave variable (as in fluid acoustics), we should try a spherically symmetric solution of the form

$$\Psi(r, t) = C(r) f(r - ct),$$

$$r^2 \equiv x_1^2 + x_2^2 + x_3^2, \tag{28}$$

where the function $f(r - ct)$ is the "profile" of the field disturbance. The function $C(r)$, which does not depend on the time, has been inserted in order to make it possible for the amplitude of the disturbance to drop as the wave travels away from the center of the disturbance (which we have placed at the coordinate origin). We have already assumed that the wave travels with the speed $c$, but this assumption would not have been necessary. If we had put in a constant but unknown speed $c_0$, as before, we should have found out in the course of the calculation that $c_0$ must equal $c$. If we substitute the trial function $\Psi$ into the single-wave equation

$$\frac{1}{c^2} \frac{\partial^2 \Psi}{\partial t^2} - \nabla^2 \Psi = 0, \tag{29}$$

we find, as the result of straightforward computation, the intermediate results

$$\frac{\partial^2 \Psi}{\partial t^2} = c^2\, C(r)\, f''(r - ct),$$

$$\Psi_{,s} = \frac{x_s}{r} \left[ C'(r)\, f(r - ct) + C(r)\, f'(r - ct) \right], \tag{30}$$

$$\Psi_{,ss} = C'' f + 2C' f' + C f'' + \frac{2}{r} (C' f + C f'),$$

which give us as the determining equations for $C(r)$

$$2 \left( C' + \frac{1}{r} C \right) f' + \left( C'' + \frac{2}{r} C' \right) f = 0; \tag{31}$$

therefore $\qquad C' + \frac{1}{r} C = 0, \qquad C'' + \frac{2}{r} C' = 0.$

It would seem that $C(r)$ must satisfy two different differential equations if $f(r - ct)$ is to remain an arbitrary function of its argument, but actually the two equations are interdependent. If the first of them is satisfied, the second one holds automatically. The solution, except for an arbitrary factor, which can be incorporated in the function $f$, is

$$C(r) = \frac{1}{r}, \tag{32}$$

so that the solution representing an outgoing spherically symmetric wave is

$$\Psi(r, t) = \frac{f(r - ct)}{r}. \tag{33}$$

Starting with this solution, we can construct a large number of more complex solutions all of which correspond to outgoing spherical waves, but these solutions no longer possess spherical symmetry. We can obtain these more complex solutions by differentiating the solution (33) with respect to the three coordinates, in any combination we like. If we have a solution of a linear, homogeneous differential equation with constant coefficients [and the wave equation (29) is of that type], then a partial derivative of that solution is itself a solution. For proof, we need merely to substitute the function $\partial\Psi/\partial x_i$ into (29); if we change the order of the partial differentiations (which is always permissible), we find that the resulting expression is the derivative of the whole left-hand side of (29), which vanishes. Of course, we can differentiate the new solution again and again and thus obtain an infinite number of new solutions of ever-increasing complexity.

The first three solutions we can obtain in this manner are

$$\Psi_{,i} = \frac{x_i}{r} \frac{\partial\Psi}{\partial r}. \tag{34}$$

There are six second-order derivatives, but they contribute only five new solutions. We have

$$\begin{aligned}
\frac{\partial^2\Psi}{\partial x_i\,\partial x_k} &= \frac{x_i\,x_k}{r^2} \frac{\partial^2\Psi}{\partial r^2} + \frac{r^2\,\delta_{ik} - x_i\,x_k}{r^3} \frac{\partial\Psi}{\partial r} \\
&= \frac{x_i\,x_k}{r^2}\left(\frac{\partial^2\Psi}{\partial r^2} - \frac{1}{r}\frac{\partial\Psi}{\partial r}\right) + \delta_{ik}\frac{1}{r}\frac{\partial\Psi}{\partial r},
\end{aligned} \tag{35}$$

but between three of these six derivatives, we have the relationship

$$\frac{\partial^2\Psi}{\partial x_s^2} = \frac{1}{c^2}\frac{\partial^2\Psi}{\partial t^2} = \frac{f''(r-ct)}{r}; \tag{36}$$

that is, one linear combination leads back to a spherically symmetric solution of the type (33). Similar but more numerous relationships reduce the number of new contributions from the higher derivatives. It can be shown in general that the $n$th partial derivatives contribute $(2n + 1)$ linearly independent new solutions, with new angular dependencies.

Among all these solutions of the wave equation, we shall have to choose certain combinations for the four field variables **A**, $\Phi$

which also satisfy the gauge condition. However, a quick survey shows that there is no spherically symmetric solution among these combinations. The solution with the least complex angular dependence is one in which the scalar potential has the same angular dependence as the scalar potential of a static dipole. With **n** being an arbitrary unit vector, this solution has the form

$$\mathbf{A} = \frac{\mathbf{n}}{c} \frac{\partial \Psi}{\partial t}, \qquad \Phi = -\mathbf{n} \cdot \nabla \Psi. \qquad (37)$$

Substitution shows that this combination of first derivatives satisfies the gauge condition. The remaining eqs. (27) are satisfied automatically.

Let us consider this solution in some more detail. First, naturally, we are interested in the components of the electric and magnetic field. We find for them the following

$$\mathbf{E} = \operatorname{curl} \operatorname{curl} (\mathbf{n} \, \Psi) = \operatorname{grad} (\mathbf{n} \cdot \operatorname{grad} \Psi) - \mathbf{n} \, \nabla^2 \Psi,$$

$$\mathbf{B} = -\frac{1}{c} \mathbf{n} \times \operatorname{grad} \Psi. \qquad (38)$$

If we wish to examine the angular dependence of these fields, we can do so by expressing all spatial derivatives in terms of derivatives with respect to $r$, multiplied by the appropriate angular functions. We get

$$\mathbf{E} = \frac{\mathbf{x}(\mathbf{x} \cdot \mathbf{n})}{r^2} \left( \frac{\partial^2 \Psi}{\partial r^2} - \frac{1}{r} \frac{\partial \Psi}{\partial r} \right) - \mathbf{n} \left( \frac{\partial^2 \Psi}{\partial r^2} + \frac{1}{r} \frac{\partial \Psi}{\partial r} \right),$$

$$\mathbf{B} = \frac{1}{c} \frac{\mathbf{x} \times \mathbf{n}}{r} \frac{\partial^2 \Psi}{\partial r \, \partial t}. \qquad (39)$$

If, in addition, we wish to bring out the dependence of the wave amplitude on the distance from the center, we have to substitute for $\Psi$ from eq. (33). The result of this substitution is

$$\mathbf{E} = \frac{\mathbf{x}(\mathbf{x} \cdot \mathbf{n})}{r^2} \left( \frac{f''}{r} - 3\frac{f'}{r^2} + 3\frac{f}{r^3} \right) - \mathbf{n} \left( \frac{f''}{r} - \frac{f'}{r^2} + \frac{f}{r^3} \right),$$

$$\mathbf{B} = \frac{\mathbf{n} \times \mathbf{x}}{r} \left( \frac{f''}{r} - \frac{f'}{r^2} \right). \qquad (40)$$

The symbol **x** denotes the three coordinates $x_s$. Our formulas show that both **E** and **B** possess components which drop off as $1/r$, and other components which drop off more rapidly. At great distance from the center, the $(1/r)$ terms are naturally the most important ones; whereas very close in, the terms with the highest power of $(1/r)$ determine the field. There is a transitional zone, roughly defined as that distance at which the ratio of the $n$th derivative of the function $f(r - ct)$ to its $(n - 1)$th derivative is of the same order of magnitude as $1/r$.

At all distances from the origin, the direction of the magnetic field is at right angles both to the radius vector and to the direction of the axis of symmetry of our field of radiation, **n**. In other words, the magnetic lines of force form circles in planes perpendicular to **n**. In talking about these geometric relations, we shall call the plane through the center and perpendicular to the axis of symmetry the *equatorial plane* and the angle of "latitude" $\theta$. The magnitude of the magnetic field at a given instant $t$ and at a particular distance from the center $r$ is proportional to $\cos \theta$. With the electric field strength, conditions are somewhat more complex. Its direction lies everywhere in the meridian plane, but it is neither parallel nor perpendicular to the radius vector. At great distance from the center, **E** is perpendicular to the radius vector, and its magnitude for given $r$ and $t$ is proportional to $\cos \theta$. Thus, at great distances from the center, the wave approaches the characteristic form of a plane wave, with **E** and **B** normal to each other and to the direction of propagation. The amplitude of that wave is inversely proportional to $r$ and directly proportional to the cosine of the angle of latitude. The plane of polarization (which by general convention is always taken as the plane of the electric field strength and the direction of propagation) is the meridian plane.

If we wish to examine conditions close to the center, we can confine our attention to the terms proportional to $(1/r)^3$. The magnetic field strength contains no such term, but the terms that appear in the electric field strength are

$$\mathbf{E}\Big|_{r \to 0} = 3 \left[ \frac{\mathbf{x}(\mathbf{x} \cdot \mathbf{n})}{r^2} - \mathbf{n} \right] \frac{f}{r^3}$$
$$= -\operatorname{grad} \left[ \frac{(\mathbf{n} \cdot \mathbf{x})}{r} \frac{f}{r^2} \right]. \tag{41}$$

In other words, the field close in may be described as the field of an electric dipole parallel to the axis. This result shows that the field we have constructed is the one that would be produced by an electric dipole which oscillates along its axis, changing its magnitude, but not its direction, in the course of time. The function $f(-ct)$ is the magnitude of the dipole moment as a function of time. The field in the "wave zone," that is, at great distance, depends not on the dipole moment itself but on its second time derivative.

We shall now determine the energy radiated by such an electric dipole into the surrounding space. The energy flux is given by Poynting's vector,

$$\mathbf{F} = \frac{c}{4\pi} \mathbf{E} \times \mathbf{H}. \tag{42}$$

While in the wave zone Poynting's vector is parallel to the radius vector, the energy flux close in is not wholly outward bound but, to some extent, represents circulation of energy in closed orbits. Since we are primarily interested in the energy *leaving* the vicinity of the radiating dipole, we shall immediately compute the expression

$$F_r = \frac{\mathbf{x}}{r} \cdot \mathbf{F} = \frac{c}{4\pi} \frac{\mathbf{x}}{r} \cdot (\mathbf{E} \times \mathbf{H}), \tag{43}$$

which represents the radial component of the energy flux density. We find, by substitution, that $F_r$ is given by the expression

$$F = \frac{c}{4\pi} \cos^2 \theta \left[ \frac{1}{r^2} f''^2 + \frac{1}{r^3} \left( \frac{ff'}{r} - f'^2 \right)' \right]. \tag{44}$$

The radial energy flux is proportional to $\cos^2 \theta$. If the wave profile has a finite length in time or, at least, dies out quickly enough, we can compute the energy passing through a unit solid angle in the course of the entire pulse. This amount of energy is

$$W_\theta = \int_{t=-\infty}^{\infty} F_r r^2 \, dt = \frac{c}{4\pi} \cos^2 \theta \int_{t=-\infty}^{\infty} f''^2 \, dt. \tag{45}$$

If we integrate this expression over the whole solid angle, we obtain

$$W = 2\pi \int_{\theta=-\frac{\pi}{2}}^{\frac{\pi}{2}} W_\theta \cos \theta \, d\theta = \frac{c}{2} \int_{t=-\infty}^{\infty} f''^2 \, dt \int_{\theta=-\frac{\pi}{2}}^{\frac{\pi}{2}} \cos^3 \theta \, d\theta$$

$$= \frac{2c}{3} \int_{-\infty}^{\infty} f''^2 \, dt, \tag{46}$$

the total energy radiated by our dipole. If the dipole describes a sustained periodic oscillation, the integral (46), extended over one period of the oscillation, will give the energy radiated per cycle; if this amount is multiplied by the frequency of oscillation, the product will be the radiated power.

So far, we have treated the case of the radiating dipole on the assumption that the electromagnetic wave travels away from the center. Mathematically, we can also start with another function instead of $\Psi$, eq. (33), one in which the spherical wave travels inward,

$$\tilde{\Psi} = \frac{1}{r} f(r + ct). \tag{47}$$

Without much difficulty, the reader will find that this function, too, is a solution of the wave equation and that a complete electromagnetic solution can be constructed with its help, a solution which represents an electric dipole that absorbs rather than radiates energy. If all the calculations above are repeated, it will be found that the energy flux has the same magnitude as before but is directed inward instead of outward. Whereas the first type of solution worked out above closely corresponds to the employment of retarded potentials, the solution constructed from the expression (47) corresponds to the use of advanced potentials.

Both of the solutions constructed from $\Psi$ and from $\tilde{\Psi}$ possess infinities at the origin. It is a very curious fact that we can construct, by linear superposition, a solution free of such singularities. If we start with a solution of the wave equation of the form

$$\Sigma\,(r,\,t) = \frac{1}{r}\left[\,g\left(t + \frac{r}{c}\right) - g\left(t - \frac{r}{c}\right)\right], \tag{48}$$

and if the function $g$ and its derivatives have no singularities, then not only the function $\Sigma(r, t)$ but likewise all its partial derivatives will remain finite at the center. This solution corresponds to an incoming plus an outgoing wave, both of which have the same shape and which meet each other at the center in such a manner that the infinite contributions cancel. If the wave is a pulse of finite length and if we observe the pulse at a point an appreciable distance from the center, we shall first observe the pulse inward bound and carrying energy with it, and then we shall see that same pulse coming past again, in the opposite direction and carrying with it the same amount of energy. The net amount of energy radiated toward or away from the center is, therefore, zero. If the wave is a sustained periodic oscillation, then at each point of space the electromagnetic field will be a periodic function of time, and the integral of the radial energy flux, taken over one full period, will vanish. In other words, such a wave will permit the field energy to whip back and forth, but with zero net radiation. Such a solution of the field equations is often called a *stationary* or *standing* wave pattern. It is not known whether such stationary patterns have any significance in connection with the emission and absorption of radiant energy.

A few words are in order concerning other spherical waves. If we retrace the construction of the dipole field, we can note that we chose from the derivatives of the "generating function" certain linear combinations which satisfied the gauge condition. Apparently, we can obtain other solutions by either changing to another type of generating function or by changing the mode of selection of the derivatives. It is not necessary for the generating function to be spherically symmetric, nor have we any reason to believe that the selection of first derivatives for the potentials is the only one possible.

As for a different selection of derivatives, it is easy to show that the only essentially different selection from the one made first is the following:

$$\mathbf{A} = \mathbf{n} \times \operatorname{grad} \Psi, \qquad \Phi = 0. \tag{49}$$

If in these expressions we introduce either (33) or (47) as the generating function we find that the resulting electric and magnetic field strengths form a pattern which is the same as before, except that the roles of the magnetic and the electric field are interchanged. In other words, the field is that of an oscillating *magnetic dipole*. The magnetic field is now in the meridian plane, and the electric lines of force form concentric circles about the axis of symmetry. The expression for the radiated (or absorbed) energy is the same.

What if we go over to another generating function? Any derivative of the spherically symmetric generating functions (33), (47), or (48) is again a solution of the wave equation and can, therefore, be used as a generating function in its own right. The higher the derivatives chosen for the generating function (only the space derivatives matter, since differentiation with respect to time does not change the angular or radial dependence of the function), the more complex will be the angular dependence of the resulting field. Depending on whether the electromagnetic potentials are formed in accordance with eq. (37) or eq. (49), we obtain the fields of oscillating electric or magnetic higher poles, quadrupoles, octupoles, and so on. It is possible to combine several of these possibilities linearly and to obtain almost any desired pattern for the angular dependence of the energy flux in the wave zone. The techniques for achieving desirable patterns form the foundation of antenna design for directional transmission of electromagnetic waves.

## 8.3. Harmonic waves. Fourier theory

Plane and spherical waves in empty space can be treated irrespective of the shape of the wave pulse; the pulse profile in the generating function is arbitrary, and neither the amplitude nor the speed of the propagated wave depends on that profile. Of course, both the plane and the spherical wave propagate without distortion only in empty space. If we consider situations in which the progress of the electromagnetic disturbance is in any way affected by matter placed into the vicinity of the disturbance, we can no longer treat the wave shape so cavalierly. If space is filled with absorptive and dispersive dielectrics, the transmitting medium will act like a broadly tuned electric circuit. The attenuation of the wave in the course of its progress will depend on its frequency, because the polarization of the dielectric at high frequencies lags behind the applied field. Likewise, if we force the wave to be reflected from conducting surfaces, then the resulting transmitted wave will be the result of the superposition of the original wave and its own reflections, and the resulting interference will be constructive for some frequencies, destructive for others.

Only for one type of wave shape, the sinusoidal or *harmonic* waves, are we assured that the shape of the pulse remains undistorted, no matter how cluttered up the path of transmission. These waves remain undistorted because the sinusoidal functions reproduce themselves (with a phase shift and a constant coefficient) when they are differentiated. Therefore, whenever we have reason to believe that a given transmitting medium or path is dispersive, we first attempt to find harmonic solutions of the wave equations before tackling more difficult wave shapes.

Not only are harmonic waves the easiest to deal with, but, by their linear superposition, almost any wave shape can be obtained. The mathematical theory concerned with the decomposition of arbitrary functions into linear combinations of harmonic functions and, conversely, with the synthesis of harmonic functions into arbitrary functions, is known as *harmonic analysis* or *Fourier theory*. There are essentially two types of functions which lend themselves to Fourier analysis, (1) periodic functions and (2) functions which have the property that the square of the function, integrated over the whole domain of the argument(s), remains finite. Fourier analysis is possible both for functions of a single argument (such as functions of time) and for functions of several arguments (such as functions of the three space coordinates), if only one or the other of the above two conditions is satisfied. In this section, no attempt will be made to develop Fourier theory completely; that project would require a book by itself. All that can be done is to sketch the fundamental ideas of the theory, which is decisive for an understanding not only of wave theory but also of quantum mechanics and modern physics in general. We shall simplify the formulas and abbreviate all intermediate steps by adopting the complex notation of trigonometric functions, which is based on the formulas

$$e^{ix} = \cos x + i \sin x, \qquad \cos x = \frac{1}{2} (e^{ix} + e^{-ix}),$$

$$e^{-ix} = \cos x - i \sin x, \qquad \sin x = \frac{1}{2i} (e^{ix} - e^{-ix}). \tag{50}$$

Differentiation of these exponentials with imaginary exponent follows the same rules as differentiation of real exponentials; that is,

$$\frac{d}{dx} (e^{ix}) = i \, e^{ix}, \qquad \frac{d}{dx} (e^{-ix}) = -i \, e^{-ix}. \tag{51}$$

It is this simple formula for differentiation that makes the use of complex notation so attractive.

**One-dimensional Fourier series.** Suppose we are given a periodic function of a single argument $f(t)$, with the period $\tau$. We wish to approximate this function as precisely as possible by a sum of harmonic functions which possess the same period. Such functions are (in the complex notation) $e^{2\pi int/\tau}$, where $n$ can be zero or any negative or positive integer. Before our problem is properly defined, we must decide how many of these harmonic functions are to be used in the approximation, and we must establish a figure of merit for the goodness of the approximation. As for the first question, we shall use all those harmonics in which $n$ lies between $-N$ and $+N$. As our figure of merit, we shall use a nonnegative number which summarizes the closeness of approximation throughout the interval of one period, one which will approach zero if the approximation is perfect. Such a figure of merit is the integral over the absolute squared difference between the function $f(t)$ and the approximation, which we might call $F(t)$:

$$D = \int_{t=0}^{\tau} |f(t) - F(t)|^2 \, dt, \qquad F(t) = \sum_{n=-N}^{N} c_n e^{2\pi in\frac{t}{\tau}}. \tag{52}$$

$D$ is our figure of merit, which we wish to make as small as possible. $c_n$ are the $(2n + 1)$ coefficients of the harmonic functions that are to be used in the approximation. Now, obviously, $D$ is a function of these parameters. If we wish to minimize $D$, we must adjust the $c_n$ so that all the partial derivatives of $D$ with respect to these parameters vanish. Now, if we wish to represent $D$ as a function of these parameters, we must work out the various integrals occurring in (52). Most of them turn out to vanish, and we are left with the expression

$$D = \int_{t=0}^{\tau} [f(t)]^2 \, dt - \sum_{n=-N}^{N} \int_{t=0}^{\tau} f(t)(c_n e^{2\pi in\frac{t}{\tau}} + c_n^* e^{-2\pi in\frac{t}{\tau}}) \, dt$$
$$+ \sum_{n=-N}^{N} c_n c_n^* \tau. \tag{53}$$

In this expression for $D$, asterisks attached to complex quantities denote the conjugate complex of that quantity (a notation that is becoming more and more frequent in theoretical physics). The expression was obtained by setting the absolute square in eq. (52) equal to the product of $(f - F)$ by its conjugate complex. If now $D$ is differentiated with respect to any of the parameters $c_n$, the result is

$$\frac{\partial D}{\partial c_n} = \tau\, c_n^* - \int_{t=0}^{\tau} f(t) e^{2\pi i n \frac{t}{\tau}}\, dt,$$

$$\frac{\partial D}{\partial c_n^*} = \tau\, c_n - \int_{t=0}^{\tau} f(t) e^{-2\pi i n \frac{t}{\tau}}\, dt. \tag{54}$$

All these partial derivatives must be set equal to zero. Strangely enough, each of them contains only one unknown, and our condition is obviously satisfied if

$$c_n = \frac{1}{\tau} \int_{t=0}^{\tau} f(t) e^{-2\pi i n \frac{t}{\tau}}\, dt. \tag{55}$$

Since $D$ is a nonnegative quantity and, therefore, must possess a minimum, and since eqs. (55) determine exactly one stationary value of $D$, we can be sure that this stationary value is exactly the minimum we are looking for. First, let us note that the best value for each coefficient $c_n$ is independent of the total number of terms included in the approximation. Then, let us compute the value of $D$ under the assumption that we have satisfied the conditions (55). By substitution into eq. (53), we find that

$$D = \int_{t=0}^{\tau} [f(t)]^2\, dt - \tau \sum_{n=-N}^{N} c_n\, c_n^* \geq 0. \tag{56}$$

This relation gives us *Bessel's inequality,*

$$\sum_{n=-N}^{N} c_n\, c_n^* \leq \frac{1}{\tau} \int_0^{\tau} [f(t)]^2\, dt. \tag{57}$$

Bessel's inequality shows that even if we permit $N$ to increase without limit, that is, if we use the infinity of all possible harmonic functions of the correct periodicity to make our approximation, the sum of the absolute squares of the coefficients of the series approximation remains bounded.

If $N$ is made infinite, the series $F(t)$ is called a *Fourier series* or, more particularly, the *Fourier representation* of the function $f(t)$. The coefficients $c_n$ are called the *Fourier coefficients* of the function $f(t)$. The question is whether this infinite series converges toward the function that is to be approximated or whether there remains a finite difference that cannot be removed. The answer, which we shall not attempt to prove here, is that the approximation is indeed perfect if the function $f(t)$ is everywhere continuous. If it is not but instead is merely bounded and piecewise continuous, the Fourier series converges toward the function everywhere except at the jumps, where the Fourier series converges toward the mean between the right and the left value of the function.

If we substitute the values of the Fourier coefficients into the expression for the series, then, provided that $f(t)$ is continuous, the theorem just formulated leads to the equation

$$f(t) = \frac{1}{\tau} \int_{t'=0}^{\tau} f(t') \sum_{n=-\infty}^{\infty} e^{2\pi i n \frac{t-t'}{\tau}} \, dt', \tag{58}$$

and we conclude that Dirac's delta function, modified so as to become a periodic function, can be approximated by the series

$$\{\delta(t)\}_{\text{mod } \tau} = \frac{1}{\tau} \sum_{n=-\infty}^{\infty} e^{-2\pi i n \frac{t}{\tau}}$$

$$= \frac{1}{\tau} \left[ 1 + 2 \sum_{n=1}^{\infty} \cos\left(2\pi \, n \, \frac{t}{\tau}\right) \right]. \tag{59}$$

**One-dimensional Fourier integral.** The Fourier series represents a periodic function; the Fourier integral, a pulse. Consider a function $g(t)$ which is *square integrable*, meaning that the integral of its square, extended over all values of the argument $t$, exists:

$$\int_{-\infty}^{+\infty} [g(t)]^2 \, dt < \infty. \tag{60}$$

Such a function must drop off rapidly enough for large positive and negative values of the argument so that the integral, when its limits are extended to infinity, does not diverge. Now it is possible to approximate such a square-integrable function again by means of a linear superposition of harmonic functions, but the series (the summation) must be replaced by an integral, thus:

$$G(t) = \int_{\omega=-\infty}^{\infty} \gamma(\omega) e^{i\omega t} \, d\omega. \tag{61}$$

The function $\gamma(\omega)$ is a continuously variable amplitude function which indicates the contribution of the function $e^{i\omega t}$ to the approximating function $G(t)$. Our task is again to adjust the amplitude function $\gamma(\omega)$ so that the approximation is as good as possible. As the figure of merit we choose again the square integral of the deviation, this time extended over the whole domain of $t$,

$$D = \int_{t=-\infty}^{\infty} |g(t) - G(t)|^2 \, dt$$

$$= \int_{-\infty}^{\infty} [g(t)]^2 \, dt$$

$$- \int_{t=-\infty}^{\infty} g(t) \int_{\omega=-\infty}^{\infty} [\gamma(\omega)e^{i\omega t} + \gamma^*(\omega)e^{-i\omega t}] \, d\omega \, dt$$

$$+ \int_{t=-\infty}^{\infty} \int\int_{\omega_1,\omega_2=-\infty}^{\infty} \gamma(\omega_1)\gamma^*(\omega_2)e^{i(\omega_1-\omega_2)t} \, d\omega_1 \, d\omega_2 \, dt. \quad (62)$$

Through a careful consideration of the limits involved, it can be shown that the last triple integral equals a single integral,

$$\int_{t=-\infty}^{\infty} \int\int_{\omega_1,\omega_2=-\infty}^{\infty} \gamma(\omega_1) \, \gamma^*(\omega_2)e^{i(\omega_1-\omega_2)t} \, d\omega_1 \, d\omega_2 \, dt$$

$$= 2\pi \int_{\omega=-\infty}^{\infty} \gamma(\omega) \, \gamma^*(\omega) \, d\omega. \quad (63)$$

If we vary the amplitude function, the resulting variation in $D$ will be

$$\delta D = \int_{\omega=-\infty}^{\infty} \left\{ \left[ 2\pi \, \gamma^*(\omega) - \int_{t=-\infty}^{\infty} g(t) \, e^{i\omega t} \, dt \right] \delta\gamma(\omega) \right.$$

$$\left. + \left[ 2\pi \, \gamma(\omega) - \int_{-\infty}^{\infty} g(t) \, e^{-i\omega t} \, dt \right] \delta\gamma^*(\omega) \right\} \, d\omega. \quad (64)$$

If $D$ is to assume the smallest possible value, then the amplitude function must, for every value of its argument $\omega$, satisfy the condition

$$\gamma(\omega) = \frac{1}{2\pi} \int_{-\infty}^{\infty} g(t) \, e^{-i\omega t} \, dt. \quad (65)$$

Again, it can be shown that if this condition is satisfied, then $G(t)$ is a perfect approximation of the function $g(t)$ (assumed to be piecewise continuous) except at points of discontinuity, where $G(t)$ converges toward the mean between the left and right limits of $g(t)$. If we substitute the proper value of $\gamma(\omega)$ into eq. (61) at a point where $G$ equals $g$, we find that

$$g(t) = \frac{1}{2\pi} \int_{\omega=-\infty}^{\infty} \int_{t'=-\infty}^{\infty} g(t') \, e^{i\omega(t-t')} \, dt' \, d\omega, \quad (66)$$

and this is the *Fourier integral formula*. $g(t)$ and $\gamma(\omega)$ are also called each other's *Fourier transforms*.

If we want to translate eq. (66) into a formula containing only the real trigonometric functions, we can do so very easily by adding together the contributions from equal positive and negative values of the argument $\omega$. This operation leads to the alternative versions of the Fourier integral theorem

$$
\begin{aligned}
g(t) &= \frac{1}{\pi} \int_{\omega=0}^{\infty} \int_{t'=-\infty}^{\infty} g(t') \cos \omega(t - t') \, dt' \, d\omega \\
&= \frac{1}{\pi} \int_{\omega=0}^{\infty} \left\{ \cos \omega t \int_{t'=-\infty}^{\infty} g(t') \cos \omega t' \, dt' \right. \\
&\qquad \left. + \sin \omega t \int_{t'=-\infty}^{\infty} g(t') \sin \omega t' \, dt' \right\} \, d\omega.
\end{aligned}
\tag{67}
$$

The theorem can also be formulated with the help of Dirac's delta function, whereupon it assumes the form

$$
\frac{1}{\pi} \int_{\omega=0}^{\infty} \cos \omega t \cdot d\omega = \frac{1}{2\pi} \int_{\omega=-\infty}^{\infty} e^{i\omega t} \cdot d\omega = \delta(t).
\tag{68}
$$

**Three-dimensional Fourier analysis.** The Fourier formulas, both the series and the integral formulas, can be generalized without essential changes into domains of any dimension. In applications to physics, Fourier analysis in three dimensions is of considerable significance. Three-dimensional Fourier series are used extensively in the theory of X-ray diffraction by crystals, which form triply periodic arrangements of X-ray scatterers in space. Three-dimensional Fourier integrals serve, for instance, to examine the spread of a square integrable wave pulse in space in the course of time. The *three-dimensional Fourier integral formula* for a square integrable function $g(\mathbf{x})$ is

$$
\begin{aligned}
g(\mathbf{x}) &= \int \int \int_{-\infty}^{\infty} \gamma(\mathbf{k}) \, e^{i(\mathbf{k} \cdot \mathbf{x})} \, dk_1 \, dk_2 \, dk_3, \\
\gamma(\mathbf{k}) &= \left(\frac{1}{2\pi}\right)^3 \int \int \int_{-\infty}^{\infty} g(\mathbf{x}) \, e^{-i(\mathbf{k} \cdot \mathbf{x})} \, dx_1 \, dx_2 \, dx_3.
\end{aligned}
\tag{69}
$$

We can say that the Fourier transform of $g(\mathbf{x})$, the amplitude function $\gamma(\mathbf{k})$, is defined in a symbolical $\mathbf{k}$-space. Each point in $\mathbf{k}$-space corresponds to a sinusoidal "wave" in **x**-space whose wave length equals $(2\pi/|\mathbf{k}|)$ and whose wave fronts are perpendicular to the vector **k**.  But the converse is also true: to each point in **x**-space there belongs a sinusoidal wave in **k**-space, because, except for a trivial normalizing factor and except for the sign in the exponential, the equation leading from $g(\mathbf{x})$ to $\gamma(\mathbf{k})$ is the same as the equation leading from $\gamma(\mathbf{k})$ to $g(\mathbf{x})$.

An application of *multidimensional Fourier series* will be found in the next section.

## 8.4. Guided waves

Generally speaking, a guided wave is a wave whose spread is hemmed in by the presence of reflecting walls, sufficiently so that over a certain distance the wave pulse transports energy along a fairly well-defined path.  The prime example of a guided wave is an electromagnetic pulse traveling in the interior of a hollow tube (the *wave guide*) the walls of which consist of an excellent conductor. Since the conductor cannot maintain an electric field in its interior, because of the immediate shifting of charges sufficient to reduce the electric field to zero, Poynting's vector in the walls must vanish, and all the radiative energy that enters one end of the tube must emerge at the other end.  Ordinarily, the cross section of the wave guide is the same throughout its length, and the most common cross sections used in microwave techniques are rectangular, circular, and concentric annular (coaxial line).  In this section, we shall develop primarily the theory of the rectangular wave guide, also indicating the results to be expected for more general cross sections. Before doing so, we shall have to indicate what is meant by the term "a perfect conductor."

The reader will recall that conductors are materials (primarily metals) which in the face of an applied electric field are capable of having a sustained electric current pass through them.  The *resistivity* of a material is defined as the ratio between the magnitude of the electric field strength and the magnitude of the resulting current density.  If the material is isotropic, these two vectors will be parallel.  A perfect conductor is a conductor with zero resistivity, an idealization not realizable in nature.  However, the concept is very useful as an approximation, since many of the heavy metals, particularly copper, silver, and gold, have such low resistivities that for many purposes they behave just like a perfect conductor. Naturally, like all approximations, this one will break down if used uncritically. Inside a perfect conductor, the electric field strength is permanently zero; and since across an interface the tangential components of the electric field strength are continuous, *the electric field strength on the surface of a perfect conductor must always be normal to that surface.* The result of this law is that the normal component of the curl of the electric field strength on the surface vanishes; and since this curl is proportional to the time rate of change of the magnetic induction **B**, it follows further that *the normal component of* **B** *on the surface of a perfect conductor vanishes or is constant in time;* at any rate it cannot be part of a wave. Therefore, in a wave guide whose interior is free of matter, our problem is to find all those solutions of Maxwell's equations which satisfy the two conditions that the tangential component of the electric field and the normal component of the magnetic field vanish at all times on the interior surfaces of the wall.

To solve the field equations with these boundary conditions is still a somewhat difficult task, particularly since different components of the field are required to satisfy boundary conditions on different portions of the guide wall. However, it is possible to reduce the number of variables and, at the same time, to simplify the boundary conditions by returning to the electromagnetic potentials and by further strengthening the gauge condition. In Chapter 7 we proved that any field can be represented in terms of electromagnetic potentials that satisfy the gauge condition. In the case of wave fields, that is, nonconstant fields in the absence of charges and currents, we can go a step further and show that it is possible to eliminate the electric potential $\Phi$ without destroying the gauge condition. Let us assume that we have a wave field (in empty space) and that we possess a set of electromagnetic potentials satisfying the gauge condition and, therefore, individually the wave equation. Then there will exist a function $\Psi$ which has the property that

$$\frac{1}{c} \frac{\partial \Psi}{\partial t} = \Phi \tag{70}$$

and which, at the same time, satisfies the wave equation. Such a function can be obtained, for instance, by choosing a particular instant $t_0$, setting

$$G(\mathbf{x}, t) = c \int_{\tau=t_0}^{t} \Phi(\mathbf{x}, \tau) \, d\tau, \tag{71}$$

where the function $G$ has the property that

$$\frac{\partial}{\partial t} \left( \frac{1}{c^2} \frac{\partial^2 G}{\partial t^2} - \nabla^2 G \right) = 0, \tag{72}$$

and then finally adding to $G$ a function $f(\mathbf{x})$ so that the sum satisfies the wave equation at the time $t_0$. Then the wave equation will be satisfied for all $t$. Now we can use the function $\Psi$ to carry out a gauge transformation. According to eqs. (7.36) and (7.51) the result of this gauge transformation will be the new potentials

$$\Phi^* = \Phi - \frac{1}{c} \frac{\partial \Psi}{\partial t} = 0, \qquad \mathbf{A}^* = \mathbf{A} + \text{grad } \Psi. \tag{73}$$

To see whether the gauge condition remains satisfied if it was satisfied originally, we form the divergence of $\mathbf{A}^*$. We find

$$\begin{aligned}
\nabla \cdot \mathbf{A}^* &= \nabla \cdot \mathbf{A} + \nabla^2 \Psi = \nabla \cdot \mathbf{A} + \frac{1}{c^2} \frac{\partial^2 \Psi}{\partial t^2} \\
&= \nabla \cdot \mathbf{A} + \frac{1}{c} \frac{\partial \Phi}{\partial t} = 0.
\end{aligned} \tag{74}$$

To sum up the results of this proof: a wave field can be constructed by finding solutions of the equations

$$\frac{1}{c^2} \frac{\partial^2 \mathbf{A}}{\partial t^2} - \nabla^2 \mathbf{A} = 0, \qquad \nabla \cdot \mathbf{A} = 0, \tag{75}$$

and by setting the field strengths equal to

$$\mathbf{B} = \text{curl } \mathbf{A}, \qquad \mathbf{E} = -\frac{1}{c} \frac{\partial \mathbf{A}}{\partial t}. \tag{76}$$

Always discarding constants of integration, which would correspond to constant potentials, we find that both our boundary conditions on the wall will be satisfied if on the walls the tangential components of $\mathbf{A}$ vanish; not only the tangential components of $\mathbf{E}$ but also the normal component of $\mathbf{B}$ will be zero.

So far, we have succeeded in describing the boundary conditions which must be satisfied on any perfectly conducting wall in terms of the vector field **A**, but we have not yet taken into consideration the special symmetry of a cylindrical wave guide. We shall do so now. If we place the wave guide so that the $x_3$-axis is the axis of the wave guide, we find that $A_3$ vanishes everywhere at the wall. At the same time, we know that the remainder, the "transverse vector potential," must also be tangential to the wall. The special symmetry conditions of the case suggest that we consider the $A_3$-component apart from the other two.

One way of solving our problem would be to attempt solutions in which $A_3$ vanishes everywhere, not only at the walls. Then the remaining two components must satisfy the divergence condition by themselves, and they will do so if we set

$$A_1 = \frac{\partial P}{\partial x_2}, \qquad A_2 = -\frac{\partial P}{\partial x_1}. \tag{77}$$

In fact, such a "superpotential" must then always exist. It follows immediately that the normal derivative of $P$ at the walls vanishes. If we can find a function $P$ which satisfies the wave solution and also the boundary condition that at the walls its normal derivative vanishes, then such a function will generate, with the help of eqs. (77) and (76), a solution of the complete problem. Since this type of solution has no longitudinal component of the electric field, it is called *transverse electric*.

The other possibility is that $A_3$ does not vanish in the interior and that the transverse part of **A** is a pure gradient. (Any non-gradient contribution can be split off and treated as a transverse electric case.) It can be shown that there exists a single function $Q$ so that

$$
\begin{aligned}
A_1 &= Q_{,13}, \\
A_2 &= Q_{,23}, \\
A_3 &= -(Q_{,11} + Q_{,22}) = Q_{,33} - \frac{1}{c^2}\frac{\partial^2 Q}{\partial t^2}.
\end{aligned} \tag{78}
$$

The boundary conditions will be satisfied in this case if $Q$ vanishes at the wall. This boundary-value problem is somewhat different from the first, in which it was not the function itself but its normal derivatives that had to vanish at the boundary. In the second case, the component $B_3$ vanishes everywhere; that is why it is called the *transverse magnetic* type of wave. It can be shown that all acceptable solutions are linear combinations of just these two special types of solution.

The further treatment of each case proceeds as follows. We consider waves that can be subjected to Fourier analysis with respect to time and with respect to the axis of the wave guide, in other words, waves that may be considered as the linear superposition of sinusoidal wave trains traveling down the $x_3$-axis. For each component of this double Fourier analysis, we attempt to solve the whole problem separately. Depending on whether we wish to treat the transverse electric or the transverse magnetic case, we start by considering functions possessing the form

$$P = \cos(\omega t - k_3 x_3) \cdot u(x_1, x_2),$$
$$Q = \cos(\omega t - k_3 x_3) \cdot v(x_1, x_2). \tag{79}$$

The ratio $\omega/k_3$ equals the velocity of propagation of the guided wave down the axis $x_3$. The remaining functions $u$ and $v$ satisfy the equations

$$u_{,11} + u_{,22} + \left(\frac{\omega^2}{c^2} - k_3^2\right) u = 0 \qquad \left(\frac{\partial u}{\partial n} = 0 \text{ at boundary}\right),$$
$$v_{,11} + v_{,22} + \left(\frac{\omega^2}{c^2} - k_3^2\right) v = 0 \qquad (v = 0 \text{ at boundary}). \tag{80}$$

Now here we have straight two-dimensional boundary-value problems of the kind treated in standard textbooks on partial differential equations. The general theory tells us that these equations with boundary conditions possess nonzero solutions only if the coefficient of the undifferentiated term is positive, and further that, for any given cross section of the wave guide, solutions will exist only for certain discrete (positive) values of that coefficient, known as the *eigenvalues* or *characteristic values* of the problem.

If the problem can be solved completely, a condition that depends primarily on the shape of the cross section, the eigenvalues can be designated by numbers (or pairs of numbers), arranged, for instance, in ascending order. For a particular eigenvalue, $\omega$ is always a definite function of $k_3$, or vice versa. If we designate the eigenvalue by $\kappa^2$, then

$$\omega^2 = c^2(\kappa^2 + k_3^2). \tag{81}$$

This expression shows that for each characteristic value of either problem (80) there will be a lowest possible value of $\omega$ equal to $c\kappa$ and known as the *cutoff frequency*, below which a progressive wave is no longer possible. It is very easy to show that a solution still exists for frequencies below the cutoff but that it depends on $x_3$ exponentially rather than trigonometrically. Such a solution does not represent a wave capable of transporting energy along the wave-guide axis.

The number of possible solutions of either problem (80) is infinite, but they are discrete, and the eigenvalues are so distributed that below any finite number only a finite number of eigenvalues will be found. These solutions are called *normal modes* and represent the infinitely many, but discrete, ways in which a wave guide can transmit electromagnetic energy. If the wave guide is excited at a particular frequency, it can respond only with a finite number of normal modes, whose cutoff lies below the frequency of excitation.

We shall now illustrate these general laws, by the specific example of the rectangular wave guide, which can be done practically by inspection. Let its width in the $x_1$-direction be $a$; that in the $x_2$-direction, $b$. The solutions of the first problem (80) are, except for a constant factor,

$$u_{mn} = \cos m\frac{\pi x_1}{a} \cos n\frac{\pi x_2}{b} \qquad \binom{m, n = 0, 1, \cdots, \infty}{m + n \geq 1,},$$
$$\kappa^2 = \pi^2\left(\frac{m^2}{a^2} + \frac{n^2}{b^2}\right); \tag{82}$$

those of the second,

$$v_{mn} = \sin m\frac{\pi x_1}{a} \sin n\frac{\pi x_2}{b} \qquad (m, n = 1, 2, \cdots, \infty),$$
$$\kappa^2 = \pi^2\left(\frac{m^2}{a^2} + \frac{n^2}{b^2}\right). \tag{83}$$

Below are tables for the field components in the two cases. For the first case, the transverse electric modes, these expressions are, except for a common arbitrary factor,

$$E_1 = k_2 \frac{\omega}{c} \cos k_1 x_1 \sin k_2 x_2 \sin (\omega t - k_3 x_3),$$

$$E_2 = -k_1 \frac{\omega}{c} \sin k_1 x_1 \cos k_2 x_2 \sin (\omega t - k_3 x_3),$$

$$E_3 = 0,$$
$$B_1 = k_1 k_3 \sin k_1 x_1 \cos k_2 x_2 \sin (\omega t - k_3 x_3),$$
$$B_2 = k_2 k_3 \cos k_1 x_1 \sin k_2 x_2 \sin (\omega t - k_3 x_3), \qquad (84)$$
$$B_3 = -(k_1^2 + k_2^2) \cos k_1 x_1 \cos k_2 x_2 \cos (\omega t - k_3 x_3)$$
$$\left( k_1 \equiv \pi \frac{m}{a}, \qquad k_2 \equiv \pi \frac{n}{b}, \qquad k_s k_s - \frac{\omega^2}{c^2} = 0 \right).$$

For a transverse magnetic mode, the corresponding expressions are

$$E_1 = k_1 k_3 \cos k_1 x_1 \sin k_2 x_2 \sin (\omega t - k_3 x_3),$$
$$E_2 = k_2 k_3 \sin k_1 x_1 \cos k_2 x_2 \sin (\omega t - k_3 x_3),$$
$$E_3 = (k_1^2 + k_2^2) \sin k_1 x_1 \sin k_2 x_2 \cos (\omega t - k_3 x_3),$$
$$B_1 = -k_2 \frac{\omega}{c} \sin k_1 x_1 \cos k_2 x_2 \sin (\omega t - k_3 x_3), \qquad (85)$$
$$B_2 = +k_1 \frac{\omega}{c} \cos k_1 x_1 \sin k_2 x_2 \sin (\omega t - k_3 x_3),$$
$$B_3 = 0.$$

For almost all combinations of $m$ and $n$, there are a transverse electric and a transverse magnetic mode with the same values for the cutoff frequency. There are only two exceptions, the combinations (0,1) and (1,0), which exist for the transverse electric but not for the transverse magnetic case. If the two corresponding cutoff frequencies can be kept sufficiently different, then there will exist a whole band of frequencies in which only one transverse electric mode can carry energy through the wave guide. In practice, rectangular wave guides are usually built so that one dimension is exactly half of the other. Thus, of these two lowest cutoff frequencies one is twice the other, and for a whole octave only one (a transverse electric) mode of the wave guide can be excited. Since the efficiency of the guide as a power line is greatest near the cutoff frequency (there $k_3$ becomes very small and with it the longitudinal field, which from the point of view of power flow is wasted), wave guides are usually used near that lowest cutoff; the

greater of the two internal widths of the wave guide is then half
of the wave length.

## Problems

**8.1.** In a spherical wave, for instance the wave of an electric dipole,
   (a) Compute the expressions for the energy density and the energy
flow in the field, on the special assumption that the time dependence is
sinusoidal.
   (b) Construct a stationary wave by adding an outgoing and an incoming
wave with the same amplitude and frequency together, and again determine energy density and energy flux. Also consider the total energy
stored up in the field.

**8.2.** Determine the angular dependence of the energy flux and density
for oscillating quadrupoles and octupoles. Also examine the energy flow
distribution for fields which are the linear superposition of a dipole and a
quadrupole of the same frequency. Finally, add an electric and a magnetic
dipole radiator together, for various angles between the two axes, and see
what happens. The primary interest is in the "wave zone" ($r$ large compared with the wave length).

**8.3.** In a wave guide construct a stationary wave by letting two waves
in the same mode and at the same frequency travel in opposite directions.
Examine the existence of nodes and antinodes in the guide. In particular,
force the guide to develop a stationary wave by sealing it at one end with
the help of a single perfectly conducting diaphragm at right angles to the
axis. Discuss both transverse electric and transverse magnetic modes.

**8.4.** Seal both ends of a rectangular wave guide with a diaphragm of
the same type as in Problem 8.3 and attempt to construct solutions that
satisfy all conditions. It will be found that only certain frequencies in
each mode are possible. Find all possible solutions and systematize them.
The box so constructed is a specially simple example of a "cavity resonator."

**8.5.** In a progressive guided wave, examine both the velocity of propagation and the power transmitted for a given normal mode as a function
of frequency.

**8.6.** Examine the normal modes of a cylindrical wave guide. This
problem can be attacked best in cylinder coordinates, and the solution of
the radial part of the wave equation leads to Bessel functions.

**8.7.** Determine the radiated wave of an electron on a periodic orbit
(for instance a circular orbit traversed at constant speed) by treating the
actual charge-current distribution as the linear superposition of sinusoidal
charge-current distributions both in space and in time.

# Chapter 9

# Relativity

## 9.1. The speed of light

Through the introduction of the field concept, it is possible to construct a theory which describes the various electromagnetic phenomena and, at the same time, permits the reestablishment of the conservation laws of mechanics. It succeeds in doing so by modifying somewhat the role assigned to "empty space." In classical mechanics, forces between mass points can reach right across empty space and produce accelerations at points distant from the source of the force, without being affected by the space or matter between source and point of application. In a field theory, action at a distance is feasible only through the intervention of the field, which pervades all space, which spreads at a definite finite rate of speed, and which may be affected by matter between the source and the point of application.

The theories of Maxwell and Hertz were successful in more than making optics a part of electromagnetic theory. Hertz, using ordinary electric devices, produced waves whose wave length could be predicted by theory and confirmed by measurement. So it appeared for a while that a mechanical theory of gravitation and a field theory of electromagnetism would have to exist side by side. Maxwell, and after him Hertz, attempted to explain the electromagnetic field as a state of stress of a mysterious and all-pervading material medium, the *ether*, but these attempts were unsuccessful, since such an ether would have to possess mechanical and other properties not shown by any other material. It would, for instance, be necessary to explain why there are transverse waves (as shown by the possibility of polarization), which could be taken as an indication of shear rigidity, but no compressional (longitudinal) waves. Unification along elastomechanical lines is therefore ruled out.

Apart from the aesthetic or philosophical objections against a mechanics-field dualism in nature, a very serious point was observed soon after the formulation of the theory. Maxwell's theory does not satisfy the (classical) principle of relativity, which was discussed in Section 6.5. This principle, it will be recalled, states that the formulation of the laws of nature is the same in all inertial frames of reference; the principle holds throughout mechanics, no matter what particular force law is obeyed. It is a simple matter to show that electrodynamic theory is in contradiction to the principle of relativity: One of the consequences of the theory is the existence of waves that travel in empty space with the velocity $c$; it would appear that the speed, when referred to another inertial frame of reference, cannot also be $c$ in all directions and that Maxwell's equations, if true at all, must hold with respect to a particular frame, the frame representing "absolute rest."

With this realization came attempts in two directions: to modify the theory so that the principle of relativity could be saved; or, if there were a frame of absolute rest, to devise experiments to discover it. In the theoretical work designed to "save" the principle, the ether hypothesis again played a role. If the electromagnetic field can be interpreted as a state of stress of a material medium, then naturally the equations governing the elastic behavior of this fluid will be simplest in the frame with respect to which this carrier medium is at rest. If the medium is a fluid or resembles a fluid, this state may be different in different locations; that is, we could have a streaming ether, and the "frame of absolute rest" would be simply the local state of motion of the ether.

The most famous experiment designed to discover the frame of absolute rest is the Michelson-Morley experiment, in which phase differences were observed between light waves traveling along two paths at right angles to each other. If there were a difference in the speed of light along the two paths in the instrument, and if this difference were determined by the orientation of the instrument in space, the phase differences (which were observed as interference fringes) should change when the interferometer is turned 90°. The first result of the experiment was negative; that is, it was found that the speed of light was independent of orientation in space. Because of its crucial importance, the experiment has been repeated by a number of investigators, with ever greater attention to hidden sources of error. Although some workers reported finding a positive result, big enough to indicate an "ether wind" of about two miles per second on the surface of the earth, the preponderance of the most recent evidence still confirms the original negative result.

Other experiments and observations prove that the earth itself does not occupy a special position in this respect, that it does not, for instance, "drag" the ether along on its surface. Probably most important in this respect is the so-called *aberration* of fixed stars; their apparent position in the sky describes a small ellipse each year, indicating that the wave fronts of an incident light wave appear "slanted" to the moving earth observer. Aberration can be explained quantitatively by the simple assumption that the light waves arrive on the surface of the earth and are picked up by the observer's telescope as if there were *no* ether drag.

It is not possible, within the frame of a single chapter, to give an exhaustive or even reasonably adequate account of the arguments that led up to the necessity of modifying the classical concepts of space and time and then to go on and develop the theory of relativity as such. All we shall do now is to state in outline which ideas were important in the development of the so-called *special theory of relativity* ("restricted" would probably be a better name, but "special" is now used almost exclusively, because of the original translation from the German *"Speziell"*) and to develop a few of its major results as they affect electromagnetic theory itself.

We can summarize the prerelativity situation by stating that although most of the consequences of the Maxwell-Hertz theory were proved correct by experiment, its apparent requirement that there be a frame of absolute rest could not be confirmed at all. Finally, Einstein showed that Maxwell's theory was perfectly consistent with the principle of relativity and that with respect to *any* inertial frame of reference the speed of electromagnetic waves could be the same in all directions, provided that the basic concepts of space and time underlying our whole structure of physical theory were revamped.

## 9.2. Space and time

Einstein recognized that our usual notions of space and time are necessary for the development of mechanics but not for that of electrodynamics. Leaving aside at first the question what to do ultimately with Newton's theory of gravitation (a question which is dealt with in the *general theory of relativity*), Einstein concentrated first on a critical evaluation of what we really know about space-time measurements and their absolute character.

In Newton's mechanics, it is of decisive importance that we know what is meant by the "simultaneity of distant events." That is to say, since every force law in mechanics is based on the distance between the two interacting particles, there is the implicit but necessary assumption that the statement "Particle $A$ was here *at the same time* at which particle $B$ was there" has an absolute meaning.  But when we wish to establish the simultaneity of two distant events by experiment, we encounter difficulties which are not merely matters of technique.

If we could pass a signal with infinite speed from one point in space to another one, there would be no particular difficulty. Actually, there is no physical effect known that would permit us to send a signal faster than light; $c$ is an upper bound for the speed of signal transmission.  This statement means that observers, wherever they may be stationed, must allow for the speed of signal transmission when judging the simultaneity of distant events.  If they assume that this speed is the speed of light, no matter what their own state of motion, then it is easy to see that the findings of two observers who are in different states of motion will not agree.  One observer will find that two events are taking place at the same time while to another observer they do not appear simultaneous.  But if the two observers agree which is to be their reference state of motion, or rather of rest, then they are creating this reference state by fiat.  Einstein's historical decision was to accept the first alternative—to conclude that simultaneity is not an absolute but a relative physical fact, dependent on the frame of reference chosen.

If that point of view is adopted, at least provisionally, it can be shown immediately that the absolute character of length and time measurements breaks down, too.  In other words, a judgment by one observer that a particular rod has a length of $a$ cm will not be confirmed by an observer in a different state of motion.

So far, we have made negative statements.  Can the notions of absolute space and time measurements be replaced by new ones, equally useful to serve as a matrix of physical events?  Einstein proceeded to answer this question by attempting to find a set of transformation laws between inertial systems which would satisfy the following requirements:

(1) The transformation law was to be *linear*, that is, space and time coordinates in one system should be linear combinations of the coordinates in the other inertial system.

(2) A signal traveling with respect to one observer with the velocity of light $c$ should possess the same speed with respect to all other observers.

(3) The transformation law should be *reflexive* in the sense that if system $B$ had a velocity $\mathbf{v}$ with respect to system $A$, then system $A$ should have the velocity $-\mathbf{v}$ with respect to $B$, and the respective transformation coefficients should depend on these two relative velocities in the same manner. He showed that these three conditions suffice to determine the transformation law completely.

Let us formulate these conditions mathematically. Suppose that we consider the inertial system $A$ and the second inertial system $B$, whose origin moves along the $x_1$-axis of the system $A$ at the constant rate $v$. Let the axes of the second system be located so that they are permanently parallel to those of the system $A$. For identification, let the coordinates of $B$ be primed, $x_s'$. This choice of special coordinates does not restrict the generality of the physical problem that we are set to solve; it merely makes use of (trivial) coordinate rotations within each given frame of reference ($A$ and $B$) so that a maximum of geometrical symmetry is achieved.

To formulate condition (1), the requirement of linearity, is not difficult. If it were not for our special choice of coordinates, our linear relations might contain 16 constant but unknown coefficients. As it is, we have only the following:

$$x_1' = \alpha x_1 + \beta t, \qquad x_2' = \gamma x_2, \qquad x_3' = \gamma x_3,$$
$$t' = \delta x_1 + \epsilon t. \tag{1}$$

All those coefficients which we have omitted would, if they did not vanish, introduce an asymmetry about the joint $x_1, x_1'$-axis. Therefore the total number of unknowns at this stage is five. To reduce the number of unknowns further, we shall set up the conditions that the system $B$ has the velocity $v$ along the positive $x_1$-axis whereas the system $A$ has the velocity $-v$ along the $x_1$-axis. Consequently, $x_1'$ vanishes if $x_1$ equals $vt$, and $x_1$ vanishes when $x_1'$ equals $-vt'$,

$$0 = (\alpha v + \beta)t, \qquad (\beta + v\epsilon)t = 0. \tag{2}$$

If we solve these two equations for $\beta$ and for $\epsilon$, only three unknowns remain, and eqs. (1) take the form

$$x_1' = \alpha(x - vt), \qquad x_2' = \gamma x_2, \qquad x_3' = \gamma x_3,$$
$$t' = \delta x + \alpha t. \tag{3}$$

At this point, we shall apply our most powerful requirement: that a signal traveling at the speed $c$ with respect to frame $A$ will also do so with respect to frame $B$, no matter what the direction of propagation. In mathematical terms:

$$x_1'^2 + x_2'^2 + x_3'^2 - c^2 t'^2 = 0$$
$$= (\alpha^2 - c^2\delta^2)x_1^2 - 2\alpha(c^2\delta + \alpha v)x_1 t$$
$$- \alpha^2(c^2 - v^2)t^2 + \gamma^2(x_2^2 + x_3^2) \tag{4}$$

if $\qquad\qquad x_1^2 + x_2^2 + x_3^2 - c^2 t^2 = 0.$

This requirement is satisfied if

$$\delta = -\frac{v}{c^2}\alpha, \qquad \gamma = \sqrt{1 - v/c^2}\,\alpha. \tag{5}$$

The last remaining unknown, $\gamma$, can be determined by the application of the condition of reflexivity. If we substitute our expressions for all the other constants into eqs. (1) and then proceed to obtain the *inverse* transformation equations (the equations giving us unprimed coordinates in terms of primed coordinates), we find that these inverted equations have the same form as (1), with the difference that $v$ is replaced by $-v$ and $\gamma$ by $\gamma^{-1}$. But if the principle of reflexivity is to hold, then $\gamma$ must be the same function of $v$ as $\gamma^{-1}$ is of $-v$. Actually, $\gamma$ can depend only on the absolute value of $v$, not its sign, since the relationship between $x_2$ and $x_2'$ cannot be changed if in a simple perversion we invert the direction of the positive $x_1$- and $x_1'$-axes. Thus, we are forced to conclude that $\gamma$ equals unity. With this final determination, eqs. (1) turn into the famous equations of the *Lorentz transformation*,

$$x_1' = \frac{x_1 - vt}{\sqrt{1 - v^2/c^2}}, \qquad x_2' = x_2, \qquad x_3' = x_3,$$
$$t' = \frac{t - v/c^2 \cdot x_1}{\sqrt{1 - v^2/c^2}}. \tag{6}$$

The corresponding classical transformation equations, the so-called *Galilean transformation equations*, are a good approximation to eqs. (6) if the relative velocity of the two inertial frames, $v$, is small compared with $c$. The Galilean equations which describe the same situation are

$$x_1' = x - vt, \qquad x_2' = x_2, \qquad x_3' = x_3, \qquad t' = t. \qquad (7)$$

According to the Lorentz equations, length measurements at right angles to the direction of relative motion have identical results, whether carried out with respect to frame $A$ or with respect to frame $B$. This result is not surprising, since two foot rules, each at rest with respect to one system and both at right angles to the direction of relative motion, can be made to coincide in their entire lengths at the same time (independently of which observer determines the coincidence). Bodies will, however, appear contracted in the direction of motion to the observer relative to whom they are moving, and the ratio of this observed contraction will be $(1 - v^2/c^2)^{1/2}$. Likewise, clocks which are moving with respect to the observer will apparently go slow, and the factor of retardation is the same square root. These contractions and retardations are *mutual;* that is, a body at rest in $A$ will appear shorter in the $x_1'$-direction when viewed by an observer in $B$, whereas a similar body in $B$ will appear contracted to the $A$-observer.

## 9.3. Lorentz covariance of the field equations

We have succeeded in modifying our space-time concepts in such a manner that it is possible for a physical process to propagate with the speed $c$ relative to all inertial frames of reference at once. It remains to be seen whether the equations of the electromagnetic field can be modified so that they have the same form with respect to all inertial frames of reference connected with each other through Lorentz transformation equations, that is, whether they are *Lorentz covariant*. This is indeed the case. The proof can be carried out in either of two ways. The more elegant of these is first to introduce "tensor calculus in four-dimensional Minkowski space" and then to show, as a special application of the complete theory of Lorentz covariants, that the electromagnetic laws are covariant. We shall follow in this presentation a more pedestrian course, one which does not require an extensive mathematical preparation. Like

Einstein in his original paper, we shall express the partial derivatives with respect to one coordinate system $(A)$ in terms of those with respect to another coordinate system $(B)$, and then we shall find linear combinations of the resulting equations which reproduce the original form of the field equations.

Starting with those four equations which contain **E** and **B** only, we find

$$\frac{1}{\sqrt{1-v^2/c^2}}\left(\frac{\partial B_1}{\partial x_1'} - \frac{v}{c^2}\frac{\partial B_1}{\partial t'}\right) + \frac{\partial B_2}{\partial x_2'} + \frac{\partial B_3'}{\partial x_3'} = 0,$$

$$\frac{\partial E_3}{\partial x_2'} - \frac{\partial E_2}{\partial x_3'} + \frac{1}{\sqrt{1-v^2/c^2}}\left(\frac{1}{c}\frac{\partial B_1'}{\partial t'} - \frac{v}{c}\frac{\partial B_1'}{\partial x_1'}\right) = 0,$$

$$\frac{1}{\sqrt{1-v^2/c^2}}\left[\frac{\partial}{\partial x_1'}\left(E_2 - \frac{v}{c}B_3\right) + \frac{1}{c}\frac{\partial}{\partial t'}\left(B_3 - \frac{v}{c}E_2\right)\right]$$
$$- \frac{\partial E_1}{\partial x_2'} = 0, \qquad (8)$$

$$\frac{1}{\sqrt{1-v^2/c^2}}\left[-\frac{\partial}{\partial x_1'}\left(E_3 + \frac{v}{c}B_2\right) + \frac{1}{c}\frac{\partial}{\partial t'}\left(B_2 + \frac{v}{c}E_3\right)\right]$$
$$+ \frac{\partial E_1}{\partial x_3'} = 0.$$

In each of the original field equations, the partial derivatives with respect to one of the four arguments $x_s$, $t$ do not occur. The last two of the four eqs. (8) also possess this property, and of the first two equations we can form appropriate linear combinations and achieve the same. As a result, the six quantities appear in certain combinations, and we are led to the identification

$$E_1' = \lambda E_1, \qquad\qquad B_1' = \lambda B_1,$$

$$E_2' = \frac{\lambda}{\sqrt{1-v^2/c^2}}\left(E_2 - \frac{v}{c}B_3\right),$$

$$B_2' = \frac{\lambda}{\sqrt{1-v^2/c^2}}\left(B_2 + \frac{v}{c}E_3\right), \quad (9)$$

$$E_3' = \frac{\lambda}{\sqrt{1-v^2/c^2}}\left(E_3 + \frac{v}{c}B_2\right),$$

$$B_3' = \frac{\lambda}{\sqrt{1-v^2/c^2}}\left(B_3 - \frac{v}{c}E_2\right),$$

in which there appears one undetermined common factor $\lambda$. By requiring again reflexivity in the transformation law, $\lambda$ is found to be 1, and the transformation laws for **E** and **B** become

$$E_1' = E_1, \qquad\qquad B_1' = B_1,$$

$$E_2' = \frac{E_2 - \dfrac{v}{c} B_3}{\sqrt{1 - v^2/c^2}}, \qquad B_2' = \frac{B_2 + \dfrac{v}{c} E_3}{\sqrt{1 - v^2/c^2}}, \qquad (10)$$

$$E_3' = \frac{E_3 + \dfrac{v}{c} B_2}{\sqrt{1 - v^2/c^2}}, \qquad B_3' = \frac{B_3 - \dfrac{v}{c} E_2}{\sqrt{1 - v^2/c^2}}.$$

If we apply the same method to the four remaining field equations, we find that the components of **D** and **H** transform with each other in precisely the same manner as those of **E** and **B**. At the same time, we obtain the transformation law for the charge and current density. Without going through the details of the calculations, we shall state the result:

$$\sigma' = \frac{\sigma - \dfrac{v}{c^2} j_1}{\sqrt{1 - v^2/c^2}}, \qquad j_1 = \frac{j_1 - v\sigma}{\sqrt{1 - v^2/c^2}}, \qquad (11)$$

$$j_2' = j_2, \qquad\qquad j_3' = j_3.$$

## 9.4. Dynamics

The basic laws of mechanics, which connect the force, the mass, and the acceleration with each other, are covariant with respect to Galilean transformations but not with respect to Lorentz transformations. Thus, it would appear that the duality between mechanics and the electromagnetic field leads to an irreconcilable conflict concerning which of the two transformation laws is correct.

When we survey the whole field of physics, we find that at present we know of only three types of interaction between particles: gravitation, electromagnetism, and nuclear forces. Omitting the nuclear forces altogether, since we cannot treat them without a quantum theoretical approach, we find that gravitation, the historical source of the mechanical approach to physics, has also remained the single outstanding triumph of the mechanical theory. On the other hand, motions of astronomical bodies are extremely slow compared with $c$, the ratio being of the order of $10^{-4}$. If it should turn out that a relativistic theory of gravitation can be developed, the corrections in terms of observable deviations are likely to be small. On the other hand, light does travel at the speed *c*, and so does every other kind of electromagnetic wave. It appeared reasonable to overthrow mechanics altogether in favor of relativistic electrodynamics and to attempt to develop a relativistic theory of gravitation. This is, of course, exactly what Einstein did, and today we possess a relativistic theory of gravitation in the form of the general theory of relativity, which is even more satisfactory than Newton's classical theory of gravitation.

Mechanics is in conflict with the Lorentz equations chiefly because of the concept of action at a distance. For an invariant or covariant force law, it is necessary that the instantaneous distance between two interacting mass points be uniquely defined. And that condition is, of course, incompatible with the Lorentz equations. We cannot hope to replace Newton's framework of classical mechanics by an equally all-embracing framework of "relativistic mechanics." However, there are two situations in which the development of relativistic mechanical concepts appears both possible and necessary, namely, in the theory of collisions and the equations of motion in electrodynamics.

The theory of collisions deals with forces between mass points which act only at such short ranges that two mass points interact with each other only while they practically coincide. A collision, classically speaking, is a special case of a mechanical interaction, and, therefore, it must obey the general conservation laws: that total linear momentum, total angular momentum, and total energy of the system before and after collision remain the same. Collisions occur in gases between molecules and in the laboratory between ivory balls. The conservation laws can be tested and are satisfied. A consistent theory of relativity must be capable of formulating these conservation laws invariantly.

In electrodynamics, the Lorentz force on a point charge is not determined by distant mass points but by the local field. The local field has certain transformation properties, which we have already indicated. If the force law is to have any meaning, left-hand and right-hand sides must transform in the same manner.

Either of these two sets of laws may serve as a starting point for the relativistic revision of the mechanical concepts of mass,

momentum, and force.   The details of either development would
lead far beyond the confines of this chapter, requiring for lucidity
the development of the above-mentioned invariant theory of
Minkowski space.   Let it be sufficient to say here that both of
these paths lead to identical results.   The results themselves are
the following.

Considering the mass of a particle invariant (the *rest mass*), we
find that the linear momentum to be assigned to a mass point with
the velocity **u** is

$$\mathbf{p} = \frac{m\,\mathbf{u}}{\sqrt{1 - u^2/c^2}}. \tag{12}$$

The expression $m/(1 - u^2/c^2)^{\frac{1}{2}}$, the coefficient of the velocity in
this formula, is often called the *relativistic mass* of the body.   The
total linear momentum of a system is the vector sum of the individual momenta.   The angular momentum of a mass point is
related to the linear momentum in precisely the same manner as
in ordinary mechanics.

The kinetic energy of a mass point is given by the formula

$$T = m\,c^2 \left( 1 - \frac{1}{\sqrt{1 - u^2/c^2}} \right). \tag{13}$$

A power-series development of this expression shows that it goes
over into the classical expression, $\frac{1}{2}m\,u^2$, if $u$ is very small compared
to $c$.   With these expressions for linear and angular momentum
and for the kinetic energy, the usual conservation laws are Lorentz
covariant.

There remains the expression for the force.   If we wish to define
force as the time rate of change of the linear momentum, then the
force expression follows from eq. (12),

$$f_i = \frac{d}{dt} \left( \frac{m\,u_i}{\sqrt{1 - u^2/c^2}} \right). \tag{14}$$

It can also be shown that this expression transforms in the same
manner as the right-hand side of the electrodynamic equations of
motion, (6.51).

Both in classical and in relativistic electrodynamics, it is possible
to bring the equations of motion into the form of the Euler-Lagrange
equations of a variational principle.   We shall immediately proceed

to find the appropriate *relativistic Lagrangian*, since the corresponding nonrelativistic expression can be obtained by going over to the limit of very slow motion. The equations of motion have the form

$$- \frac{d}{dt}\left(\frac{m\,\mathbf{u}}{\sqrt{1 - u^2/v^2}}\right) + e\left(\mathbf{E} + \frac{\mathbf{u}}{c} \times \mathbf{B}\right) = 0, \qquad (15)$$

and our task is to find a function $L$ of the coordinates as well as the velocity components so that these equations take the Euler-Lagrange form. The field components which appear here must be understood as the values of the "incident" field at the location of the particle at a particular time $t$, and they are, therefore, functions of the particle coordinates as well as $t$. Our task is greatly simplified if we introduce the electromagnetic potentials into eq. (15). Writing the equations in component notation, we get

$$e\left[-\Phi_{,i} - \frac{1}{c}\frac{\partial A_i}{\partial t} + \frac{u_s}{c}\left(A_{s,i} - A_{i,s}\right)\right] - \frac{d}{dt}\left(\frac{m\,u_i}{\sqrt{1 - u^2/c^2}}\right) = 0. \quad (16)$$

Two terms contain derivatives with respect to $x_i$, and we may conjecture that, among other terms, the Lagrangian contains these:

$$L = e\left(\frac{\mathbf{u} \cdot \mathbf{A}}{c} - \Phi\right) + \cdots. \qquad (17)$$

The last term in eq. (16) further leads us to try whether among other terms we have also

$$\frac{\partial L}{\partial u_s} = \frac{m\,u_s}{\sqrt{1 - u^2/c^2}} + \cdots, \qquad (18)$$

which would lead to a term in the Lagrangian of the form

$$L = m\,c^2(1 - \sqrt{1 - u^2/c^2}) + \cdots. \qquad (19)$$

Substitution of all these conjectured terms into the form of the Euler-Lagrange equations,

$$\frac{\partial L}{\partial x_s} - \frac{d}{dt}\left(\frac{\partial L}{\partial u_s}\right) = 0, \qquad (20)$$

shows that we have already obtained the complete expression for the Lagrangian,

$$L = m\,c^2(1 - \sqrt{1 - u^2/c^2}) - e\left(\Phi - \frac{\mathbf{u}}{c}\cdot\mathbf{A}\right). \qquad (21)$$

It follows that the appropriate expression for the canonically conjugate momentum in electrodynamics is

$$p_s = \frac{\partial L}{\partial u_s} = \frac{m\,u_s}{\sqrt{1 - u^2/c^2}} + \frac{e}{c}\,A_s, \qquad (22)$$

which leads to the Hamiltonian

$$H(x_s,\,p_s) = e\,\Phi + m\,c^2\left[\sqrt{1 + \frac{1}{m^2\,c^2}\left(\mathbf{p} - \frac{e}{c}\,\mathbf{A}\right)^2} - 1\right]. \qquad (23)$$

These expressions look rather formidable. They are, however, useful in applications, since they permit the computation of particle orbits in complex applied electromagnetic fields. One interesting application of our equations can be obtained for the theory of accelerating devices. The expression (23), like any Hamiltonian, represents the sum of the kinetic and potential energies of a particle in the field. Most accelerating devices (with the exception of electrostatic generators) accelerate the particles not by merely letting them pass through a stationary potential drop but by letting the applied field vary with time. In other words, in such devices the sum of potential and kinetic energy at the end of the particle orbit is greater than at the beginning. We can find an expression for the energy gain by means of eq. (2.35). The partial derivative of $H$ with respect to $t$ is

$$\frac{dH}{dt} \equiv \frac{\partial H}{\partial t} = e\,\frac{\partial \Phi}{\partial t} - \frac{\dfrac{e}{m\,c}\left(\mathbf{p} - \dfrac{e}{c}\,\mathbf{A}\right)\cdot\dfrac{\partial \mathbf{A}}{\partial t}}{\sqrt{1 + \dfrac{1}{m^2c^2}\left(\mathbf{p} - \dfrac{e}{c}\,\mathbf{A}\right)^2}}$$

$$= e\left(\frac{\partial \Phi}{\partial t} - \frac{\mathbf{u}}{c}\cdot\frac{\partial \mathbf{A}}{\partial t}\right), \qquad (24)$$

and this is the expression for the rate at which the particle gains energy.

## Problems

**9.1.** For a particle having a velocity along the $x_1$-axis $u$ with respect to system $B$, determine the velocity with respect to system $A$. The resulting formula is known as the *relativistic law for the addition of velocities*. Show that a body that has a velocity less than $c$ in one system will not have a velocity in excess of $c$ in another system.

**9.2.** With the help of the Lorentz transformation equations, derive the Lorentz contraction of scales and the formula for the rate of clocks in motion.

**9.3.** Show that the relativistic energy of a particle, just like the classical kinetic energy, increases at a rate that equals the dot product of its velocity and the rate of change of its linear momentum.

**9.4.** Carry out in detail the calculations which lead from the Lagrangian (21) to the Hamiltonian (23).

**9.5.** Discuss the principle of any of the well-known particle accelerators in terms of eq. (24).

**9.6.** Derive the equations of the Lorentz transformation if the velocity **v** of the system $B$ relative to $A$ has an arbitrary direction.

# Chapter 10

# Optics

As long as physics was divided into separate fields in accordance with the human senses of perception, optics was a well-defined field, that of visible light. But when Maxwell and Hertz discovered that light is no more than electromagnetic radiation in a particular frequency range in which the human eye happens to be sensitive, the realm of optics was expanded to include all high-frequency electromagnetic radiation, whether visible or not. At the same time, optics became a subdivision of electrodynamics. Naturally, the types of interaction of electromagnetic radiation with matter and the methods of producing and absorbing electromagnetic waves are very different in different frequency ranges. Nevertheless, the laws of propagation are broadly the same.

Primarily, optics is concerned with the effect of matter on the propagation of electromagnetic waves. When plane or spherical waves are made to pass through regions of space containing conductors or dielectrics, with inhomogeneities and with surfaces, then the original shape of the wave fronts is changed. Although we can envisage unlimited variations on the types of inhomogeneities that may affect the progress of traveling waves, certain types are of preeminent importance, and mathematical methods have been developed to cope with these situations.

If a dielectric or a conductor fills some well-defined domains of space and if $\kappa$ and $\mu$ are constant inside each domain, we must be concerned primarily with the *refraction* and *reflection* by the surfaces on which the index of refraction changes discontinuously. If the bounding surfaces possess sharp edges or corners, we have, moreover, *diffraction*. On the other hand, $\kappa$ and $\mu$ may be continuous, slowly variable functions of the space coordinates. In such a situation, reflection and diffraction are usually negligible, but refraction may still be significant. Piecewise-constant optical properties are realized in optical instruments with lenses and mirrors, and the atmosphere provides an example of continuously variable optical parameters, since the dielectric constant of air depends both on its density and its temperature.  If very small inhomogeneities are dispersed in an otherwise homogeneous medium, each inhomogeneity will act as a secondary source of a spherical wave; it will *scatter*.  If the scatterers possess a regular arrangement, as they do in diffraction gratings and in crystals, then these many secondary spherical waves will interfere with each other and lead to sharp diffraction maxima.  These maxima are very pronounced when X-rays are scattered by the lattice points of crystals, and X-ray diffraction patterns are a powerful tool for the investigation of molecular and atomic arrangements in the crystal.

In this chapter, we shall treat refraction and reflection in isotropic media in which any nonlinearity of the relationship between applied field and resulting polarization can be disregarded.  Occasionally, we shall also assume that the permeability is 1, usually a very good approximation.  Even with these restrictions, we shall be able to discuss most of the typically optical phenomena.

## 10.1. The wave equation

For the discussion of optics, we shall again separate electric from magnetic quantities by going over to the second-order wave equations.  We repeat here the derivation of the wave equation from Maxwell's equations because it is necessary to consider the *variability* of $\kappa$ and $\mu$, something which we had no occasion to do before.  We shall rewrite Maxwell's equations in terms of **E** and **B,** assuming that $\kappa$ and $\mu$ are functions of the $x_s$ but not of the time $t$.  As always in the study of waves, we shall assume the absence of free charges and currents.  The field equations are then

$$\operatorname{div} (\kappa \, \mathbf{E}) = 0, \qquad \operatorname{div} \mathbf{B} = 0,$$
$$\operatorname{curl} \mathbf{E} + \frac{1}{c} \frac{\partial \mathbf{B}}{\partial t} = 0, \tag{1}$$
$$\operatorname{curl} \left( \frac{\mathbf{B}}{\mu} \right) - \frac{\kappa}{c} \frac{\partial \mathbf{E}}{\partial t} = 0.$$

Since we are now interested only in waves, not in static fields, the first two equations are already contained in the remainder: If we take the divergence of each of the last two sets of equations, the first term in each case vanishes identically, and it follows that the time rate of change of the divergences of **D** and of **B** vanishes. These equations permit, at most, constant fields that violate the divergence relations. If we wish to eliminate the magnetic field from the last two equations, we can do so, but with some effort. We have to set

$$\frac{\partial}{\partial t}\left[\operatorname{curl}\left(\frac{\mathbf{B}}{\mu}\right) - \frac{\kappa}{c}\frac{\partial \mathbf{E}}{\partial t}\right] - \operatorname{curl}\left[\frac{1}{\mu}\left(\operatorname{curl}\mathbf{E} + \frac{1}{c}\frac{\partial \mathbf{B}}{\partial t}\right)\right]$$

$$= -\frac{\kappa}{c}\frac{\partial^2 \mathbf{E}}{\partial t^2} - \operatorname{curl}\left(\frac{1}{\mu}\operatorname{curl}\mathbf{E}\right) \tag{2}$$

$$= -\frac{\kappa}{c}\frac{\partial^2 \mathbf{E}}{\partial t^2} + \frac{1}{\mu}(\nabla^2 \mathbf{E} - \operatorname{grad}\operatorname{div}\mathbf{E}) + \frac{\operatorname{grad}\mu}{\mu^2} \times \operatorname{curl}\mathbf{E} = 0.$$

After further simplifications, we end up with the three equations

$$\nabla^2 E_i - \frac{\kappa\mu}{c^2}\frac{\partial^2 E_i}{\partial t^2} + \frac{\mu_{,s}}{\mu}(E_{s,i} - E_{i,s}) + \left(\frac{\kappa_{,s}}{\kappa}E_s\right)_{,i} = 0, \tag{3}$$

which are not entirely separated, although **B** does no longer occur in them.

The equations would, of course, be easier to handle if they could be entirely separated. However, all the terms which introduce components of **E** into the "wrong" equations contain either the gradient of the permeability or that of the dielectric constant. As long as these quantities change much more slowly than the field variables (more precisely, as long as the product of the logarithmic gradient of either of these quantities, multiplied by the wave length, is small compared with 1), these first- and zero-order terms can be safely omitted for many purposes. In such cases, we have to deal just with the ordinary wave equation, but with a slowly varying index of refraction.

Naturally, the cross terms may not be omitted when the change in $\mu$ or in $\kappa$ is abrupt. On the contrary, in that case it is just the cross terms which produce the standard *transition conditions*. These transition conditions can be obtained by considering first a finite change of $\kappa$ and $\mu$ over a very short distance and then going over to the limit of that distance converging toward zero. Let us carry our calculations through at a point where the gradient of these two quantities is in the $x_1$-direction. We start out with the component equations

$$E_{1,11} + (E_{1,22} + E_{1,33}) - \frac{\kappa \mu}{c^2} \frac{\partial^2 E_1}{\partial t^2} + (\ln \mu)_{,s}(E_{s,1} - E_{1,s})$$

$$+ [(\ln \kappa)_{,1} E_1]_{,1} + [(\ln \kappa)_{,2} E_2 + (\ln \kappa)_{,3} E_3]_{,1} = 0,$$

$$E_{2,11} + (E_{2,22} + E_{2,33}) - \frac{\kappa \mu}{c^2} \frac{\partial^2 E_2}{\partial t^2} + (\ln \mu)_{,s}(E_{s,2} - E_{2,s}). \tag{4}$$

$$+ [(\ln \kappa)_{,s} E_s]_{,2} = 0,$$

etc.

They contain quantities which are differentiated with respect to $x_1$ twice, once, and not at all. In order to examine conditions for the limit in which we are interested, we can carry out an integration across the direction of rapid change and choose our integral so that none of the terms in the integrand will give an infinite contribution in the limit. In the choice of such an integral, we shall use a formula that relates a function to its second derivative,

$$y(x) - y(x_0) = (x - x_0) y'(x_0) + \int_{\xi = x_0}^{x} (x - \xi) y''(\xi) \, d\xi. \tag{5}$$

This equation can be verified easily by continued differentiation and by careful attention to the constants of integration that are dropped through differentiation. If we now choose our path of integration as a short straight line parallel to the $x_1$-axis and so that the two end points lie on opposite sides of the region of rapid rise, we can, by first taking the first eq. (4), obtain the relationship

$$\Delta E_1 + \int_{x_0}^{x} (x - \xi)\{(\ln \mu)_{,2} \, dE_2 + (\ln \mu)_{,3} \, dE_3 + d[(\ln \kappa)_{,s} E_s]\}$$

$$- (x - x_0) E_{1,1}(x_0) + \int_{x_0}^{x} (x - \xi) \left[ E_{1,22} + E_{1,33} \right. \tag{6}$$

$$\left. - \frac{\kappa \mu}{c^2} \frac{\partial^2 E_1}{\partial t^2} - (\ln \mu)_{,2} E_{1,2} - (\ln \mu)_{,3} E_{1,3} \right] d\xi = 0.$$

The first term is the difference in the value of $E_1$ at the two end points of integration. Before we can shrink the region of change, it is advisable to carry out an integration by parts on the last term in the first integral. We get

$$\int_{x_0}^{x} (x - \xi) d[(\ln \kappa)_{,s} E_s] = \left[ \int_{x_0}^{x} (x - \xi)(\ln \kappa)_{,s} E_s \right]$$

$$+ \int_{x_0}^{x} (\ln \kappa)_{,s} E_s \, d\xi = \left[ \int_{x_0}^{x} (x - \xi)(\ln \kappa)_{,s} E_s \right] + \int_{x_0}^{x} [(\ln \kappa)_{,2} E_2 \tag{7}$$

$$+ (\ln \kappa)_{,3} E_3] \, d\xi + \int_{x_0}^{x} E_1 \, d(\ln \kappa).$$

By this series of transformations, we have obtained a number of integrals and other expressions which will all remain convergent even if some of the variables change discontinuously. We shall now shrink the path of integration toward zero, but so that the end points lie outside the singular region. That is, at the end points themselves none of the derivatives will become infinite. Let us look at all the terms.

The first term in eq. (6) will remain just the difference in $E_1$ on the two sides of the interface. In the first integral, only the last term will make a contribution, which we shall evaluate in a moment with the help of eq. (7). The remaining terms in eq. (6) all converge toward zero. Turning back to the term that has been treated in eq. (7), we find that after the transformation all contributions will converge toward zero except for the last integral on the right-hand side. We find, therefore, that our lengthy expressions reduce to

$$\Delta E_1 + \int_{x_0}^{x} E_1 \, d(\ln \kappa) = 0. \tag{8}$$

This expression can also be written in the form

$$\int_{x_0}^{x} [dE_1 + E_1 \, d(\ln \kappa)] = \int_{x_0}^{x} \frac{1}{\kappa} \, d(\kappa \, E_1) = 0, \tag{9}$$

and we come to the conclusion that this condition can be satisfied only if the differentiated expression does not change a finite amount along the path of integration,

$$\Delta(\kappa \, E_1) = 0. \tag{10}$$

An analogous but somewhat simpler evaluation of the remaining eqs. (6) leads to the further results

$$\Delta E_2 = \Delta E_3 = 0. \tag{11}$$

If we had eliminated the electric field in order to get wave equations for the components of the magnetic field, we should have obtained quite similar cross terms, leading to the transition conditions

$$\Delta B_1 = \Delta \left( \frac{B_2}{\mu} \right) = \Delta \left( \frac{B_3}{\mu} \right) = 0. \tag{12}$$

The transition conditions (10), (11), and (12) are identical with those obtained in Problem 5.4, but the present derivation is based on the wave equations exclusively, without the divergence relations. The earlier result had been predicated on electrostatic and magnetostatic laws.

Instead of dealing with the field strengths directly, we can also work with the vector potential. First, by means of a gauge transformation, we shall eliminate the scalar potential $\Phi$. The quantities **E** and **B** are then given by the expressions

$$\mathbf{B} = \text{curl } \mathbf{A}, \qquad \mathbf{E} = -\frac{1}{c}\frac{\partial \mathbf{A}}{\partial t}, \tag{13}$$

and two of the four field equations (1) are satisfied identically. The remaining equations take the form

$$\text{div}\left(\frac{\kappa}{c}\frac{\partial \mathbf{A}}{\partial t}\right) = 0,$$

$$\frac{1}{\mu}\text{ curl curl } \mathbf{A} - \frac{\text{grad }\mu}{\mu^2} \times \text{curl } \mathbf{A} + \frac{\kappa}{c^2}\frac{\partial^2 \mathbf{A}}{\partial t^2} = 0. \tag{14}$$

The first of these equations can be integrated once, leading to

$$\text{div }(\kappa \mathbf{A}) = \kappa[\text{div } \mathbf{A} + \text{grad }(\ln \kappa) \cdot \mathbf{A}] = 0. \tag{15}$$

Time-independent components are to be discarded, as usual in wave-field investigations. The remaining equations can be separated with respect to the second-order terms with the help of the divergence relationship (15). The wave equations for **A** become

$$\nabla^2 \mathbf{A} - \frac{\kappa \mu}{c^2}\frac{\partial^2 \mathbf{A}}{\partial t^2} + \text{grad }[\text{grad }(\ln \kappa) \cdot \mathbf{A}] + \text{grad }(\ln \mu) \times \text{curl } \mathbf{A} = 0. \tag{16}$$

They have exactly the same form as the wave equations for **E**. Given a vector field which satisfies eqs. (16) and (15), **E** and **B** can be found without further integrations, with the help of eqs. (13).

## 10.2. Interfaces

In this section, we shall examine what happens to a plane wave that strikes the interface separating two dielectrics. The interface shall be chosen as simply as possible, an infinitely extended plane. On each side of this plane, the dielectric constant and the permeability are constant; but they are not the same on both sides. We shall identify the two sides of the interface by means of the subscripts $a$ and $b$. It is well known that part of the energy passes the interface and continues into the other medium, while part is reflected back. Both the refracted and the reflected waves are plane waves again. Their directions as well as their amplitudes can be obtained by means of the transition conditions. We shall begin by recapitulating the pertinent facts about the plane waves in the interior of the dielectric.

A plane wave can be represented in the form

$$\mathbf{A} = \mathbf{A}_0 f\left(t - \frac{\mathbf{n} \cdot \mathbf{x}}{c_0}\right) \qquad \left(\mathbf{n} \cdot \mathbf{H}_0 = 0, \quad c_0 = \frac{c}{\sqrt{\kappa \mu}}\right). \qquad (17)$$

$\mathbf{n}$ is a unit vector that represents the direction of propagation. It is normal to the wave fronts. $\mathbf{A}_0$ is a constant vector that represents both the amplitude and the polarization of the plane wave. $f$ is an arbitrary function of its argument. If the wave is sinusoidal, it can be represented in the form

$$\mathbf{A} = \mathbf{A}_0 \cos\left[\omega\left(t - \frac{\mathbf{n} \cdot \mathbf{x}}{c_0}\right)\right]. \qquad (18)$$

The electric and magnetic field strengths are

$$\mathbf{E} = -\frac{1}{c}\mathbf{A}_0 f', \qquad \mathbf{H} = -\frac{1}{c}\sqrt{\frac{\kappa}{\mu}}(\mathbf{n} \times \mathbf{A}_0) f', \qquad (19)$$

and the energy flux, which is determined by Poynting's vector, turns out to be

$$\mathbf{P} = \frac{1}{4\pi c}\sqrt{\frac{\kappa}{\mu}} A_0^2 f'^2 \mathbf{n}. \qquad (20)$$

We shall now determine three plane waves—the incident and the reflected wave in the medium $(a)$ and the transmitted (refracted) wave in the medium $(b)$—in such a manner that on the interface the transition conditions are satisfied; that is, the tangential components of $\mathbf{A}$ and the normal component of $\kappa \mathbf{A}$ are continuous across the interface.

We shall choose a coordinate system so that the interface passes through the origin, and we shall call the unit vector normal to this plane $\mathbf{m}$. The quantities relating to the incident wave shall be identified by means of the roman numeral subscript I, those relating to the reflected wave by the subscript II, and those belonging to the refracted wave by III. The coordinates of points that lie on the interface can be written in the form

$$\mathbf{x} = \boldsymbol{\xi} - \mathbf{m}(\mathbf{m} \cdot \boldsymbol{\xi}) \equiv (\mathbf{m} \times \boldsymbol{\xi}) \times \mathbf{m}, \qquad (21)$$

where $\boldsymbol{\xi}$ is three *arbitrary* numbers. The vector potential in one medium will be

$$\mathbf{A}_a = \mathbf{A}_\mathrm{I} \cdot f\left(t - \frac{\sqrt{\kappa_a \mu_a}}{c} \mathbf{n}_\mathrm{I} \cdot \mathbf{x}\right) + \mathbf{A}_\mathrm{II} \cdot f\left(t - \frac{\sqrt{\kappa_a \mu_a}}{c} \mathbf{n}_\mathrm{II} \cdot \mathbf{x}\right); \quad (22)$$

that in the other medium,

$$\mathbf{A}_b = \mathbf{A}_\mathrm{III} \cdot f\left(t - \frac{\sqrt{\kappa_b \mu_b}}{c} \mathbf{n}_\mathrm{III} \cdot \mathbf{x}\right). \qquad (23)$$

The transition conditions can be written in the form

$$\begin{aligned}
\mathbf{m} &\times (\mathbf{A}_a - \mathbf{A}_b) = 0, \\
\mathbf{m} &\cdot (\kappa_a \mathbf{A}_a - \kappa_b \mathbf{A}_b) = 0, \\
\mathbf{m} &\times \left(\frac{1}{\mu_a} \operatorname{curl} \mathbf{A}_a - \frac{1}{\mu_b} \operatorname{curl} \mathbf{A}_b\right) = 0,
\end{aligned} \qquad [\mathbf{x} = \boldsymbol{\xi} - \mathbf{m}(\mathbf{m} \cdot \boldsymbol{\xi})]. \quad (24)$$

These conditions can be satisfied for all conceivable $\boldsymbol{\xi}$ only if the arguments of the three functions $f$ are all the same. In other words, we have as the first requirements

$$(\mathbf{n}_\mathrm{I} - \mathbf{n}_\mathrm{II}) \cdot [\boldsymbol{\xi} - \mathbf{m}(\mathbf{m} \cdot \boldsymbol{\xi})] \equiv 0,$$
$$\text{or} \qquad (\mathbf{n}_\mathrm{I} - \mathbf{n}_\mathrm{II}) \times \mathbf{m} = 0, \qquad (25)$$

for the reflected wave and

$$(\sqrt{\kappa_a \mu_a}\, \mathbf{n}_\mathrm{I} - \sqrt{\kappa_b \mu_b}\, \mathbf{n}_\mathrm{III}) \cdot [\boldsymbol{\xi} - \mathbf{m}(\mathbf{m} \cdot \boldsymbol{\xi})] \equiv 0,$$
$$\text{or} \qquad (\sqrt{\kappa_a \mu_a}\, \mathbf{n}_\mathrm{I} - \sqrt{\kappa_b \mu_b}\, \mathbf{n}_\mathrm{III}) \times \mathbf{m} = 0, \qquad (26)$$

for the refracted wave. With given $\mathbf{n}_\mathrm{I}$, each of these two equations has two solutions, pointing toward opposite sides of the interface. The $\mathbf{n}_\mathrm{II}$ that points back into medium ($a$) and the $\mathbf{n}_\mathrm{III}$ that points forward into the medium ($b$) are physically significant. These solutions are

$$n_{II} = n_I - 2(m \cdot n_I)m,$$

$$n_{III} = \sqrt{\frac{\kappa_a \mu_a}{\kappa_b \mu_b}} \, n_I - \left[ \sqrt{\frac{\kappa_a \mu_a}{\kappa_b \mu_b}} \, (m \cdot n_I) \right. \tag{27}$$
$$\left. - \sqrt{1 - \frac{\kappa_a \mu_a}{\kappa_b \mu_b} [1 - (m \cdot n_I)^2]} \right] m.$$

They contain the laws of reflection and of refraction. First of all, both the reflected and the refracted wave normals lie in the plane of the incident wave normal $n_I$ and the interface normal $m$. The sine of the angle of incidence is equal in magnitude to the cross product of $n_I$ and $m$, and similar expressions formed with $n_{II}$ and with $n_{III}$, respectively, give the sines of the angles of reflection and refraction. By direct computation, the angle of reflection equals the angle of incidence; and the ratio of the sines of the angles of refraction and of incidence equals a constant, the ratio of the refractive indices

$$\nu = \frac{\nu_a}{\nu_b} = \frac{\sqrt{\kappa_a \mu_a}}{\sqrt{\kappa_b \mu_b}}. \tag{28}$$

This last law is Snell's law.

Once the various normals have been made to satisfy the relations (28), the transition conditions (24) reduce to relationships between the amplitude vectors,

$$m \times (A_I + A_{II} - A_{III}) = 0,$$
$$m \cdot [\kappa_a(A_I + A_{II}) - \kappa_b A_{III}] = 0,$$
$$m \times \left[ \sqrt{\frac{\kappa_a}{\mu_a}} (n_I \times A_I + n_{II} \times A_{II}) - \sqrt{\frac{\kappa_b}{\mu_b}} n_{III} \times A_{III} \right] = 0, \tag{29}$$
$$n_I \cdot A_I = n_{II} \cdot A_{II} = n_{III} \cdot A_{III} = 0.$$

In order to solve these equations, we shall decompose the incident plane wave into two plane-polarized components, one parallel to the interface, the other parallel to the plane of incidence (the plane defined by $n_I$ and $m$). The transmissivity of the interface to these two components is not the same, and as a result the reflected and the transmitted waves in general change their planes of polarization. The decomposition into the two components described above is the decomposition into the two "principal" directions, those in which the relationship of the incident wave to the plane of incidence remains unchanged.

Let us first treat the component in which $\mathbf{A}_I$, $\mathbf{A}_{II}$, and $\mathbf{A}_{III}$ are all perpendicular to $\mathbf{m}$. In that case, the eqs. (29) reduce to

$$A_I + A_{II} - A_{III} = 0,$$

$$\sqrt{\frac{\kappa_a}{\mu_a}} \cos \theta_I \cdot (A_I - A_{II}) - \sqrt{\frac{\kappa_b}{\mu_b}} \cos \theta_{III} \cdot A_{III} = 0, \qquad (30)$$

$$\cos \theta_I = \mathbf{m} \cdot \mathbf{n}_I, \qquad \cos \theta_{III} = \mathbf{m} \cdot \mathbf{n}_{III},$$

the other equations being satisfied automatically. The $A$-quantities (italics) represent the components under consideration. The solution of these equations is

$$\frac{A_{II}}{A_I} = \frac{\sqrt{\kappa_a/\mu_a} \cos \theta_I - \sqrt{\kappa_b/\mu_b} \cos \theta_{III}}{\sqrt{\kappa_a/\mu_a} \cos \theta_I + \sqrt{\kappa_b/\mu_b} \cos \theta_{III}},$$

$$\frac{A_{III}}{A_I} = \frac{2 \sqrt{\kappa_a/\mu_a} \cos \theta_I}{\sqrt{\kappa_a/\mu_a} \cos \theta_I + \sqrt{\kappa_b/\mu_b} \cos \theta_{III}}. \qquad (31)$$

We can give these equations a more convenient form by application of Snell's law in the form

$$\sqrt{\frac{\kappa_a}{\mu_a}} \sqrt{\frac{\mu_b}{\kappa_b}} = \frac{\mu_b}{\mu_a} \frac{\sin \theta_{III}}{\sin \theta_I}. \qquad (32)$$

After the application of some trigonometric addition formulas, the expressions (31) take the form

$$\frac{A_{II}}{A_I} = \frac{(\mu_b - \mu_a) \sin (\theta_I + \theta_{III}) - (\mu_b + \mu_a) \sin (\theta_I - \theta_{III})}{(\mu_b + \mu_a) \sin (\theta_I + \theta_{III}) - (\mu_b - \mu_a) \sin (\theta_I - \theta_{III})},$$

$$\frac{A_{III}}{A_I} = \frac{2\mu_b[\sin (\theta_I + \theta_{III}) - \sin (\theta_I - \theta_{III})]}{(\mu_b + \mu_a) \sin (\theta_I + \theta_{III}) - (\mu_b - \mu_a) \sin (\theta_I - \theta_{III})}, \qquad (33)$$

which is specially suitable in the important case that the permeabilities are both equal to 1. The division of energy into the reflected and into the refracted wave can be computed by the application of eq. (20).

We shall now turn to the treatment of the other case, in which the vector potentials all lie in the plane of incidence. Here it is best to introduce the components of the magnetic field strength $\mathbf{H}$, since

$$\mathbf{H} = -\frac{1}{c}\sqrt{\frac{\kappa}{\mu}}\,(\mathbf{n} \times \mathbf{A}_0)\,f',$$

$$\mathbf{A}_0 = c\sqrt{\frac{\mu}{\kappa}}\frac{1}{f'}\,(\mathbf{n} \times \mathbf{H}). \tag{34}$$

These equations show that if the vector potential lies in the plane of incidence, then the magnetic field strength is parallel to the interface or, in other words, perpendicular to both $\mathbf{m}$ and $\mathbf{n}$. Furthermore, the amplitude of the magnetic field strength can be related algebraically to the amplitude vector of the vector potential. It follows that we can express the transition conditions (29) conveniently in terms of the three amplitude quantities $H_{\mathrm{I}}$, $H_{\mathrm{II}}$, and $H_{\mathrm{III}}$, which represent the mutually parallel magnetic field strength amplitudes of the incident, the reflected, and the transmitted wave, respectively. Substitution of the expression (34) into the transition equations (29) yields only two equations which are independent of each other,

$$H_{\mathrm{I}} + H_{\mathrm{II}} - H_{\mathrm{III}} = 0,$$

$$\sqrt{\frac{\mu_a}{\kappa_a}}\cos\theta_{\mathrm{I}}\,(H_{\mathrm{I}} - H_{\mathrm{II}}) - \sqrt{\frac{\mu_b}{\kappa_b}}\cos\theta_{\mathrm{III}}\,H_{\mathrm{III}} = 0. \tag{35}$$

These equations are very similar to eqs. (30). The roles of $\kappa$ and $\mu$ have been exchanged, a natural consequence, since now the magnetic field strengths occupy the position held previously by the electric field strengths. The solution of this system of equations is

$$\frac{H_{\mathrm{II}}}{H_{\mathrm{I}}} = \frac{\sqrt{\dfrac{\mu_a}{\kappa_a}}\cos\theta_{\mathrm{I}} - \sqrt{\dfrac{\mu_b}{\kappa_b}}\cos\theta_{\mathrm{III}}}{\sqrt{\dfrac{\mu_a}{\kappa_a}}\cos\theta_{\mathrm{I}} + \sqrt{\dfrac{\mu_b}{\kappa_b}}\cos\theta_{\mathrm{III}}},$$

$$\frac{H_{\mathrm{III}}}{H_{\mathrm{I}}} = \frac{2\sqrt{\dfrac{\mu_a}{\kappa_a}}\cos\theta_{\mathrm{I}}}{\sqrt{\dfrac{\mu_a}{\kappa_a}}\cos\theta_{\mathrm{I}} + \sqrt{\dfrac{\mu_b}{\kappa_b}}\cos\theta_{\mathrm{III}}}. \tag{36}$$

If we now eliminate again the dielectric constants, as we did previously with the help of Snell's law, eq. (32), it turns out that we can transform the solution with the help of trigonometric transformations into either of two forms:

$$\frac{H_{\text{II}}}{H_{\text{I}}} = \frac{\mu_a \sin 2\,\theta_{\text{I}} - \mu_b \sin 2\theta_{\text{III}}}{\mu_a \sin 2\,\theta_{\text{I}} + \mu_b \sin 2\theta_{\text{III}}}$$

$$= \frac{(\mu_a - \mu_b) \tan (\theta_{\text{I}} + \theta_{\text{III}}) + (\mu_a + \mu_b) \tan (\theta_{\text{I}} - \theta_{\text{III}})}{(\mu_a + \mu_b) \tan (\theta_{\text{I}} + \theta_{\text{III}}) + (\mu_a - \mu_b) \tan (\theta_{\text{I}} - \theta_{\text{III}})},$$

$$\frac{H_{\text{III}}}{H_{\text{I}}} = \frac{2\mu_a \sin 2\theta_{\text{I}}}{\mu_a \sin 2\theta_{\text{I}} + \mu_b \sin 2\theta_{\text{III}}} \tag{37}$$

$$= \frac{2\mu_a \left[\tan (\theta_{\text{I}} + \theta_{\text{III}}) + \tan (\theta_{\text{I}} - \theta_{\text{III}})\right]}{(\mu_a + \mu_b) \tan (\theta_{\text{I}} + \theta_{\text{III}}) + (\mu_a - \mu_b) \tan (\theta_{\text{I}} - \theta_{\text{III}})}.$$

If the permeabilities are very close to 1, as they almost always are, the differences between the results (33) and (37), which apply to different states of polarization for the incident waves, can be given a striking interpretation. If the electric vector is in the plane of the interface, there will always be a reflected wave, no matter what the angle of incidence. But if the magnetic vector is parallel to the plane of the interface, then there is one angle of incidence for which the reflected wave has zero amplitude. There will be no reflection when the sum of the angle of incidence and the angle of refraction, $(\theta_{\text{I}} + \theta_{\text{III}})$, equals $\pi/2$. In that case, a reflecting dielectric surface will act as a perfect polarizer. If the states of polarization of the incident wave are mixed, then the reflected wave will contain only waves whose magnetic vector is parallel to the reflecting surface. This particular angle of incidence is, therefore, called the *polarizing angle* of the interface. If the permeabilities are not precisely 1, the polarizing angle still exists, but it is not the angle at which the incident and the refracted angle are exactly complementary. The general formula for the polarizing angle is

$$\tan \theta_{\text{I}} = \sqrt{\frac{\kappa_b\,\mu_b}{\kappa_a\,\mu_a}} \sqrt{\frac{\dfrac{\mu_a}{\mu_b}\,\kappa_b - \kappa_a}{\dfrac{\mu_b}{\mu_a}\,\kappa_b - \kappa_a}}. \tag{38}$$

## 10.3. Waves and rays

In this section, we shall deal primarily with an electromagnetic wave that is spreading in a medium in which the dielectric constant and the magnetic permeability are continuous and slowly varying functions of the space coordinates only. By "slowly varying" we mean that $\kappa$ and $\mu$ change their values only slightly over a distance of the order of the pulse length or wave length of the traveling wave.

Later we shall formulate this condition mathematically. For the time being, we shall merely attempt to describe the wave pattern at each location as if it could be approximated by a plane wave.

For such an approximation to make sense, two conditions must be satisfied. Not only must the optical properties of the transmitting medium be fairly constant over the period of one wave length, as indicated above, but the wave fronts must be fairly straight. Our experience with the Hertz oscillator in Chapter 8 has shown that close to a center of excitation the electromagnetic wave is far different from a plane wave traveling in the same medium. At great distances, in the wave zone, the local wave has in good approximation all the properties of a plane electromagnetic wave: its electric and magnetic field strengths are mutually perpendicular to each other and to the direction of (radial) propagation, and they are equal in magnitude. "At great distances" is again defined in terms of the wave length or, in the case of a nonsinusoidal pulse shape, in terms of some similar characteristic length.

If we wish to approximate an unknown wave in terms of a plane wave, we might try to separate local amplitude from local phase. If the pulse is traveling through space without distortion, we could attempt to represent the magnetic potential in the form

$$\mathbf{A}(\mathbf{x},\, t) = \mathbf{A}_0(\mathbf{x}) \cdot f\left[ t - \frac{1}{c}\, S(\mathbf{x}) \right]. \tag{39}$$

$\mathbf{A}_0$ would be the local amplitude and time-independent. $f(t)$ would be the pulse profile at the origin of the wave, and $S$ would again be a time-independent function of the location, possessing the dimension of a length (sometimes called the *optical path length*) and, when divided by $c$, indicating the time the wave takes to travel to the point $\mathbf{x}$ from the center of excitation.

Again, the experience gained in Chapter 8 shows that this approach is not feasible. Even in the absence of dielectric media, the very curvature of the wave fronts makes for dispersion and for the attendant distortion of the original pulse shape. If we were to carry out a Fourier analysis of this original pulse shape $f(t)$ and follow each Fourier component on its travel throughout space, we should find that the attenuation, the ratio between the local amplitude and the amplitude at or near the center, is a function of frequency. Since the process of wave propagation is dispersive, with the single exception of a truly plane wave traveling through empty space, we can attempt our "quasi plane-wave representation" (39) only for trigonometric waves; we shall start with the trial solution

$$\mathbf{A}(\mathbf{x},\, t) = \mathbf{A}_0(\mathbf{x}) \cdot \cos\left[\omega\left(t - \frac{1}{c}\,S(\mathbf{x})\right)\right] \tag{40}$$

and substitute it into eqs. (15) and (16).

The result of these substitutions is a set of equations that contain terms multiplied either by the sine or by the cosine of the argument $[\omega(t - S/c)]$. If the equations are to hold for all values of $t$, then the sine terms and the cosine terms must vanish separately. By carrying out the necessary steps himself, the reader can verify easily that the resulting time-free equations are

$$\frac{\omega^2}{c^2}\,(\kappa\,\mu - S_{,s}\,S_{,s})A_i + A_{i,ss} + \left(\frac{\kappa_{,s}}{\kappa}\,A_s\right)_{\!,i}$$

$$+\,\frac{\mu_{,s}}{\mu}\,(A_{s,i} - A_{i,s}) = 0,$$

$$2A_{i,s}\,S_{,s} + A_i\,S_{ss} + \left(\frac{\kappa_{,s}}{\kappa} + \frac{\mu_{,s}}{\mu}\right)S_{,i}\,A_s - \frac{\mu_{,s}}{\mu}\,S_{,s}\,A_i = 0, \tag{41}$$

$$(\kappa\,A_s)_{,s} = 0,$$

$$A_s\,S_{,s} = 0.$$

This set of equations has one extremely conspicuous property: it is much more involved than the original set (15), (16). Its complexity need not deter us, though, if we can obtain simpler equations by means of an approximation method. Equations (41) possess another, and more desirable, property: the angular frequency $\omega$ occurs in only one spot, in the first set of equations. That is, most of the laws contained in this set of equations will be independent of the frequency.

A further interpretation of the equations is greatly facilitated if we consider that the surfaces $S$ = constant are the wave fronts of the pattern; that is, the electric field strength as a function of time goes through its zeros simultaneously all along these surfaces. The gradient of $S$ is, therefore, parallel to the wave normal. It differs from our usual unit vector $\mathbf{n}$ only in that its magnitude is not normalized. However, the meaning of the last equation (41) is quite clear: the vector potential amplitude is perpendicular to the wave normal everywhere in space. We can, thus, again speak of a local plane of polarization, the one defined by the directions of the vectors $\mathbf{A}_0$ and grad $S$.

We shall now turn to the interpretation of the second set of eqs. (41). We shall find that they contain three separate physical laws governing the propagation of the waves. The first law is obtained by multiplying these equations by $A_i \atop 0$. We find, as a result of this operation,

$$A_i \atop 0 \left[ 2 A_{i,s} \atop 0 S_{,s} + A_i \atop 0 S_{,ss} + \left( \frac{\kappa_{,s}}{\kappa} + \frac{\mu_{,s}}{\mu} \right) \underline{S_{,i} A_s \atop 0} - \frac{\mu_{,s}}{\mu} S_{,s} A_i \atop 0 \right]$$
$$= \mu \left( \frac{1}{\mu} A^2 \atop 0 S_{,s} \right)_{,s} = 0, \qquad (42)$$
$$\text{div} \left( \frac{1}{\mu} A^2 \atop 0 \text{ grad } S \right) = 0.$$

The underscored term vanishes identically, because of the last eq. (41). The remaining terms can be put together easily to yield a divergence relationship. This divergence relationship is closely linked to the conservation law of energy. It states, as we shall see shortly, that the divergence of the average value of Poynting's vector, eq. (20), vanishes in this stationary wave field.

Before we can prove that the parenthesis in the last eq. (42) is proportional to Poynting's vector, we shall have first to evaluate the first eq. (41). We have previously stated that our approximation can be meaningful only if both the radii of curvature of the wave fronts and the distance over which $\kappa$ and $\mu$ change appreciably are large compared to the wave length. Given the distribution of matter and the rough shape of the wave fronts, we can turn our conditions around and declare that our approximation is realistic only if we choose the angular frequency $\omega$ sufficiently large. Since the wave length is inversely proportional to the frequency, choice of a high frequency implies a small wave length. Now we can choose $\omega$ so large that the first term of the first eq. (41) is very large compared with the remainder and vanishes by itself. To put it differently, we could consider all quantities expanded into power series in descending powers of $(\omega/c)$; the equation satisfied by the lowest approximation would then be

$$(\text{grad } S)^2 = \kappa \mu. \tag{43}$$

This equation is sometimes called the *eiconal equation* of ray optics (because the function $S$ is also called the eiconal). We shall return to it later, but now we shall use it only to remark that the magnitude of grad $S$ is, in this approximation, given by

$$|\text{grad } S| = \sqrt{\kappa \mu}. \tag{44}$$

Substitution in eq. (42) leads to

$$\text{div}\left(\sqrt{\frac{\kappa}{\mu}} A^2_{\ 0} \mathbf{n}\right) = 0. \tag{45}$$

The proportionality of the expression in the parenthesis to Poynting's vector, eq. (20), is now obvious.

The second relationship contained in the second eq. (41) is obtained by multiplication by $S_{,i}$. We find

$$S_{,i}\left[2A_{i,s}S_{,s} + A_i S_{,ss} + \left(\frac{\kappa_{,s}}{\kappa} + \frac{\mu_{,s}}{\mu}\right)S_{,i}A_s - \frac{\mu_{,s}}{\mu}S_{,s}A_i\right]$$

$$= -2A_i S_{,s}S_{,is} + (\text{grad } S)^2\left(\frac{\kappa_{,s}}{\kappa} + \frac{\mu_{,s}}{\mu}\right)A_s \tag{46}$$

$$= -\kappa \mu \mathbf{A} \cdot \text{grad}\left[\frac{(\text{grad } S)^2}{\kappa \mu}\right] = 0$$

This equation is a rigorous relationship, valid even if the approximation leading to the eiconal equation (43) is not. It states that the squared magnitude of grad $S$, divided through by the square of the refractive index, is constant along these curves to which the vector potential is everywhere tangential and which, because of the last eq. (41), lie wholly in their respective wave-front surfaces. If the eiconal equation is assumed to hold, then eq. (46) is, of course, satisfied identically.

If we multiply the second eq. (41) by a vector perpendicular both to grad $S$ and to $\mathbf{A}_0$, we must obtain the third and final law contained in it. Accordingly, we shall multiply by the cross product grad $S \times \mathbf{A}_0$. We have

$$\delta_{ikl}S_{,k}A_l\left[2A_{i,s}S_{,s} + A_i S_{,ss} + \left(\frac{\kappa_{,s}}{\kappa} + \frac{\mu_{,s}}{\mu}\right)S_{,i}A_s - \frac{\mu_{,s}}{\mu}S_{,s}A_i\right] = 0. \tag{47}$$

Each of the underscored terms gives a zero contribution because of the complete antisymmetry of the Levi-Civita pseudotensor. The lone remaining term can be rewritten in the form

$$\delta_{ikl} \underset{0}{A_{i,s}} S_{,k} \underset{0}{A_l} S_{,s} = (\delta_{ikl} \underset{0}{A_i} S_{,k})_{,s} S_{,s} \underset{0}{A_l}$$
$$= \mathbf{A}_0 \cdot [\text{grad } S \cdot \nabla(\mathbf{A}_0 \times \text{grad } S)] = 0. \quad (48)$$

The cross product of $\mathbf{A}_0$ and grad $S$ is perpendicular to the plane of polarization and, therefore, is in first approximation parallel to the magnetic field strength. It may certainly be used as an "indicator" of the plane of polarization. Equation (48) now states that the dot product of $\mathbf{A}_0$ and the change in the "indicator" in the direction of the wave normal vanishes. Now the changes in the "indicator" can be in three directions: parallel to itself (this would involve a change in magnitude only), parallel to grad $S$ (involving a rotation of the plane of polarization about $\mathbf{A}_0$ as the axis), and parallel to $\mathbf{A}_0$ (involving a rotation about grad $S$ or $\mathbf{n}$ as the axis). Equation (48) then states that a rotation about $\mathbf{n}$ cannot take place as we follow the progress of the wave along $\mathbf{n}$. The plane of polarization cannot "twist" like a screw.

As for the third eq. (41), it merely states that $\kappa \, \mathbf{A}_0$ is a divergence-free field. The remarkable fact is that once $S$ has been determined in accordance with the eiconal equation (43), the third and fourth eqs. (41) and eqs. (42), (46), and (48) can be satisfied merely by appropriate choice of $\mathbf{A}_0$. In other words, the conditions imposed on $\mathbf{A}_0$ by all the other relationships in no way restrict the freedom of choice among the solutions of the eiconal equation. In discussing the possible types of wave front patterns, we may restrict ourselves to an examination of eq. (43) alone.

Equation (43) is the mathematical expression for *Huygens's principle;* as such it provides the mathematical key to *geometrical optics.* Huygens's principle is a method for constructing wave fronts. Starting with one given wave front, we construct about each point on the wave front a small hemisphere whose radius is inversely proportional to the local index of refraction. The next wave front is then the envelope of all the hemispherical surfaces. Geometrically, Huygens's principle amounts to the requirement that the distances between two neighboring wave fronts at two different locations should be inversely proportional to the indices of refraction there.   Now if the wave fronts are the equipotential surfaces of some function $S$, then the gradient of $S$ represents the slope of $S$ at right anges to the equipotential surfaces and is inversely proportional to the distance between two wave fronts representing two fixed values $S_1$ and $S_2$.   |grad $S$|, according to Huygens's principle, must therefore be proportional to the index of refraction, and that is the requirement of eq. (43).

From Huygens's principle, we should be able to go over to the ordinary laws of ray optics, which refer to the trajectories of individual light rays.   In fact, we shall show that *eq. (43) leads to a set of ordinary differential equations for the orthogonal trajectories of the wave fronts.*   For this proof, we shall introduce the unit normal **n** into the eiconal equation.   About **n** the eiconal equation (43) gives us just one piece of information: multiplied by the index of refraction, $\nu$, it is the gradient of a function $S$.   In Chapter 7, we found that a vector field will be a gradient if and only if its curl vanishes.   The import of the eiconal equation for **n** is, therefore, that

$$\text{curl } (\nu \, \mathbf{n}) \equiv \text{grad } \nu \times \mathbf{n} + \nu \, \text{curl } \mathbf{n} = 0,$$
$$\text{curl } \mathbf{n} = \mathbf{n} \times \text{grad log } \nu \qquad (\nu = \sqrt{\kappa \, \mu}). \tag{49}$$

This equation can be decomposed into two separate equations, one expressing the change of **n** in the direction **n,** the other its change at right angles to itself.   By forming both the dot product and the cross product of the second equation (49) by **n**, we get, after a few changes, and observing that the magnitude of **n** as a unit vector remains constant, the equations

$$(\mathbf{n} \times \nabla) \cdot \mathbf{n} = 0 \tag{50}$$

and $\qquad (\mathbf{n} \cdot \nabla)\mathbf{n} = \text{grad log } \nu - \mathbf{n}(\mathbf{n} \cdot \text{grad log } \nu). \tag{51}$

Both equations are concerned with changes in the values of the components of **n** observed on moving from one point to a neighboring point.   But whereas the first equation deals with displacements at right angles to **n** itself, the second equation is concerned with displacements parallel to **n**.   We shall now proceed to show that if merely the second equation is satisfied, then the first equation assumes the character of an initial condition; that is, if it is satisfied on a single surface, then it will be satisfied everywhere.

We shall start with a surface which completely cuts space in two

and which is otherwise arbitrary. At each point, there exists a
normal to the surface, **m**. We shall now choose throughout the
surface a field of normals **n**, which shall satisfy merely one condition:
nowhere is **n** to be tangential to $S$ (that is, perpendicular to **m**).
In extending the field **n** beyond the surface $S$, we shall satisfy eq.
(51), without as yet paying any attention to eq. (50).

Now let us consider a closed curve lying wholly in $S$ and let us
form the closed-path integral

$$I = \oint \nu \, \mathbf{n} \cdot \mathbf{dl} = \oint \nu \, n_s \frac{dx_s}{d\lambda} \, d\lambda, \tag{52}$$

where $\lambda$ is some parameter along the curve introduced for the purpose of carrying out the integration. Next, we shall consider a
family of closed curves (including the original one) which are generated by moving each point of the original curve in a direction
parallel to **n**. In order to identify these generated curves, we shall
introduce a second parameter, $\beta$, which is constant along each one
of the closed curves and varies continuously as we pass on to
neighboring closed curves. We shall now examine the change in $I$
as we pass from curve to curve.

The principle by which we generate our family of closed curves
is described by the requirement that

$$\frac{\partial x_s(\lambda, \beta)}{\partial \beta} = a(\lambda, \beta) \, n_s, \tag{53}$$

where $a$ is an arbitrary function of its two arguments. With this
condition in mind, we find, for $dI/d\beta$:

$$
\begin{aligned}
\frac{dI}{d\beta} &= \oint \left[ \frac{\partial x_s}{\partial \lambda} (\nu \, n_s)_{,k} \, a \, n_k + \nu \, n_s \frac{\partial^2 x_s}{\partial \beta \, \partial \lambda} \right] d\lambda \\
&= \oint \left[ \frac{\partial x_s}{\partial \lambda} (\nu \, n_s)_{,k} \, a \, n_k + \nu \, n_s \frac{\partial}{\partial \lambda} (a \, n_s) \right] d\lambda \\
&= \oint \left[ (\nu \, n_s)_{,k} \, n_k \, a \, dx_s + \nu \frac{\partial a}{\partial \lambda} \, d\lambda \right] \\
&= \oint a[(\nu \, n_s)_{,k} \, n_k - \nu_{,s}] \, dx_s \\
&= \oint \nu \, a \left[ n_{s,k} \, n_k - \left( \frac{\nu_{,s}}{\nu} - n_s \frac{\nu_{,k}}{\nu} \, n_k \right) \right] dx_s = 0.
\end{aligned}
\tag{54}
$$

The last expression vanishes because of eq. (51). It turns out that the value of $I$ is the same for the whole family of generated closed curves. If now, on the surface $S$, eq. (49) is satisfied [and, therefore, both (50) and (51)], $I$ vanishes for the original closed curve because of Stokes's theorem. It follows, then, that if we satisfy both (50) and (51) on $S$ and (51) throughout space, all closed-path integrals (52) will vanish everywhere, and therefore the eiconal equation has been satisfied throughout space.

Except for the initial conditions on $S$, we may merely satisfy eq. (51) throughout space. But eq. (51) is a differential equation for individual curves of which **n** is the unit tangent vector. As a matter of fact, the left-hand side of eq. (51), representing the change in **n** per unit length along the curve, is what in differential geometry is called the *curvature vector*. It has the direction of the radius of curvature, and its magnitude is the reciprocal of the radius of curvature. It is always at right angles to the tangent vector **n**. In other words, once we start out at a particular point on $S$ with a chosen direction for **n**, then eq. (51) will generate an **n**-curve that is independent of the choice of **n**-directions elsewhere on $S$. This **n**-curve can be embedded in any solution of the eiconal equation which has the right **n**-direction in the one chosen point on $S$ and elsewhere on $S$ satisfies the initial conditions (50). We have found in eq. (51) the differential equation for *ray trajectories*. The whole concept of the light ray is based on the fact that in the short-wave limit we can separate the problem of finding a solution of the wave equation throughout space into the infinitely many partial problems of finding individual ray trajectories. Equation (51) embodies Snell's law for continuously variable index of refraction.

Equation (51) is capable of still another interpretation. It is the set of Euler-Lagrange equations of a variational problem. If we introduce an arbitrary parameter $\beta$ along a particular ray trajectory, so that the curve may be described in terms of three parametric equations

$$x_i = x_i(\beta), \tag{55}$$

then the unit vector **n** has the significance

$$n_i = \frac{dx_i/d\beta}{\sqrt{\dfrac{1x_k}{d\beta}\dfrac{dx_k}{d\beta}}}, \tag{56}$$

and eq. (51) can be given the form

$$0 = \nu_{,i} - n_i n_s \nu_{,s} - \nu n_s n_{i,s} = \nu_{,i} - n_s(\nu n_i)_{,s}$$

$$= \nu_{,i} - \left(\frac{dx_k}{d\beta}\frac{dx_k}{d\beta}\right)^{-\frac{1}{2}} \frac{dx_i}{d\beta} \frac{\partial}{\partial x_i}(\nu n_i)$$

$$= \nu_{,i} - \left(\frac{dx_k}{d\beta}\frac{dx_k}{d\beta}\right)^{-\frac{1}{2}} \frac{d}{d\beta}(\nu n_i), \tag{57}$$

$$\sqrt{\frac{dx_k}{d\beta}\frac{dx_k}{d\beta}}\frac{\partial \nu}{\partial x_i} - \frac{d}{d\beta}\left[\nu \frac{dx_i/d\beta}{\left(\dfrac{dx_k}{d\beta}\dfrac{dx_k}{d\beta}\right)^{\frac{1}{2}}}\right] = 0.$$

This equation has the form of a set of Euler-Lagrange equations. The corresponding Lagrangian is

$$\Lambda = \nu(\mathbf{x})\sqrt{\frac{dx_k}{d\beta}\frac{dx_k}{d\beta}}, \tag{58}$$

and the line integral that is to be stationary will be

$$T = \frac{1}{c}\int_{\beta_1}^{\beta_2} \nu(\mathbf{x})\sqrt{\frac{dx_k}{d\beta}\frac{dx_k}{d\beta}}\,d\beta = \frac{1}{c}\int_{\mathbf{x}_1}^{\mathbf{x}_2}\nu(\mathbf{x})\,dl \qquad (\delta T = 0). \tag{59}$$

$T$ is nothing but the travel time of a wave following the ray trajectory and having at each point the speed corresponding to the local value of the refractive index. The principle that the actual ray trajectory is the one over which an electromagnetic disturbance will travel between two fixed end points in the shortest possible time is called *Fermat's principle*. The eiconal equation (43) is nothing but the *Hamilton-Jacobi equation* associated with the variational problem (59).

Ray optics can, thus, be developed in close analogy with classical mechanics. There exists a variational principle, Fermat's principle, which corresponds to Hamilton's principle of least action of mechanics. Huygens's principle is the analogue of the Hamilton-Jacobi partial differential equation. Every general theorem in mechanics possesses an analogous theorem in ray optics. This parallelism, discovered by Hamilton, is known as *Hamilton's optical-mechanical analogy*. It has been of great historical importance in the development of quantum mechanics; quantum mechanics is the "wave mechanics" which bears the same mathematical relationship to classical mechanics that wave optics has to ray optics.

## Problems

**10.1.** Derive the equations of sound waves in a fluid in which both the density and the bulk modulus are functions of location. Discuss these equations, deriving both Snell's law and the transition conditions where two fluids are separated by an interface.

**10.2.** The permeability of glass is very nearly 1, and the optical properties are due to the dielectric constant. To what extent is the polarizing action of a reflecting glass surface impaired per unit angle of deviation from the correct value of the polarizing angle?

**10.3.** White light is incident at right angles on a thin plate having the permeability 1 and the dielectric constant $\kappa$, which shall be assumed to be independent of the frequency. If the thickness of the plate is $s$ and if the plate surfaces are plane and parallel to a very high degree of accuracy, determine the effective transmissivity of the plate as a function of wave length.

**10.4.** Modify the situation of the preceding problem by assuming that $N$ identical plates are stacked with a repeating distance (center to center) $d > s$.

**10.5.** To what extent are lens coatings incapable of doing all that might be hoped for, namely, to make an air-glass interface 100 per cent transmissive under all conditions? Supplement your qualitative analysis by appropriate sample computations.

**10.6.** Derive the equations of ray acoustics from the wave equation obtained in Problem 10.1. Attempt to set up a systematic approximation method for solving the wave equation for high but finite frequencies, so that the equations of ray acoustics and their solutions form a first approximation stage.

**10.7.** In an otherwise homogeneous fluid (say water), there is embedded a small sphere of another fluid (an air bubble) possessing much smaller density and bulk modulus. If a plane wave passes across the location of the bubble, it is possible to satisfy the transition conditions by setting up inside the bubble, as well as outside, additional solutions of the respective wave equations having (a) spherical symmetry, (b) the symmetry of a radiating dipole, (c) the symmetry of a radiating quadrupole, and so on. Inside the bubble, one has to use the solutions which are combinations of advanced and retarded potentials, so that there will be no singularity at the center. Outside, the wave must propagate outward. Find an approximate solution for the important case that the bubble diameter is much smaller than the wave length of the sound wave in water. The outgoing wave in the surrounding fluid is called the *scattered wave*. It has a maximum amplitude (in terms of the amplitude of the incident plane wave) for a particular wave length, which is called the *resonant wave length*.

# Chapter 11

## Conclusion

In this book, we have covered the theories known as the classical theories of physics, with the possible exception of the special theory of relativity. Classical mechanics is probably the first systematic attempt in the history of mankind to describe the motions of material bodies quantitatively and to explain their behavior in terms of a theory based on a very small number of basic assumptions. We owe to Newton and his predecessors the clear formulation of the force concept. He discovered that interaction in the physical universe results in changes in the state of motion of bodies, not in changes of location, as had been believed previously in the Scholastic period. Since force results in acceleration of material bodies, he attempted to place the source of the force also in a material body, and to the extent that he was able to obtain quantitative experimental evidence, this attempt appeared to be fully successful.

Even Newton was troubled by the need for explaining the nature of light. But since at his time a measurement of the speed of light was completely out of the question, and since almost nothing was known concerning light diffraction and interference, a mechanical (ray-optical) theory of light appeared feasible and was, in fact, adopted as the correct approach to optics.

Fresnel's mirror experiments first established the essential wave nature of light, and Oersted's and Faraday's work showed that electromagnetic forces did not fit into the Newtonian scheme of things. Maxwell and Hertz were able to give Faraday's qualitative field concepts the form of a quantitative theory, which was brought to its completion by the work of Lorentz and Einstein.

In the field theory of electrodynamics, the nature of the particle is the same as in mechanics, to the extent that it is pointlike and that it possesses certain inherent properties which determine (a) the acceleration it will suffer when subject to external influences, and (b) the nature and magnitude of its effect on its surroundings. These inherent properties are its mass and its electric charge, both quantities that have the same significance as in mechanics and, more particularly, in electrostatics. However, the point charge, as this particle is usually called, does not directly affect another point charge at a distance; it acts by means of an intermediary, the electromagnetic field. The electromagnetic field is determined only incompletely by the distribution of charges and their motions, since there are fields that obey the field laws (Maxwell's equations) without being associated with charge distributions. Thus, in contrast to a mechanical system, an electrodynamic system is not completely determined if the initial locations and velocities of the particles are known; the initial field distribution must also be given. Then the future behavior of the system is completely determined by the laws of electrodynamics. These laws fall into three groups: the *field equations*, linear partial differential equations for the electric and magnetic field strengths, determine the development of a field in the course of time if the initial field as well as the distribution of charges at all times are known; the *force law* determines the acceleration of a particle in the presence of a given "incident field," [the (finite) difference between the total field and the "self-field"]; and a third law must define the "self-field" of a particle.

Classical field physics possesses laws of the same degree of determinacy as classical mechanics. Once a situation is sufficiently well defined at a chosen "starting time" $t_0$, the future of the system is completely predictable. In a field theory, such as electrodynamics, the number of facts of which initial knowledge is required is, however, considerably larger than in a mechanical theory, involving not only the initial locations and velocities of the particles, but also the initial values of the field variables at every space point.

Electromagnetic disturbances propagate in empty space at a certain uniform rate of speed, $c$, which equals approximately $3.0 \times 10^{10}$ cm-sec$^{-1}$. It appeared, therefore, at first that Maxwell's laws could not possibly hold with respect to every inertial frame of reference, that is, every frame with respect to which Newton's laws of mechanics are valid, but that their validity was restricted either to a universal frame of reference representing "absolute rest" or else to a local frame representing the local state of motion of a material medium capable of propagating electromagnetic waves, the "ether." Experimental evidence, however, showed both of these alternatives to be untenable, and further theoretical examination of this question led to a fundamental revision of the then current space-time concepts; this revision is known as the (*special*) *theory of relativity*. With the help of this theory, it was possible to establish a logically consistent transformation theory of the equations of electrodynamics which was compatible with all known experimental facts. Unfortunately, the new space-time concepts are irreconcilable with Newtonian mechanics and, in particular, with Newton's theory of the gravitational field. Einstein succeeded, however, in expanding the original theory of relativity so that gravitation became an integral part of the new space-time concepts, thus leading to the culmination of classical field physics in the general theory of relativity. (The general theory is not covered in this book, because it requires too many special mathematical tools.)

This book contains all but one of the fundamental physical theories which had been developed by the turn of the century, and it goes beyond this date in the presentation of the theory of relativity. No attention has been given at all to the theory of heat, which properly forms part of classical theoretical physics and which is closely associated with the gradual recognition of the microscopic structure of matter. We have treated "mass points" or "particles" by acknowledging their existence and by showing that in certain respects systems of particles can be treated without a knowledge of the properties of the constituent particles. Such treatment, as the reader may well suspect, has its limitations.

When matter in bulk is being described in terms of the average local density and the average local velocity, we can assign to each point in space an average local linear momentum density and an average local angular momentum density; and the integral of these quantities, extended over space, will equal the sum of the corresponding particle quantities, carried out over all the constituent particles. But the total kinetic energy of all the constituent particles is always greater than the integral of the expression $\frac{1}{2}\rho\,v^2$, taken over space. The difference between the sum and the integral represents the kinetic energy contained in the random motion of the individual particles. This extra energy is known as *heat energy*.

The treatment of random motion can take place on two different levels. We may actually descend to molecular dimensions and develop a statistical theory of those effects which, because of incomplete knowledge of the situation *in detail,* are not accessible to rigorous, deterministic prediction. This theory is known as *statistical mechanics.* We may also restrict our attention to those macroscopic effects which are subject to direct experimental determination, that is, primarily to temperature, pressure, density, and heat exchange. There are laws relating just to these macroscopic quantities, and their systematization is known as *thermodynamics.* It is clear that the thermodynamic laws must be contained in the laws of statistical mechanics, but the reverse is not true.

The statistical treatment of molecular processes extends the power of theoretical examination to a very large body of physical phenomena that otherwise would fall outside the frame of classical mechanics. It is possible to treat satisfactorily the bulk laws of heat transfer (the first and second laws of thermodynamics) and to connect by a single theoretical scheme such apparently widely separated effects as heat conduction and viscosity of fluids. It turns out that the "perfect gas" not only has a mathematically simple equation of state but also corresponds to the simplest possible assumption concerning the forces of interaction between individual molecules. It is further possible to predict the distribution of velocities among the molecules contained in a gas and to relate the parameters of the velocity distribution to the macroscopically determined temperature.

In view of the power of the statistical approach to molecular phenomena, two separate deficiencies of the classical theory became very conspicuous. One was the inability of the classical theory to account qualitatively or quantitatively for the fact that radiation emanating from hot gases occurs primarily at certain, well-defined frequencies (atomic line spectra). The other deficiency has to do with the equilibrium frequency distribution of heat radiation (blackbody radiation). The continued discussion of these phenomena brought about a revolution in our basic concepts of the physical universe which in its depth is at least comparable to the development of field physics and the theory of relativity. The new structure is known as *quantum mechanics.*

Quantum mechanics started out as a recipe how to select, among all the possible situations permitted by the rules of mechanics and electrodynamics, discrete sets of "permitted" solutions of the equations. This approach was not only unsatisfactory from a logical point of view but also was found to cover only some of the atomic phenomena for which a general theoretical explanation was sought. Schrödinger succeeded in developing an idea of de Broglie to the point where it became clear that atomic line spectra could be explained by means of a theory in which a wave equation had to be solved and in which the observed discrete states of the atom corresponded to "normal modes." Classical mechanics had to be considered as a first approximation to "wave mechanics," in the same manner in which ray optics constitutes the "short wave limit" of wave optics.

Naturally, attention focussed very soon on the physical significance of the wave variable which appears in Schrödinger's wave equation. It was found soon that this variable (or variables) lacks the robust significance which is possessed, for instance, by the electric and magnetic field strengths. Schrödinger's wave function turned out to be nothing but a "probability amplitude," a measure by which the *probable* outcome of proposed experiments (measurements) could be predicted. In its present form, quantum physics has destroyed the rigid determinism of classical physics and has introduced, in its stead, a probability calculus which, in contrast to classical statistical mechanics, is not concerned with the statistical treatment of deterministic but incompletely known systems, but which deals with an *essentially statistical physical universe*.

Present-day quantum mechanics has succeeded in dealing satisfactorily with all problems of atomic mechanics, and it has, to some extent, also succeeded in describing the interaction between charged particles and the electromagnetic field. The description of the field itself is not yet completely satisfactory, and our theoretical grasp of nuclear phenomena and of the structure and the formation of elementary particles is still basically defective. These questions are now in the focus of theoretical and experimental investigations. Very possibly the conceptual framework of quantum mechanics requires another basic revision before we can achieve further significant progress.

A second book will present the theory of heat and furnish an introduction to modern quantum physics. The purpose of this concluding chapter was to indicate the shortcomings of the classical theories that led to our present theoretical views.

# Further Reading

In the body of this book, no reference has been made to suggested supplementary reading, because most of the presentation, it is hoped, is self-contained. Nevertheless, the reader of a book on the graduate level will find it necessary, not only for a complete understanding but also for his development as an independent thinker, to read widely in order to have the benefit of a variety of points of view. Naturally, many of the developments that have been merely sketched in this work will be found presented in more detail elsewhere.

For a presentation of the mathematical tools of the theoretical physicist, a number of books are available which are not straight mathematics texts. Among these are Houston, *Principles of Mathematical Physics* (McGraw-Hill). Margenau and Murphy, *The Mathematics of Physics and Chemistry* (Van Nostrand). Frank and von Mises, *Die Differential- und Integralgleichungen der Mechanik und Physik* (Vieweg and M. Rosenberg), two Vols. Courant and Hilbert, *Methoden der mathematischen Physik* (Springer), two Vols. Joos, *Theoretical Physics* (First Part) (Blackie and Stechert-Hafner).

Among the well-known textbooks of theoretical physics which cover ground similar to that contained in this book are: Page, *Introduction to Theoretical Physics* (Van Nostrand). Slater and Frank, *Mechanics*, and, by the same authors, *Electromagnetism* (McGraw-Hill). Joos, *Theoretical Physics* (Blackie and Stechert-Hafner). Some of the older, more elaborate German texts, are available in translation; those of M. Planck, C. Schäfer, and A. Haas are probably the most important. R. Fuerth's *Theoretische Physik* (Springer), an excellent German textbook, is almost unavailable in the United States.

Among the texts on mechanics, the reader may find helpful the very thorough discussions in Frank and Mises, which has been mentioned above; special attention is called to the treatment of variational calculus by Caratheodory in Vol. I. Whittaker's *A Treatise on Analytical Mechanics* (Cambridge University Press) is a standard text of mechanics. The classic on hydrodynamics is undoubtedly the work by Lamb, *Hydrodynamics* (Cambridge); an excellent German text, by Ewald, Pöschl, and Prandtl, has been translated into English as *Physics of Solids and Fluids* (Blackie). The theory of sound is covered very extensively in a text by Lord Rayleigh, *Theory of Sound* (Dover), of which it is said that everything can be found in it if you only know how to go about finding it. Morse's *Vibration and Sound* (McGraw-Hill, 2d ed., 1948) is a modern and excellent work on a somewhat less lofty level.

Texts on electrodynamics include the old work by Abraham and Becker, *Classical Electricity and Magnetism* (Blackie), the contemporary works by Page and Adams, *Principles of Electricity* (Van Nostrand) and by Stratton, *Electromagnetic Theory* (McGraw-Hill). Books which are particularly concerned with optics are the German *Optik* by M. Born (Springer and Edwards Bros.) and *Physical Optics* by R. W. Wood (Macmillan). A beautiful treatment of guided waves is available by J. C. Slater, *Microwave Transmission* (McGraw-Hill). The old *Elektronentheorie* by H. A. Lorentz (Teubner) is still very readable.

# Index

CATALOGUE OF DOVER BOOKS

# BOOKS EXPLAINING SCIENCE AND MATHEMATICS
## General

**WHAT IS SCIENCE?, Norman Campbell.** This excellent introduction explains scientific method, role of mathematics, types of scientific laws. Contents: 2 aspects of science, science & nature, laws of science, discovery of laws, explanation of laws, measurement & numerical laws, applications of science. 192pp. 5⅜ x 8. S43 Paperbound **$1.25**

**THE COMMON SENSE OF THE EXACT SCIENCES, W. K. Clifford.** Introduction by James Newman, edited by Karl Pearson. For 70 years this has been a guide to classical scientific and mathematical thought. Explains with unusual clarity basic concepts, such as extension of meaning of symbols, characteristics of surface boundaries, properties of plane figures, vectors, Cartesian method of determining position, etc. Long preface by Bertrand Russell. Bibliography of Clifford. Corrected, 130 diagrams redrawn. 249pp. 5⅜ x 8. T61 Paperbound **$1.60**

**SCIENCE THEORY AND MAN, Erwin Schrödinger.** This is a complete and unabridged reissue of SCIENCE AND THE HUMAN TEMPERAMENT plus an additional essay: "What is an Elementary Particle?" Nobel laureate Schrödinger discusses such topics as nature of scientific method, the nature of science, chance and determinism, science and society, conceptual models for physical entities, elementary particles and wave mechanics. Presentation is popular and may be followed by most people with little or no scientific training. "Fine practical preparation for a time when laws of nature, human institutions . . . are undergoing a critical examination without parallel," Waldemar Kaempffert, N. Y. TIMES. 192pp. 5⅜ x 8. T428 Paperbound **$1.35**

**FADS AND FALLACIES IN THE NAME OF SCIENCE, Martin Gardner.** Examines various cults, quack systems, frauds, delusions which at various times have masqueraded as science. Accounts of hollow-earth fanatics like Symmes; Velikovsky and wandering planets; Hoerbiger; Bellamy and the theory of multiple moons; Charles Fort; dowsing, pseudoscientific methods for finding water, ores, oil. Sections on naturopathy, iridiagnosis, zone therapy, food fads, etc. Analytical accounts of Wilhelm Reich and orgone sex energy; L. Ron Hubbard and Dianetics; A. Korzybski and General Semantics; many others. Brought up to date to include Bridey Murphy, others. Not just a collection of anecdotes, but a fair, reasoned appraisal of eccentric theory. Formerly titled IN THE NAME OF SCIENCE. Preface. Index. x + 384pp. 5⅜ x 8. T394 Paperbound **$1.50**

**A DOVER SCIENCE SAMPLER, edited by George Barkin.** 64-page book, sturdily bound, containing excerpts from over 20 Dover books, explaining science. Edwin Hubble, George Sarton, Ernst Mach, A. d'Abro, Galileo, Newton, others, discussing island universes, scientific truth, biological phenomena, stability in bridges, etc. Copies limited; no more than 1 to a customer. FREE

**POPULAR SCIENTIFIC LECTURES, Hermann von Helmholtz.** Helmholtz was a superb expositor as well as a scientist of genius in many areas. The seven essays in this volume are models of clarity, and even today they rank among the best general descriptions of their subjects ever written. "The Physiological Causes of Harmony in Music" was the first significant physiological explanation of musical consonance and dissonance. Two essays, "On the Interaction of Natural Forces" and "On the Conservation of Force," were of great importance in the history of science, for they firmly established the principle of the conservation of energy. Other lectures include "On the Relation of Optics to Painting," "On Recent Progress in the Theory of Vision," "On Goethe's Scientific Researches," and "On the Origin and Significance of Geometrical Axioms." Selected and edited with an introduction by Professor Morris Kline. xii + 286pp. 5⅜ x 8½. T799 Paperbound **$1.45**

# BOOKS EXPLAINING SCIENCE AND MATHEMATICS
## Physics

**CONCERNING THE NATURE OF THINGS, Sir William Bragg.** Christmas lectures delivered at the Royal Society by Nobel laureate. Why a spinning ball travels in a curved track; how uranium is transmuted to lead, etc. Partial contents: atoms, gases, liquids, crystals, metals, etc. No scientific background needed; wonderful for intelligent child. 32pp. of photos, 57 figures. xii + 232pp. 5⅜ x 8. T31 Paperbound **$1.50**

**THE RESTLESS UNIVERSE, Max Born.** New enlarged version of this remarkably readable account by a Nobel laureate. Moving from sub-atomic particles to universe, the author explains in very simple terms the latest theories of wave mechanics. Partial contents: air and its relatives, electrons & ions, waves & particles, electronic structure of the atom, nuclear physics. Nearly 1000 illustrations, including 7 animated sequences. 325pp. 6 x 9. T412 Paperbound **$2.00**

**FROM EUCLID TO EDDINGTON: A STUDY OF THE CONCEPTIONS OF THE EXTERNAL WORLD, Sir Edmund Whittaker.** A foremost British scientist traces the development of theories of natural philosophy from the western rediscovery of Euclid to Eddington, Einstein, Dirac, etc. The inadequacy of classical physics is contrasted with present day attempts to understand the physical world through relativity, non-Euclidean geometry, space curvature, wave mechanics, etc. 5 major divisions of examination: Space; Time and Movement; the Concepts of Classical Physics; the Concepts of Quantum Mechanics; the Eddington Universe. 212pp. 5⅜ x 8.                                                    T491 Paperbound **$1.35**

**PHYSICS, THE PIONEER SCIENCE, L. W. Taylor.** First thorough text to place all important physical phenomena in cultural-historical framework; remains best work of its kind. Exposition of physical laws, theories developed chronologically, with great historical, illustrative experiments diagrammed, described, worked out mathematically. Excellent physics text for self-study as well as class work. Vol. 1: Heat, Sound: motion, acceleration, gravitation, conservation of energy, heat engines, rotation, heat, mechanical energy, etc. 211 illus. 407pp. 5⅜ x 8. Vol. 2: Light, Electricity: images, lenses, prisms, magnetism, Ohm's law, dynamos, telegraph, quantum theory, decline of mechanical view of nature, etc. Bibliography. 13 table appendix. Index. 551 illus. 2 color plates. 508pp. 5⅜ x 8.

Vol. 1 S565 Paperbound **$2.00**
Vol. 2 S566 Paperbound **$2.00**
The set **$4.00**

**A SURVEY OF PHYSICAL THEORY, Max Planck.** One of the greatest scientists of all time, creator of the quantum revolution in physics, writes in non-technical terms of his own discoveries and those of other outstanding creators of modern physics. Planck wrote this book when science had just crossed the threshold of the new physics, and he communicates the excitement felt then as he discusses electromagnetic theories, statistical methods, evolution of the concept of light, a step-by-step description of how he developed his own momentous theory, and many more of the basic ideas behind modern physics. Formerly "A Survey of Physics." Bibliography. Index. 128pp. 5⅜ x 8.                    S650 Paperbound **$1.15**

**THE ATOMIC NUCLEUS, M. Korsunsky.** The only non-technical comprehensive account of the atomic nucleus in English. For college physics students, etc. Chapters cover: Radioactivity, the Nuclear Model of the Atom, the Mass of Atomic Nuclei, the Disintegration of Atomic Nuclei, the Discovery of the Positron, the Artificial Transformation of Atomic Nuclei, Artificial Radioactivity, Mesons, the Neutrino, the Structure of Atomic Nuclei and Forces Acting Between Nuclear Particles, Nuclear Fission, Chain Reaction, Peaceful Uses, Thermonuclear Reactions. Slightly abridged edition. Translated by G. Yankovsky. 65 figures. Appendix includes 45 photographic illustrations. 413 pp. 5⅜ x 8.                             S1052 Paperbound **$2.00**

**PRINCIPLES OF MECHANICS SIMPLY EXPLAINED, Morton Mott-Smith.** Excellent, highly readable introduction to the theories and discoveries of classical physics. Ideal for the layman who desires a foundation which will enable him to understand and appreciate contemporary developments in the physical sciences. Discusses: Density, The Law of Gravitation, Mass and Weight, Action and Reaction, Kinetic and Potential Energy, The Law of Inertia, Effects of Acceleration, The Independence of Motions, Galileo and the New Science of Dynamics, Newton and the New Cosmos, The Conservation of Momentum, and other topics. Revised edition of "This Mechanical World." Illustrated by E. Kosa, Jr. Bibliography and Chronology. Index. xiv + 171pp. 5⅜ x 8½.                                         T1067 Paperbound **$1.00**

**THE CONCEPT OF ENERGY SIMPLY EXPLAINED, Morton Mott-Smith.** Elementary, non-technical exposition which traces the story of man's conquest of energy, with particular emphasis on the developments during the nineteenth century and the first three decades of our own century. Discusses man's earlier efforts to harness energy, more recent experiments and discoveries relating to the steam engine, the engine indicator, the motive power of heat, the principle of excluded perpetual motion, the bases of the conservation of energy, the concept of entropy, the internal combustion engine, mechanical refrigeration, and many other related topics. Also much biographical material. Index. Bibliography. 33 illustrations. ix + 215pp. 5⅜ x 8½.                                                     T1071 Paperbound **$1.25**

**HEAT AND ITS WORKINGS, Morton Mott-Smith.** One of the best elementary introductions to the theory and attributes of heat, covering such matters as the laws governing the effect of heat on solids, liquids and gases, the methods by which heat is measured, the conversion of a substance from one form to another through heating and cooling, evaporation, the effects of pressure on boiling and freezing points, and the three ways in which heat is transmitted (conduction, convection, radiation). Also brief notes on major experiments and discoveries. Concise, but complete, it presents all the essential facts about the subject in readable style. Will give the layman and beginning student a first-rate background in this major topic in physics. Index. Bibliography. 50 illustrations. x + 165pp. 5⅜ x 8½. T978 Paperbound **$1.00**

**THE STORY OF ATOMIC THEORY AND ATOMIC ENERGY, J. G. Feinberg.** Wider range of facts on physical theory, cultural implications, than any other similar source. Completely non-technical. Begins with first atomic theory, 600 B.C., goes through A-bomb, developments to 1959. Avogadro, Rutherford, Bohr, Einstein, radioactive decay, binding energy, radiation danger, future benefits of nuclear power, dozens of other topics, told in lively, related, informal manner. Particular stress on European atomic research. "Deserves special mention . . . authoritative," Saturday Review. Formerly "The Atom Story." New chapter to 1959. Index. 34 illustrations. 251pp. 5⅜ x 8.                                T625 Paperbound **$1.60**

**THE STRANGE STORY OF THE QUANTUM, AN ACCOUNT FOR THE GENERAL READER OF THE GROWTH OF IDEAS UNDERLYING OUR PRESENT ATOMIC KNOWLEDGE, B. Hoffmann.** Presents lucidly and expertly, with barest amount of mathematics, the problems and theories which led to modern quantum physics. Dr. Hoffmann begins with the closing years of the 19th century, when certain trifling discrepancies were noticed, and with illuminating analogies and examples takes you through the brilliant concepts of Planck, Einstein, Pauli, de Broglie, Bohr, Schroedinger, Heisenberg, Dirac, Sommerfeld, Feynman, etc. This edition includes a new, long postscript carrying the story through 1958. "Of the books attempting an account of the history and contents of our modern atomic physics which have come to my attention, this is the best," H. Margenau, Yale University, in "American Journal of Physics." 32 tables and line illustrations. Index. 275pp. 5⅜ x 8.                                    T518 Paperbound **$1.50**

**THE EVOLUTION OF SCIENTIFIC THOUGHT FROM NEWTON TO EINSTEIN, A. d'Abro.** Einstein's special and general theories of relativity, with their historical implications, are analyzed in non-technical terms. Excellent accounts of the contributions of Newton, Riemann, Weyl, Planck, Eddington, Maxwell, Lorentz and others are treated in terms of space and time, equations of electromagnetics, finiteness of the universe, methodology of science. 21 diagrams. 482pp. 5⅜ x 8.                                             T2 Paperound **$2.25**

**THE RISE OF THE NEW PHYSICS, A. d'Abro.** A half-million word exposition, formerly titled THE DECLINE OF MECHANISM, for readers not versed in higher mathematics. The only thorough explanation, in everyday language, of the central core of modern mathematical physical theory, treating both classical and modern theoretical physics, and presenting in terms almost anyone can understand the equivalent of 5 years of study of mathematical physics. Scientifically impeccable coverage of mathematical-physical thought from the Newtonian system up through the electronic theories of Dirac and Heisenberg and Fermi's statistics. Combines both history and exposition; provides a broad yet unified and detailed view, with constant comparison of classical and modern views on phenomena and theories. "A must for anyone doing serious study in the physical sciences," JOURNAL OF THE FRANKLIN INSTITUTE. "Extraordinary faculty . . . to explain ideas and theories of theoretical physics in the language of daily life," ISIS. First part of set covers philosophy of science, drawing upon the practice of Newton, Maxwell, Poincaré, Einstein, others, discussing modes of thought, experiment, interpretations of causality, etc. In the second part, 100 pages explain grammar and vocabulary of mathematics, with discussions of functions, groups, series, Fourier series, etc. The remainder is devoted to concrete, detailed coverage of both classical and quantum physics, explaining such topics as analytic mechanics, Hamilton's principle, wave theory of light, electromagnetic waves, groups of transformations, thermodynamics, phase rule, Brownian movement, kinetics, special relativity, Planck's original quantum theory, Bohr's atom, Zeeman effect, Broglie's wave mechanics, Heisenberg's uncertainty, Eigen-values, matrices, scores of other important topics. Discoveries and theories are covered for such men as Alembert, Born, Cantor, Debye, Euler, Foucault, Galois, Gauss, Hadamard, Kelvin, Kepler, Laplace, Maxwell, Pauli, Rayleigh, Volterra, Weyl, Young, more than 180 others. Indexed. 97 illustrations. ix + 982pp. 5⅜ x 8.          T3 Volume 1, Paperbound **$2.00**
T4 Volume 2, Paperbound **$2.00**

**SPINNING TOPS AND GYROSCOPIC MOTION, John Perry.** Well-known classic of science still unsurpassed for lucid, accurate, delightful exposition. How quasi-rigidity is induced in flexible and fluid bodies by rapid motions; why gyrostat falls, top rises; nature and effect on climatic conditions of earth's precessional movement; effect of internal fluidity on rotating bodies, etc. Appendixes describe practical uses to which gyroscopes have been put in ships, compasses, monorail transportation. 62 figures. 128pp. 5⅜ x 8.          T416 Paperbound **$1.00**

**THE UNIVERSE OF LIGHT, Sir William Bragg.** No scientific training needed to read Nobel Prize winner's expansion of his Royal Institute Christmas Lectures. Insight into nature of light, methods and philosophy of science. Explains lenses, reflection, color, resonance, polarization, x-rays, the spectrum, Newton's work with prisms, Huygens' with polarization, Crookes' with cathode ray, etc. Leads into clear statement of 2 major historical theories of light, corpuscle and wave. Dozens of experiments you can do. 199 illus., including 2 full-page color plates. 293pp. 5⅜ x 8.                          S538 Paperbound **$1.85**

**THE STORY OF X-RAYS FROM RÖNTGEN TO ISOTOPES, A. R. Bleich.** Non-technical history of x-rays, their scientific explanation, their applications in medicine, industry, research, and art, and their effect on the individual and his descendants. Includes amusing early reactions to Röntgen's discovery, cancer therapy, detections of art and stamp forgeries, potential risks to patient and operator, etc. Illustrations show x-rays of flower structure, the gall bladder, gears with hidden defects, etc. Original Dover publication. Glossary. Bibliography. Index. 55 photos and figures. xiv + 186pp. 5⅜ x 8.                 T662 Paperbound **$1.35**

**ELECTRONS, ATOMS, METALS AND ALLOYS, Wm. Hume-Rothery.** An introductory-level explanation of the application of the electronic theory to the structure and properties of metals and alloys, taking into account the new theoretical work done by mathematical physicists. Material presented in dialogue-form between an "Old Metallurgist" and a "Young Scientist." Their discussion falls into 4 main parts: the nature of an atom, the nature of a metal, the nature of an alloy, and the structure of the nucleus. They cover such topics as the hydrogen atom, electron waves, wave mechanics, Brillouin zones, co-valent bonds, radioactivity and natural disintegration, fundamental particles, structure and fission of the nucleus, etc. Revised, enlarged edition. 177 illustrations. Subject and name indexes. 407pp. 5⅜ x 8½.                                                      S1046 Paperbound **$2.25**

**OUT OF THE SKY, H. H. Nininger.** A non-technical but comprehensive introduction to "meteoritics", the young science concerned with all aspects of the arrival of matter from outer space. Written by one of the world's experts on meteorites, this work shows how, despite difficulties of observation and sparseness of data, a considerable body of knowledge has arisen. It defines meteors and meteorites; studies fireball clusters and processions, meteorite composition, size, distribution, showers, explosions, origins, craters, and much more. A true connecting link between astronomy and geology. More than 175 photos, 22 other illustrations. References. Bibliography of author's publications on meteorites. Index. viii + 336pp. 5⅜ x 8.                                                          T519 Paperbound **$1.85**

**SATELLITES AND SCIENTIFIC RESEARCH, D. King-Hele.** Non-technical account of the manmade satellites and the discoveries they have yielded up to the autumn of 1961. Brings together information hitherto published only in hard-to-get scientific journals. Includes the life history of a typical satellite, methods of tracking, new information on the shape of the earth, zones of radiation, etc. Over 60 diagrams and 6 photographs. Mathematical appendix. Bibliography of over 100 items. Index. xii + 180pp. 5⅜ x 8½.                              T703 Paperbound **$2.00**

# BOOKS EXPLAINING SCIENCE AND MATHEMATICS

## Mathematics

**CHANCE, LUCK AND STATISTICS: THE SCIENCE OF CHANCE, Horace C. Levinson.** Theory of probability and science of statistics in simple, non-technical language. Part I deals with theory of probability, covering odd superstitions in regard to "luck," the meaning of betting odds, the law of mathematical expectation, gambling, and applications in poker, roulette, lotteries, dice, bridge, and other games of chance. Part II discusses the misuse of statistics, the concept of statistical probabilities, normal and skew frequency distributions, and statistics applied to various fields—birth rates, stock speculation, insurance rates, advertising, etc. "Presented in an easy humorous style which I consider the best kind of expository writing," Prof. A. C. Cohen, Industry Quality Control. Enlarged revised edition. Formerly titled "The Science of Chance." Preface and two new appendices by the author. Index. xiv + 365pp. 5⅜ x 8.                                                          T1007 Paperbound **$1.85**

**PROBABILITIES AND LIFE, Emile Borel.** Translated by M. Baudin. Non-technical, highly readable introduction to the results of probability as applied to everyday situations. Partial contents: Fallacies About Probabilities Concerning Life After Death; Negligible Probabilities and the Probabilities of Everyday Life; Events of Small Probability; Application of Probabilities to Certain Problems of Heredity; Probabilities of Deaths, Diseases, and Accidents; On Poisson's Formula. Index. 3 Appendices of statistical studies and tables. vi + 87pp. 5⅜ x 8½.                                                          T121 Paperbound **$1.00**

**GREAT IDEAS OF MODERN MATHEMATICS: THEIR NATURE AND USE, Jagjit Singh.** Reader with only high school math will understand main mathematical ideas of modern physics, astronomy, genetics, psychology, evolution, etc., better than many who use them as tools, but comprehend little of their basic structure. Author uses his wide knowledge of non-mathematical fields in brilliant exposition of differential equations, matrices, group theory, logic, statistics, problems of mathematical foundations, imaginary numbers, vectors, etc. Original publication. 2 appendices. 2 indexes. 65 illustr. 322pp. 5⅜ x 8.        S587 Paperbound **$1.75**

**MATHEMATICS IN ACTION, O. G. Sutton.** Everyone with a command of high school algebra will find this book one of the finest possible introductions to the application of mathematics to physical theory. Ballistics, numerical analysis, waves and wavelike phenomena, Fourier series, group concepts, fluid flow and aerodynamics, statistical measures, and meteorology are discussed with unusual clarity. Some calculus and differential equations theory is developed by the author for the reader's help in the more difficult sections. 88 figures. Index. viii + 236pp. 5⅜ x 8.                                           T440 Clothbound **$3.50**

**THE FOURTH DIMENSION SIMPLY EXPLAINED, edited by H. P. Manning.** 22 essays, originally Scientific American contest entries, that use a minimum of mathematics to explain aspects of 4-dimensional geometry: analogues to 3-dimensional space, 4-dimensional absurdities and curiosities (such as removing the contents of an egg without puncturing its shell), possible measurements and forms, etc. Introduction by the editor. Only book of its sort on a truly elementary level, excellent introduction to advanced works. 82 figures. 251pp. 5⅜ x 8.                                                          T711 Paperbound **$1.35**

# MATHEMATICS—INTERMEDIATE TO ADVANCED

## General

**INTRODUCTION TO APPLIED MATHEMATICS, Francis D. Murnaghan.** A practical and thoroughly sound introduction to a number of advanced branches of higher mathematics. Among the selected topics covered in detail are: vector and matrix analysis, partial and differential equations, integral equations, calculus of variations, Laplace transform theory, the vector triple product, linear vector functions, quadratic and bilinear forms, Fourier series, spherical harmonics, Bessel functions, the Heaviside expansion formula, and many others. Extremely useful book for graduate students in physics, engineering, chemistry, and mathematics. Index. 111 study exercises with answers. 41 illustrations. ix + 389pp. 5⅜ x 8½.
S1042 Paperbound **$2.00**

**OPERATIONAL METHODS IN APPLIED MATHEMATICS, H. S. Carslaw and J. C. Jaeger.** Explanation of the application of the Laplace Transformation to differential equations, a simple and effective substitute for more difficult and obscure operational methods. Of great practical value to engineers and to all workers in applied mathematics. Chapters on: Ordinary Linear Differential Equations with Constant Coefficients;; Electric Circuit Theory; Dynamical Applications; The Inversion Theorem for the Laplace Transformation; Conduction of Heat; Vibrations of Continuous Mechanical Systems; Hydrodynamics; Impulsive Functions; Chains of Differential Equations; and other related matters. 3 appendices. 153 problems, many with answers. 22 figures. xvi + 359pp. 5⅜ x 8½.
S1011 Paperbound **$2.25**

**APPLIED MATHEMATICS FOR RADIO AND COMMUNICATIONS ENGINEERS, C. E. Smith.** No extraneous material here!—only the theories, equations, and operations essential and immediately useful for radio work. Can be used as refresher, as handbook of applications and tables, or as full home-study course. Ranges from simplest arithmetic through calculus, series, and wave forms, hyperbolic trigonometry, simultaneous equations in mesh circuits, etc. Supplies applications right along with each math topic discussed. 22 useful tables of functions, formulas, logs, etc. Index. 166 exercises, 140 examples, all with answers. 95 diagrams. Bibliography. x + 336pp. 5⅜ x 8.
S141 Paperbound **$1.75**

## Algebra, group theory, determinants, sets, matrix theory

**ALGEBRAS AND THEIR ARITHMETICS, L. E. Dickson.** Provides the foundation and background necessary to any advanced undergraduate or graduate student studying abstract algebra. Begins with elementary introduction to linear transformations, matrices, field of complex numbers; proceeds to order, basal units, modulus, quaternions, etc.; develops calculus of linears sets, describes various examples of algebras including invariant, difference, nilpotent, semi-simple. "Makes the reader marvel at his genius for clear and profound analysis," Amer. Mathematical Monthly. Index. xii + 241pp. 5⅜ x 8.
S616 Paperbound **$1.50**

**THE THEORY OF EQUATIONS WITH AN INTRODUCTION TO THE THEORY OF BINARY ALGEBRAIC FORMS, W. S. Burnside and A. W. Panton.** Extremely thorough and concrete discussion of the theory of equations, with extensive detailed treatment of many topics curtailed in later texts. Covers theory of algebraic equations, properties of polynomials, symmetric functions, derived functions, Horner's process, complex numbers and the complex variable, determinants, and methods of elimination, invariant theory (nearly 100 pages), transformations, introduction to Galois theory, Abelian equations, and much more. Invaluable supplementary work for modern students and teachers. 759 examples and exercises. Index in each volume. Two volume set. Total of xxiv + 604pp. 5⅜ x 8.
S714 Vol I Paperbound **$1.85**
S715 Vol II Paperbound **$1.85**
The set **$3.70**

**COMPUTATIONAL METHODS OF LINEAR ALGEBRA, V. N. Faddeeva,** translated by **C. D. Benster.** First English translation of a unique and valuable work, the only work in English presenting a systematic exposition of the most important methods of linear algebra—classical and contemporary. Shows in detail how to derive numerical solutions of problems in mathematical physics which are frequently connected with those of linear algebra. Theory as well as individual practice. Part I surveys the mathematical background that is indispensable to what follows. Parts II and III, the conclusion, set forth the most important methods of solution, for both exact and iterative groups. One of the most outstanding and valuable features of this work is the 23 tables, double and triple checked for accuracy. These tables will not be found elsewhere. Author's preface. Translator's note. New bibliography and index. x + 252pp. 5⅜ x 8.
S424 Paperbound **$1.95**

**ALGEBRAIC EQUATIONS, E. Dehn.** Careful and complete presentation of Galois' theory of algebraic equations; theories of Lagrange and Galois developed in logical rather than historical form, with a more thorough exposition than in most modern books. Many concrete applications and fully-worked-out examples. Discusses basic theory (very clear exposition of the symmetric group); isomorphic, transitive, and Abelian groups; applications of Lagrange's and Galois' theories; and much more. Newly revised by the author. Index. List of Theorems. xi + 208pp. 5⅜ x 8.
S697 Paperbound **$1.45**

## Differential equations, ordinary and partial; integral equations

**INTRODUCTION TO THE DIFFERENTIAL EQUATIONS OF PHYSICS, L. Hopf.** Especially valuable to the engineer with no math beyond elementary calculus. Emphasizing intuitive rather than formal aspects of concepts, the author covers an extensive territory. Partial contents: Law of causality, energy theorem, damped oscillations, coupling by friction, cylindrical and spherical coordinates, heat source, etc. Index. 48 figures. 160pp. 5⅜ x 8.
S120 Paperbound **$1.25**

**INTRODUCTION TO THE THEORY OF LINEAR DIFFERENTIAL EQUATIONS, E. G. Poole.** Authoritative discussions of important topics, with methods of solution more detailed than usual, for students with background of elementary course in differential equations. Studies existence theorems, linearly independent solutions; equations with constant coefficients; with uniform analytic coefficients; regular singularities; the hypergeometric equation; conformal representation; etc. Exercises. Index. 210pp. 5⅜ x 8.
S629 Paperbound **$1.65**

**DIFFERENTIAL EQUATIONS FOR ENGINEERS, P. Franklin.** Outgrowth of a course given 10 years at M. I. T. Makes most useful branch of pure math accessible for practical work. Theoretical basis of D.E.'s; solution of ordinary D.E.'s and partial derivatives arising from heat flow, steady-state temperature of a plate, wave equations; analytic functions; convergence of Fourier Series. 400 problems on electricity, vibratory systems, other topics. Formerly "Differential Equations for Electrical Engineers." Index 41 illus. 307pp. 5⅜ x 8.
S601 Paperbound **$1.65**

**DIFFERENTIAL EQUATIONS, F. R. Moulton.** A detailed, rigorous exposition of all the non-elementary processes of solving ordinary differential equations. Several chapters devoted to the treatment of practical problems, especially those of a physical nature, which are far more advanced than problems usually given as illustrations. Includes analytic differential equations; variations of a parameter; integrals of differential equations; analytic implicit functions; problems of elliptic motion; sine-amplitude functions; deviation of formal bodies; Cauchy-Lipschitz process; linear differential equations with periodic coefficients; differential equations in infinitely many variations; much more. Historical notes. 10 figures. 222 problems. Index. xv + 395pp. 5⅜ x 8.
S451 Paperbound **$2.00**

**DIFFERENTIAL AND INTEGRAL EQUATIONS OF MECHANICS AND PHYSICS (DIE DIFFERENTIAL-UND INTEGRALGLEICHUNGEN DER MECHANIK UND PHYSIK), edited by P. Frank and R. von Mises.** Most comprehensive and authoritative work on the mathematics of mathematical physics available today in the United States: the standard, definitive reference for teachers, physicists, engineers, and mathematicians—now published (in the original German) at a relatively inexpensive price for the first time! Every chapter in this 2,000-page set is by an expert in his field: Carathéodory, Courant, Frank, Mises, and a dozen others. Vol I, on mathematics, gives concise but complete coverages of advanced calculus, differential equations, integral equations, and potential, and partial differential equations. Index. xxiii + 916pp. Vol. II (physics): classical mechanics, optics, continuous mechanics, heat conduction and diffusion, the stationary and quasi-stationary electromagnetic field, electromagnetic oscillations, and wave mechanics. Index. xxiv + 1106pp. Two volume set. Each volume available separately. 5⅝ x 8⅜.
S787 Vol I Clothbound **$7.50**
S788 Vol II Clothbound **$7.50**
The set **$15.00**

**LECTURES ON CAUCHY'S PROBLEM, J. Hadamard.** Based on lectures given at Columbia, Rome, this discusses work of Riemann, Kirchhoff, Volterra, and the author's own research on the hyperbolic case in linear partial differential equations. It extends spherical and cylindrical waves to apply to all (normal) hyperbolic equations. Partial contents: Cauchy's problem, fundamental formula, equations with odd number, with even number of independent variables; method of descent. 32 figures. Index. iii + 316pp. 5⅜ x 8.
S105 Paperbound **$1.75**

**THEORY OF DIFFERENTIAL EQUATIONS, A. R. Forsyth.** Out of print for over a decade, the complete 6 volumes (now bound as 3) of this monumental work represent the most comprehensive treatment of differential equations ever written. Historical presentation includes in 2500 pages every substantial development. Vol. 1, 2: EXACT EQUATIONS, PFAFF'S PROBLEM; ORDINARY EQUATIONS, NOT LINEAR: methods of Grassmann, Clebsch, Lie, Darboux; Cauchy's theorem; branch points; etc. Vol. 3, 4: ORDINARY EQUATIONS, NOT LINEAR; ORDINARY LINEAR EQUATIONS: Zeta Fuchsian functions, general theorems on algebraic integrals, Brun's theorem, equations with uniform periodic coffiecients, etc. Vol. 4, 5: PARTIAL DIFFERENTIAL EQUATIONS: 2 existence-theorems, equations of theoretical dynamics, Laplace transformations, general transformation of equations of the 2nd order, much more. Indexes. Total of 2766pp. 5⅜ x 8.
S576-7-8 Clothbound: the set **$15.00**

**PARTIAL DIFFERENTIAL EQUATIONS OF MATHEMATICAL PHYSICS, A. G. Webster.** A keystone work in the library of every mature physicist, engineer, researcher. Valuable sections on elasticity, compression theory, potential theory, theory of sound, heat conduction, wave propagation, vibration theory. Contents include: deduction of differential equations, vibrations, normal functions, Fourier's series, Cauchy's method, boundary problems, method of Riemann-Volterra. Spherical, cylindrical, ellipsoidal harmonics, applications, etc. 97 figures. vii + 440pp. 5⅜ x 8.
S263 Paperbound **$2.00**

**ELEMENTARY CONCEPTS OF TOPOLOGY, P. Alexandroff.** First English translation of the famous brief introduction to topology for the beginner or for the mathematician not undertaking extensive study. This unusually useful intuitive approach deals primarily with the concepts of complex, cycle, and homology, and is wholly consistent with current investigations. Ranges from basic concepts of set-theoretic topology to the concept of Betti groups. "Glowing example of harmony between intuition and thought," David Hilbert. Translated by A. E. Farley. Introduction by D. Hilbert. Index. 25 figures. 73pp. 5⅜ x 8.            S747 Paperbound **$1.00**

## Number theory

**INTRODUCTION TO THE THEORY OF NUMBERS, L. E. Dickson.** Thorough, comprehensive approach with adequate coverage of classical literature, an introductory volume beginners can follow. Chapters on divisibility, congruences, quadratic residues & reciprocity, Diophantine equations, etc. Full treatment of binary quadratic forms without usual restriction to integral coefficients. Covers infinitude of primes, least residues, Fermat's theorem, Euler's phi function, Legendre's symbol, Gauss's lemma, automorphs, reduced forms, recent theorems of Thue & Siegel, many more. Much material not readily available elsewhere. 239 problems. Index. I figure. viii + 183pp. 5⅜ x 8.            S342 Paperbound **$1.65**

**ELEMENTS OF NUMBER THEORY, I. M. Vinogradov.** Detailed 1st course for persons without advanced mathematics; 95% of this book can be understood by readers who have gone no farther than high school algebra. Partial contents: divisibility theory, important number theoretical functions, congruences, primitive roots and indices, etc. Solutions to both problems and exercises. Tables of primes, indices, etc. Covers almost every essential formula in elementary number theory! Translated from Russian. 233 problems, 104 exercises. viii + 227pp. 5⅜ x 8.            S259 Paperbound **$1.60**

**THEORY OF NUMBERS and DIOPHANTINE ANALYSIS, R. D. Carmichael.** These two complete works in one volume form one of the most lucid introductions to number theory, requiring only a firm foundation in high school mathematics. "Theory of Numbers," partial contents: Eratosthenes' sieve, Euclid's fundamental theorem, G.C.F. and L.C.M. of two or more integers, linear congruences, etc "Diophantine Analysis": rational triangles, Pythagorean triangles, equations of third, fourth, higher degrees, method of functional equations, much more. "Theory of Numbers": 76 problems. Index. 94pp. "Diophantine Analysis": 222 problems. Index. 118pp. 5⅜ x 8.            S529 Paperbound **$1.35**

## Numerical analysis, tables

**MATHEMATICAL TABLES AND FORMULAS, Compiled by Robert D. Carmichael and Edwin R. Smith.** Valuable collection for students, etc. Contains all tables necessary in college algebra and trigonometry, such as five-place common logarithms, logarithmic sines and tangents of small angles, logarithmic trigonometric functions, natural trigonometric functions, four-place antilogarithms, tables for changing from sexagesimal to circular and from circular to sexagesimal measure of angles, etc. Also many tables and formulas not ordinarily accessible, including powers, roots, and reciprocals, exponential and hyperbolic functions, ten-place logarithms of prime numbers, and formulas and theorems from analytical and elementary geometry and from calculus. Explanatory introduction. viii + 269pp. 5⅜ x 8½.            S111 Paperbound **$1.00**

**MATHEMATICAL TABLES, H. B. Dwight.** Unique for its coverage in one volume of almost every function of importance in applied mathematics, engineering, and the physical sciences. Three extremely fine tables of the three trig functions and their inverse functions to thousandths of radians; natural and common logarithms; squares, cubes; hyperbolic functions and the inverse hyperbolic functions; $(a^2 + b^2)$ exp. ½$a$; complete elliptic integrals of the 1st and 2nd kind; sine and cosine integrals; exponential integrals Ei($x$) and Ei( $-x$); binomial coefficients; factorials to 250; surface zonal harmonics and first derivatives; Bernoulli and Euler numbers and their logs to base of 10; Gamma function; normal probability integral; over 60 pages of Bessel functions; the Riemann Zeta function. Each table with formulae generally used, sources of more extensive tables, interpolation data, etc. Over half have columns of differences, to facilitate interpolation. Introduction. Index. viii + 231pp. 5⅜ x 8.            S445 Paperbound **$1.75**

**TABLES OF FUNCTIONS WITH FORMULAE AND CURVES, E. Jahnke & F. Emde.** The world's most comprehensive 1-volume English-text collection of tables, formulae, curves of transcendent functions. 4th corrected edition, new 76-page section giving tables, formulae for elementary functions—not in other English editions. Partial contents: sine, cosine, logarithmic integral; factorial function; error integral; theta functions; elliptic integrals, functions; Legendre, Bessel, Riemann, Mathieu, hypergeometric functions, etc. Supplementary books. Bibliography. Indexed. "Out of the way functions for which we know no other source," SCIENTIFIC COMPUTING SERVICE, Ltd. 212 figures. 400pp. 5⅜ x 8.            S133 Paperbound **$2.00**

# CHEMISTRY AND PHYSICAL CHEMISTRY

**ORGANIC CHEMISTRY, F. C. Whitmore.** The entire subject of organic chemistry for the practicing chemist and the advanced student. Storehouse of facts, theories, processes found elsewhere only in specialized journals. Covers aliphatic compounds (500 pages on the properties and synthetic preparation of hydrocarbons, halides, proteins, ketones, etc.), alicyclic compounds, aromatic compounds, heterocyclic compounds, organophosphorus and organometallic compounds. Methods of synthetic preparation analyzed critically throughout. Includes much of biochemical interest. "The scope of this volume is astonishing," INDUSTRIAL AND ENGINEERING CHEMISTRY. 12,000-reference index. 2387-item bibliography. Total of x + 1005pp. 5⅜ x 8. Two volume set.
S700 Vol I Paperbound **$2.25**
S701 Vol II Paperbound **$2.25**
The set **$4.50**

**THE MODERN THEORY OF MOLECULAR STRUCTURE, Bernard Pullman.** A reasonably popular account of recent developments in atomic and molecular theory. Contents: The Wave Function and Wave Equations (history and bases of present theories of molecular structure); The Electronic Structure of Atoms (Description and classification of atomic wave functions, etc.); Diatomic Molecules; Non-Conjugated Polyatomic Molecules; Conjugated Polyatomic Molecules; The Structure of Complexes. Minimum of mathematical background needed. New translation by David Antin of "La Structure Moleculaire." Index. Bibliography. vii + 87pp. 5⅜ x 8½.
S987 Paperbound **$1.00**

**CATALYSIS AND CATALYSTS, Marcel Prettre,** Director, Research Institute on Catalysis. This brief book, translated into English for the first time, is the finest summary of the principal modern concepts, methods, and results of catalysis. Ideal introduction for beginning chemistry and physics students. Chapters: Basic Definitions of Catalysis (true catalysis and generalization of the concept of catalysis); The Scientific Bases of Catalysis (Catalysis and chemical thermodynamics, catalysis and chemical kinetics); Homogeneous Catalysis (acid-base catalysis, etc.); Chain Reactions; Contact Masses; Heterogeneous Catalysis (Mechanisms of contact catalyses, etc.); and Industrial Applications (acids and fertilizers, petroleum and petroleum chemistry, rubber, plastics, synthetic resins, and fibers). Translated by David Antin. Index. vi + 88pp. 5⅜ x 8½.
S998 Paperbound **$1.00**

**POLAR MOLECULES, Pieter Debye.** This work by Nobel laureate Debye offers a complete guide to fundamental electrostatic field relations, polarizability, molecular structure. Partial contents: electric intensity, displacement and force, polarization by orientation, molar polarization and molar refraction, halogen-hydrides, polar liquids, ionic saturation, dielectric constant, etc. Special chapter considers quantum theory. Indexed. 172pp. 5⅜ x 8.
S64 Paperbound **$1.50**

**THE ELECTRONIC THEORY OF ACIDS AND BASES, W. F. Luder and Saverio Zuffanti.** The first full systematic presentation of the electronic theory of acids and bases—treating the theory and its ramifications in an uncomplicated manner. Chapters: Historical Background; Atomic Orbitals and Valence; The Electronic Theory of Acids and Bases; Electrophilic and Electrodotic Reagents; Acidic and Basic Radicals; Neutralization; Titrations with Indicators; Displacement; Catalysis; Acid Catalysis; Base Catalysis; Alkoxides and Catalysts; Conclusion. Required reading for all chemists. Second revised (1961) edition, with additional examples and references. 3 figures. 9 tables. Index. Bibliography xii + 165pp. 5⅜ x 8.
S201 Paperbound **$1.50**

**KINETIC THEORY OF LIQUIDS, J. Frenkel.** Regarding the kinetic theory of liquids as a generalization and extension of the theory of solid bodies, this volume covers all types of arrangements of solids, thermal displacements of atoms, interstitial atoms and ions, orientational and rotational motion of molecules, and transition between states of matter. Mathematical theory is developed close to the physical subject matter. 216 bibliographical footnotes. 55 figures. xi + 485pp. 5⅜ x 8.
S95 Paperbound **$2.55**

**THE PRINCIPLES OF ELECTROCHEMISTRY, D. A. MacInnes.** Basic equations for almost every subfield of electrochemistry from first principles, referring at all times to the soundest and most recent theories and results; unusually useful as text or as reference. Covers coulometers and Faraday's Law, electrolytic conductance, the Debye-Hueckel method for the theoretical calculation of activity coefficients, concentration cells, standard electrode potentials, thermodynamic ionization constants, pH, potentiometric titrations, irreversible phenomena, Planck's equation, and much more. "Excellent treatise," AMERICAN CHEMICAL SOCIETY JOURNAL. "Highly recommended," CHEMICAL AND METALLURGICAL ENGINEERING. 2 Indices. Appendix. 585-item bibliography. 137 figures. 94 tables. ii + 478pp. 5⅝ x 8⅜.
S52 Paperbound **$2.45**

**THE PHASE RULE AND ITS APPLICATION, Alexander Findlay.** Covering chemical phenomena of 1, 2, 3, 4, and multiple component systems, this "standard work on the subject" (NATURE, London), has been completely revised and brought up to date by A. N. Campbell and N. O. Smith. Brand new material has been added on such matters as binary, tertiary liquid equilibria, solid solutions in ternary systems, quinary systems of salts and water. Completely revised to triangular coordinates in ternary systems, clarified graphic representation, solid models, etc. 9th revised edition. Author, subject indexes. 236 figures. 505 footnotes, mostly bibliographic. xii + 494pp. 5⅜ x 8.
S91 Paperbound **$2.50**

# PHYSICS

## General physics

**FOUNDATIONS OF PHYSICS, R. B. Lindsay & H. Margenau.** Excellent bridge between semi-popular works & technical treatises. A discussion of methods of physical description, construction of theory; valuable for physicist with elementary calculus who is interested in ideas that give meaning to data, tools of modern physics. Contents include symbolism, mathematical equations; space & time foundations of mechanics; probability; physics & continua; electron theory; special & general relativity; quantum mechanics; causality. "Thorough and yet not overdetailed. Unreservedly recommended," NATURE (London). Unabridged, corrected edition. List of recommended readings. 35 illustrations. xi + 537pp. 5⅜ x 8.
S377 Paperbound **$2.75**

**FUNDAMENTAL FORMULAS OF PHYSICS, ed. by D. H. Menzel.** Highly useful, fully inexpensive reference and study text, ranging from simple to highly sophisticated operations. Mathematics integrated into text—each chapter stands as short textbook of field represented. Vol. 1: Statistics, Physical Constants, Special Theory of Relativity, Hydrodynamics, Aerodynamics, Boundary Value Problems in Math. Physics; Viscosity, Electromagnetic Theory, etc. Vol. 2: Sound, Acoustics, Geometrical Optics, Electron Optics, High-Energy Phenomena, Magnetism, Biophysics, much more. Index. Total of 800pp. 5⅜ x 8.
Vol. 1 S595 Paperbound **$2.00**
Vol. 2 S596 Paperbound **$2.00**

**MATHEMATICAL PHYSICS, D. H. Menzel.** Thorough one-volume treatment of the mathematical techniques vital for classic mechanics, electromagnetic theory, quantum theory, and relativity. Written by the Harvard Professor of Astrophysics for junior, senior, and graduate courses, it gives clear explanations of all those aspects of function theory, vectors, matrices, dyadics, tensors, partial differential equations, etc., necessary for the understanding of the various physical theories. Electron theory, relativity, and other topics seldom presented appear here in considerable detail. Scores of definitions, conversion factors, dimensional constants, etc. "More detailed than normal for an advanced text . . . excellent set of sections on Dyadics, Matrices, and Tensors," JOURNAL OF THE FRANKLIN INSTITUTE. Index. 193 problems, with answers. x + 412pp. 5⅜ x 8.
S56 Paperbound **$2.00**

**THE SCIENTIFIC PAPERS OF J. WILLARD GIBBS.** All the published papers of America's outstanding theoretical scientist (except for "Statistical Mechanics" and "Vector Analysis"). Vol I (thermodynamics) contains one of the most brilliant of all 19th-century scientific papers—the 300-page "On the Equilibrium of Heterogeneous Substances," which founded the science of physical chemistry, and clearly stated a number of highly important natural laws for the first time; 8 other papers complete the first volume. Vol II includes 2 papers on dynamics, 8 on vector analysis and multiple algebra, 5 on the electromagnetic theory of light, and 6 miscellaneous papers. Biographical sketch by H. A. Bumstead. Total of xxxvi + 718pp. 5⅝ x 8⅜.
S721 Vol I Paperbound **$2.50**
S722 Vol II Paperbound **$2.00**
The set **$4.50**

**BASIC THEORIES OF PHYSICS, Peter Gabriel Bergmann.** Two-volume set which presents a critical examination of important topics in the major subdivisions of classical and modern physics. The first volume is concerned with classical mechanics and electrodynamics: mechanics of mass points, analytical mechanics, matter in bulk, electrostatics and magnetostatics, electromagnetic interaction, the field waves, special relativity, and waves. The second volume (Heat and Quanta) contains discussions of the kinetic hypothesis, physics and statistics, stationary ensembles, laws of thermodynamics, early quantum theories, atomic spectra, probability waves, quantization in wave mechanics, approximation methods, and abstract quantum theory. A valuable supplement to any thorough course or text.
Heat and Quanta: Index. 8 figures. x + 300pp. 5⅜ x 8½. S968 Paperbound **$1.75**
Mechanics and Electrodynamics: Index. 14 figures. vii + 280pp. 5⅜ x 8½.
S969 Paperbound **$1.75**

**THEORETICAL PHYSICS, A. S. Kompaneyets.** One of the very few thorough studies of the subject in this price range. Provides advanced students with a comprehensive theoretical background. Especially strong on recent experimentation and developments in quantum theory. Contents: Mechanics (Generalized Coordinates, Lagrange's Equation, Collision of Particles, etc.), Electrodynamics (Vector Analysis, Maxwell's equations, Transmission of Signals, Theory of Relativity, etc.), Quantum Mechanics (the Inadequacy of Classical Mechanics, the Wave Equation, Motion in a Central Field, Quantum Theory of Radiation, Quantum Theories of Dispersion and Scattering, etc.), and Statistical Physics (Equilibrium Distribution of Molecules in an Ideal Gas, Boltzmann statistics, Bose and Fermi Distribution, Thermodynamic Quantities, etc.). Revised to 1961. Translated by George Yankovsky, authorized by Kompaneyets. 137 exercises. 56 figures. 529pp. 5⅜ x 8½. S972 Paperbound **$2.50**

**ANALYTICAL AND CANONICAL FORMALISM IN PHYSICS, André Mercier.** A survey, in one volume, of the variational principles (the key principles—in mathematical form—from which the basic laws of any one branch of physics can be derived) of the several branches of physical theory, together with an examination of the relationships among them. Contents: the Lagrangian Formalism, Lagrangian Densities, Canonical Formalism, Canonical Form of Electrodynamics, Hamiltonian Densities, Transformations, and Canonical Form with Vanishing Jacobian Determinant. Numerous examples and exercises. For advanced students, teachers, etc. 6 figures. Index. viii + 222pp. 5⅜ x 8½. S1077 Paperbound **$1.75**

# MATHEMATICAL PUZZLES AND RECREATIONS

**AMUSEMENTS IN MATHEMATICS, Henry Ernest Dudeney.** The foremost British originator of mathematical puzzles is always intriguing, witty, and paradoxical in this classic, one of the largest collections of mathematical amusements. More than 430 puzzles, problems, and paradoxes. Mazes and games, problems on number manipulation, unicursal and other route problems, puzzles on measuring, weighing, packing, age, kinship, chessboards, joining, crossing river, plane figure dissection, and many others. Solutions. More than 450 illustrations. vii + 258pp. 5⅜ x 8.　　　　　　　　　　　　　　　　　**T473 Paperbound $1.25**

**SYMBOLIC LOGIC and THE GAME OF LOGIC, Lewis Carroll.** "Symbolic Logic" is not concerned with modern symbolic logic, but is instead a collection of over 380 problems posed with charm and imagination, using the syllogism, and a fascinating diagrammatic method of drawing conclusions. In "The Game of Logic," Carroll's whimsical imagination devises a logical game played with 2 diagrams and counters (included) to manipulate hundreds of tricky syllogisms. The final section, "Hit or Miss" is a lagniappe of 101 additional puzzles in the delightful Carroll manner. Until this reprint edition, both of these books were rarities costing up to $15 each. Symbolic Logic: Index, xxxi + 199pp. The Game of Logic: 96pp. Two vols. bound as one. 5⅜ x 8.　　　　　　　　　　　　　　　　　**T492 Paperbound $1.50**

**MAZES AND LABYRINTHS: A BOOK OF PUZZLES, W. Shepherd.** Mazes, formerly associated with mystery and ritual, are still among the most intriguing of intellectual puzzles. This is a novel and different collection of 50 amusements that embody the principle of the maze: mazes in the classical tradition; 3-dimensional, ribbon, and Möbius-strip mazes; hidden messages; spatial arrangements; etc.—almost all built on amusing story situations. 84 illustrations. Essay on maze psychology. Solutions. xv + 122pp. 5⅜ x 8.　　**T731 Paperbound $1.00**

**MATHEMATICAL RECREATIONS, M. Kraitchik.** Some 250 puzzles, problems, demonstrations of recreational mathematics for beginners & advanced mathematicians. Unusual historical problems from Greek, Medieval, Arabic, Hindu sources: modern problems based on "mathematics without numbers," geometry, topology, arithmetic, etc. Pastimes derived from figurative numbers, Mersenne numbers, Fermat numbers; fairy chess, latruncles, reversi, many topics. Full solutions. Excellent for insights into special fields of math. 181 illustrations. 330pp. 5⅜ x 8.　　　　　　　　　　　　　　　　　　　　　　　　　**T163 Paperbound $1.75**

**MATHEMATICAL PUZZLES OF SAM LOYD, Vol. I, selected and edited by M. Gardner.** Puzzles by the greatest puzzle creator and innovator. Selected from his famous "Cyclopedia of Puzzles," they retain the unique style and historical flavor of the originals. There are posers based on arithmetic, algebra, probability, game theory, route tracing, topology, counter, sliding block, operations research, geometrical dissection. Includes his famous "14-15" puzzle which was a national craze, and his "Horse of a Different Color" which sold millions of copies. 117 of his most ingenious puzzles in all, 120 line drawings and diagrams. Solutions. Selected references. xx + 167pp. 5⅜ x 8.　　　　　　**T498 Paperbound $1.00**

**MY BEST PUZZLES IN MATHEMATICS, Hubert Phillips ("Caliban").** Caliban is generally considered the best of the modern problemists. Here are 100 of his best and wittiest puzzles, selected by the author himself from such publications as the London Daily Telegraph, and each puzzle is guaranteed to put even the sharpest puzzle detective through his paces. Perfect for the development of clear thinking and a logical mind. Complete solutions are provided for every puzzle. x + 107pp. 5⅜ x 8½.　　　　　　　　　**T91 Paperbound $1.00**

**MY BEST PUZZLES IN LOGIC AND REASONING, H. Phillips ("Caliban").** 100 choice, hitherto unavailable puzzles by England's best-known problemist. No special knowledge needed to solve these logical or inferential problems, just an unclouded mind, nerves of steel, and fast reflexes. Data presented are both necessary and just sufficient to allow one unambiguous answer. More than 30 different types of puzzles, all ingenious and varied, many one of a kind, that will challenge the expert, please the beginner. Original publication. 100 puzzles, full solutions. x + 107pp. 5⅜ x 8½.　　　　　　　　　　　**T119 Paperbound $1.00**

**MATHEMATICAL PUZZLES FOR BEGINNERS AND ENTHUSIASTS, G. Mott-Smith.** 188 mathematical puzzles to test mental agility. Inference, interpretation, algebra, dissection of plane figures, geometry, properties of numbers, decimation, permutations, probability, all enter these delightful problems. Puzzles like the Odic Force, How to Draw an Ellipse, Spider's Cousin, more than 180 others. Detailed solutions. Appendix with square roots, triangular numbers, primes, etc. 135 illustrations. 2nd revised edition. 248pp. 5⅜ x 8.　　**T198 Paperbound $1.00**

**MATHEMATICS, MAGIC AND MYSTERY, Martin Gardner.** Card tricks, feats of mental mathematics, stage mind-reading, other "magic" explained as applications of probability, sets, theory of numbers, topology, various branches of mathematics. Creative examination of laws and their applications with scores of new tricks and insights. 115 sections discuss tricks with cards, dice, coins; geometrical vanishing tricks, dozens of others. No sleight of hand needed; mathematics guarantees success. 115 illustrations. xii + 174pp. 5⅜ x 8.　　　　　　　　　　　　　　　　　　　　　　　　　**T335 Paperbound $1.00**

# CATALOGUE OF DOVER BOOKS

**RECREATIONS IN THE THEORY OF NUMBERS: THE QUEEN OF MATHEMATICS ENTERTAINS, Albert H. Beiler.** The theory of numbers is often referred to as the "Queen of Mathematics." In this book Mr. Beiler has compiled the first English volume to deal exclusively with the recreational aspects of number theory, an inherently recreational branch of mathematics. The author's clear style makes for enjoyable reading as he deals with such topics as: perfect numbers, amicable numbers, Fermat's theorem, Wilson's theorem, interesting properties of digits, methods of factoring, primitive roots, Euler's function, polygonal and figurate numbers, Mersenne numbers, congruence, repeating decimals, etc. Countless puzzle problems, with full answers and explanations. For mathematicians and mathematically-inclined laymen, etc. New publication. 28 figures. 9 illustrations. 103 tables. Bibliography at chapter ends. vi + 247pp. 5⅜ x 8½. T1096 Paperbound **$1.85**

**PAPER FOLDING FOR BEGINNERS, W. D. Murray and F. J. Rigney.** A delightful introduction to the varied and entertaining Japanese art of origami (paper folding), with a full crystal-clear text that anticipates every difficulty; over 275 clearly labeled diagrams of all important stages in creation. You get results at each stage, since complex figures are logically developed from simpler ones. 43 different pieces are explained: place mats, drinking cups, bonbon boxes, sailboats, frogs, roosters, etc. 6 photographic plates. 279 diagrams. 95pp. 5⅝ x 8⅜. T713 Paperbound **$1.00**

**1800 RIDDLES, ENIGMAS AND CONUNDRUMS, Darwin A. Hindman.** Entertaining collection ranging from hilarious gags to outrageous puns to sheer nonsense—a welcome respite from sophisticated humor. Children, toastmasters, and practically anyone with a funny bone will find these zany riddles tickling and eminently repeatable. Sample: "Why does Santa Claus always go down the chimney?" "Because it soots him." Some old, some new—covering a wide variety of subjects. New publication. iii + 154pp. 5⅜ x 8½. T1059 Paperbound **$1.00**

**EASY-TO-DO ENTERTAINMENTS AND DIVERSIONS WITH CARDS, STRING, COINS, PAPER AND MATCHES, R. M. Abraham.** Over 300 entertaining games, tricks, puzzles, and pastimes for children and adults. Invaluable to anyone in charge of groups of youngsters, for party givers, etc. Contains sections on card tricks and games, making things by paperfolding—toys, decorations, and the like; tricks with coins, matches, and pieces of string; descriptions of games; toys that can be made from common household objects; mathematical recreations; word games; and 50 miscellaneous entertainments. Formerly "Winter Nights Entertainments." Introduction by Lord Baden Powell. 329 illustrations. v + 186pp. 5⅜ x 8. T921 Paperbound **$1.00**

**DIVERSIONS AND PASTIMES WITH CARDS, STRING, PAPER AND MATCHES, R. M. Abraham.** Another collection of amusements and diversion for game and puzzle fans of all ages. Many new paperfolding ideas and tricks, an extensive section on amusements with knots and splices, two chapters of easy and not-so-easy problems, coin and match tricks, and lots of other parlor pastimes from the agile mind of the late British problemist and gamester. Corrected and revised version. Illustrations. 160pp. 5⅜ x 8½. T1127 Paperbound **$1.00**

**STRING FIGURES AND HOW TO MAKE THEM: A STUDY OF CAT'S-CRADLE IN MANY LANDS, Caroline Furness Jayne.** In a simple and easy-to-follow manner, this book describes how to make 107 different string figures. Not only is looping and crossing string between the fingers a common youthful diversion, but it is an ancient form of amusement practiced in all parts of the globe, especially popular among primitive tribes. These games are fun for all ages and offer an excellent means for developing manual dexterity and coordination. Much insight also for the anthropological observer on games and diversions in many different cultures. Index. Bibliography. Introduction by A. C. Haddon, Cambridge University. 17 full-page plates. 950 illustrations. xxiii + 407pp. 5⅜ x 8½. T152 Paperbound **$2.00**

**CRYPTANALYSIS, Helen F. Gaines.** (Formerly ELEMENTARY CRYPTANALYSIS.) A standard elementary and intermediate text for serious students. It does not confine itself to old material, but contains much that is not generally known, except to experts. Concealment, Transposition, Substitution ciphers; Vigenere, Kasiski, Playfair, multafid, dozens of other techniques. Appendix with sequence charts, letter frequencies in English, 5 other languages, English word frequencies. Bibliography. 167 codes. New to this edition: solution to codes. vi + 230pp. 5⅜ x 8. T97 Paperbound **$2.00**

**MAGIC SQUARES AND CUBES, W. S. Andrews.** Only book-length treatment in English, a thorough non-technical description and analysis. Here are nasik, overlapping, pandiagonal, serrated squares; magic circles, cubes, spheres, rhombuses. Try your hand at 4-dimensional magical figures! Much unusual folklore and tradition included. High school algebra is sufficient. 754 diagrams and illustrations. viii + 419pp. 5⅜ x 8. T658 Paperbound **$1.85**

**CALIBAN'S PROBLEM BOOK: MATHEMATICAL, INFERENTIAL, AND CRYPTOGRAPHIC PUZZLES, H. Phillips ("Caliban"), S. T. Shovelton, G. S. Marshall.** 105 ingenious problems by the greatest living creator of puzzles based on logic and inference. Rigorous, modern, piquant, and reflecting their author's unusual personality, these intermediate and advanced puzzles all involve the ability to reason clearly through complex situations; some call for mathematical knowledge, ranging from algebra to number theory. Solutions. xi + 180pp. 5⅜ x 8. T736 Paperbound **$1.25**

# FICTION

**THE LAND THAT TIME FORGOT and THE MOON MAID, Edgar Rice Burroughs.** In the opinion of many, Burroughs' best work. The first concerns a strange island where evolution is individual rather than phylogenetic. Speechless anthropoids develop into intelligent human beings within a single generation. The second projects the reader far into the future and describes the first voyage to the Moon (in the year 2025), the conquest of the Earth by the Moon, and years of violence and adventure as the enslaved Earthmen try to regain possession of their planet. "An imaginative tour de force that keeps the reader keyed up and expectant," NEW YORK TIMES. Complete, unabridged text of the original two novels (three parts in each). 5 illustrations by J. Allen St. John. vi + 552pp. 5⅜ x 8½.
T1020 Clothbound **$3.75**
T358 Paperbound **$2.00**

**AT THE EARTH'S CORE, PELLUCIDAR, TANAR OF PELLUCIDAR: THREE SCIENCE FICTION NOVELS BY EDGAR RICE BURROUGHS.** Complete, unabridged texts of the first three Pellucidar novels. Tales of derring-do by the famous master of science fiction. The locale for these three related stories is the inner surface of the hollow Earth where we discover the world of Pellucidar, complete with all types of bizarre, menacing creatures, strange peoples, and alluring maidens—guaranteed to delight all Burroughs fans and a wide circle of advenutre lovers. Illustrated by J. Allen St. John and P. F. Berdanier. vi + 433pp. 5⅜ x 8½.
T1051 Paperbound **$2.00**

**THE PIRATES OF VENUS and LOST ON VENUS: TWO VENUS NOVELS BY EDGAR RICE BURROUGHS.** Two related novels, complete and unabridged. Exciting adventure on the planet Venus with Earthman Carson Napier broken-field running through one dangerous episode after another. All lovers of swashbuckling science fiction will enjoy these two stories set in a world of fascinating societies, fierce beasts, 5000-ft. trees, lush vegetation, and wide seas. Illustrations by Fortunino Matania. Total of vi + 340pp. 5⅜ x 8½. T1053 Paperbound **$1.75**

**A PRINCESS OF MARS and A FIGHTING MAN OF MARS: TWO MARTIAN NOVELS BY EDGAR RICE BURROUGHS.** "Princess of Mars" is the very first of the great Martian novels written by Burroughs, and it is probably the best of them all; it set the pattern for all of his later fantasy novels and contains a thrilling cast of strange peoples and creatures and the formula of Olympian heroism amidst ever-fluctuating fortunes which Burroughs carries off so successfully. "Fighting Man" returns to the same scenes and cities—many years later. A mad scientist, a degenerate dictator, and an indomitable defender of the right clash—with the fate of the Red Planet at stake! Complete, unabridged reprinting of original editions. Illustrations by F. E. Schoonover and Hugh Hutton. v + 356pp. 5⅜ x 8½.
T1140 Paperbound **$1.75**

**THREE MARTIAN NOVELS, Edgar Rice Burroughs.** Contains: Thuvia, Maid of Mars; The Chessmen of Mars; and The Master Mind of Mars. High adventure set in an imaginative and intricate conception of the Red Planet. Mars is peopled with an intelligent, heroic human race which lives in densely populated cities and with fierce barbarians who inhabit dead sea bottoms. Other exciting creatures abound amidst an inventive framework of Martian history and geography. Complete unabridged reprintings of the first edition. 16 illustrations by J. Allen St. John. vi + 499pp. 5⅜ x 8½.
T39 Paperbound **$1.85**

**THREE PROPHETIC NOVELS BY H. G. WELLS, edited by E. F. Bleiler.** Complete texts of "When the Sleeper Wakes" (1st book printing in 50 years), "A Story of the Days to Come," "The Time Machine" (1st complete printing in book form). Exciting adventures in the future are as enjoyable today as 50 years ago when first printed. Predict TV, movies, intercontinental airplanes, prefabricated houses, air-conditioned cities, etc. First important author to foresee problems of mind control, technological dictatorships. "Absolute best of imaginative fiction," N. Y. Times. Introduction. 335pp. 5⅜ x 8. T605 Paperbound **$1.50**

**28 SCIENCE FICTION STORIES OF H. G. WELLS.** Two full unabridged novels, MEN LIKE GODS and STAR BEGOTTEN, plus 26 short stories by the master science-fiction writer of all time. Stories of space, time, invention, exploration, future adventure—an indispensable part of the library of everyone interested in science and adventure. PARTIAL CONTENTS: Men Like Gods, The Country of the Blind, In the Abyss, The Crystal Egg, The Man Who Could Work Miracles, A Story of the Days to Come, The Valley of Spiders, and 21 more! 928pp. 5⅜ x 8.
T265 Clothbound **$4.50**

**THE WAR IN THE AIR, IN THE DAYS OF THE COMET, THE FOOD OF THE GODS: THREE SCIENCE FICTION NOVELS BY H. G. WELLS.** Three exciting Wells offerings bearing on vital social and philosophical issues of his and our own day. Here are tales of air power, strategic bombing, East vs. West, the potential miracles of science, the potential disasters from outer space, the relationship between scientific advancement and moral progress, etc. First reprinting of "War in the Air" in almost 50 years. An excellent sampling of Wells at his storytelling best. Complete, unabridged reprintings. 16 illustrations. 645pp. 5⅜ x 8½.
T1135 Paperbound **$2.00**

**SEVEN SCIENCE FICTION NOVELS, H. G. Wells.** Full unabridged texts of 7 science-fiction novels of the master. Ranging from biology, physics, chemistry, astronomy to sociology and other studies, Mr. Wells extrapolates whole worlds of strange and intriguing character. "One will have to go far to match this for entertainment, excitement, and sheer pleasure . . . ," NEW YORK TIMES. Contents: The Time Machine, The Island of Dr. Moreau, First Men in the Moon, The Invisible Man, The War of the Worlds, The Food of the Gods, In the Days of the Comet. 1015pp. 5⅜ x 8.                    T264 Clothbound **$4.50**

**BEST GHOST STORIES OF J. S. LE FANU, Selected and introduced by E. F. Bleiler.** LeFanu is deemed the greatest name in Victorian supernatural fiction. Here are 16 of his best horror stories, including 2 nouvelles: "Carmilla," a classic vampire tale couched in a perverse eroticism, and "The Haunted Baronet." Also: "Sir Toby's Will," "Green Tea," "Schalken the Painter," "Ultor de Lacy," "The Familiar," etc. The first American publication of about half of this material: a long-overdue opportunity to get a choice sampling of LeFanu's work. New selection (1964). 8 illustrations. 5⅜ x 8⅜.                    T415 Paperbound **$1.85**

**THE WONDERFUL WIZARD OF OZ, L. F. Baum.** Only edition in print with all the original W. W. Denslow illustrations in full color—as much a part of "The Wizard" as Tenniel's drawings are for "Alice in Wonderland." "The Wizard" is still America's best-loved fairy tale, in which, as the author expresses it, "The wonderment and joy are retained and the heartaches and nightmares left out." Now today's young readers can enjoy every word and wonderful picture of the original book. New introduction by Martin Gardner. A Baum bibliography. 23 full-page color plates. viii + 268pp. 5⅜ x 8.                    T691 Paperbound **$1.50**

**GHOST AND HORROR STORIES OF AMBROSE BIERCE, Selected and introduced by E. F. Bleiler.** 24 morbid, eerie tales—the cream of Bierce's fiction output. Contains such memorable pieces as "The Moonlit Road," "The Damned Thing," "An Inhabitant of Carcosa," "The Eyes of the Panther," "The Famous Gilson Bequest," "The Middle Toe of the Right Foot," and other chilling stories, plus the essay, "Visions of the Night" in which Bierce gives us a kind of rationale for his aesthetic of horror. New collection (1964). xxii + 199pp. 5⅜ x 8⅜.                    T767 Paperbound **$1.00**

# HUMOR

**MR. DOOLEY ON IVRYTHING AND IVRYBODY, Finley Peter Dunne.** Since the time of his appearance in 1893, "Mr. Dooley," the fictitious Chicago bartender, has been recognized as America's most humorous social and political commentator. Collected in this volume are 102 of the best Dooley pieces—all written around the turn of the century, the height of his popularity. Mr. Dooley's Irish brogue is employed wittily and penetratingly on subjects which are just as fresh and relevant today as they were then: corruption and hypocrisy of politicans, war preparations and chauvinism, automation, Latin American affairs, superbombs, etc. Other articles range from Rudyard Kipling to football. Selected with an introduction by Robert Hutchinson. xii + 244pp. 5⅜ x 8½.                    T626 Paperbound **$1.00**

**RUTHLESS RHYMES FOR HEARTLESS HOMES and MORE RUTHLESS RHYMES FOR HEARTLESS HOMES, Harry Graham ("Col. D. Streamer").** A collection of Little Willy and 48 other poetic "disasters." Graham's funniest and most disrespectful verse, accompanied by original illustrations. Nonsensical, wry humor which employs stern parents, careless nurses, uninhibited children, practical jokers, single-minded golfers, Scottish lairds, etc. in the leading roles. A precursor of the "sick joke" school of today. This volume contains, bound together for the first time, two of the most perennially popular books of humor in England and America. Index. vi + 69pp. 5⅜ x 8.                    T930 Paperbound **75¢**

**A WHIMSEY ANTHOLOGY, Collected by Carolyn Wells.** 250 of the most amusing rhymes ever written. Acrostics, anagrams, palindromes, alphabetical jingles, tongue twisters, echo verses, alliterative verses, riddles, mnemonic rhymes, interior rhymes, over 40 limericks, etc. by Lewis Carroll, Edward Lear, Joseph Addison, W. S. Gilbert, Christina Rossetti, Chas. Lamb, James Boswell, Hood, Dickens, Swinburne, Leigh Hunt, Harry Graham, Poe, Eugene Field, and many others. xiv + 221pp. 5⅜ x 8½.                    T195 Paperbound **$1.25**

**MY PIOUS FRIENDS AND DRUNKEN COMPANIONS and MORE PIOUS FRIENDS AND DRUNKEN COMPANIONS, Songs and ballads of Conviviality Collected by Frank Shay.** Magnificently illuminated by John Held, Jr. 132 ballads, blues, vaudeville numbers, drinking songs, cowboy songs, sea chanties, comedy songs, etc. of the Naughty Nineties and early 20th century. Over a third are reprinted with music. Many perennial favorites such as: The Band Played On, Frankie and Johnnie, The Old Grey Mare, The Face on the Bar-room Floor, etc. Many others unlocatable elsewhere: The Dog-Catcher's Child, The Cannibal Maiden, Don't Go in the Lion's Cage Tonight, Mother, etc. Complete verses and introductions to songs. Unabridged republication of first editions, 2 Indexes (song titles and first lines and choruses). Introduction by Frank Shay. 2 volumes bounds as 1. Total of xvi + 235pp. 5⅜ x 8½.                    T946 Paperbound **$1.25**

**MAX AND MORITZ, Wilhelm Busch.** Edited and annotated by H. Arthur Klein. Translated by H. Arthur Klein, M. C. Klein, and others. The mischievous high jinks of Max and Moritz, Peter and Paul, Ker and Plunk, etc. are delightfully captured in sketch and rhyme. (Companion volume to "Hypocritical Helena.") In addition to the title piece, it contians: Ker and Plunk; Two Dogs and Two Boys; The Egghead and the Two Cut-ups of Corinth; Deceitful Henry; The Boys and the Pipe; Cat and Mouse; and others. (Original German text with accompanying English translations.) Afterword by H. A. Klein. vi + 216pp. 5⅜ x 8½.
T181 Paperbound **$1.15**

**THROUGH THE ALIMENTARY CANAL WITH GUN AND CAMERA: A FASCINATING TRIP TO THE INTERIOR, Personally Conducted by George S. Chappell.** In mock-travelogue style, the amusing account of an imaginative journey down the alimentary canal. The "explorers" enter the esophagus, round the Adam's Apple, narrowly escape from a fierce Amoeba, struggle through the impenetrable Nerve Forests of the Lumbar Region, etc. Illustrated by the famous cartoonist, Otto Soglow, the book is as much a brilliant satire of academic pomposity and professional travel literature as it is a clever use of the facts of physiology for supremely comic purposes. Preface by Robert Benchley. Author's Foreword. 1 Photograph. 17 illustrations by O. Soglow. xii + 114pp. 5⅜ x 8½.
T376 Paperbound **$1.00**

**THE BAD CHILD'S BOOK OF BEASTS, MORE BEASTS FOR WORSE CHILDREN, and A MORAL ALPHABET, H. Belloc.** Hardly an anthology of humorous verse has appeared in the last 50 years without at least a couple of these famous nonsense verses. But one must see the entire volumes—with all the delightful original illustrations by Sir Basil Blackwood—to appreciate fully Belloc's charming and witty verses that play so subacidly on the platitudes of life and morals that beset his day—and ours. A great humor classic. Three books in one. Total of 157pp. 5⅜ x 8.
T749 Paperbound **$1.00**

**THE DEVIL'S DICTIONARY, Ambrose Bierce.** Sardonic and irreverent barbs puncturing the pomposities and absurdities of American politics, business, religion, literature, and arts, by the country's greatest satirist in the classic tradition. Epigrammatic as Shaw, piercing as Swift, American as Mark Twain, Will Rogers, and Fred Allen. Bierce will always remain the favorite of a small coterie of enthusiasts, and of writers and speakers whom he supplies with "some of the most gorgeous witticisms of the English language." (H. L. Mencken) Over 1000 entries in alphabetical order. 144pp. 5⅜ x 8.
T487 Paperbound **$1.00**

**THE COMPLETE NONSENSE OF EDWARD LEAR.** This is the only complete edition of this master of gentle madness available at a popular price. A BOOK OF NONSENSE, NONSENSE SONGS, MORE NONSENSE SONGS AND STORIES in their entirety with all the old favorites that have delighted children and adults for years. The Dong With A Luminous Nose, The Jumblies, The Owl and the Pussycat, and hundreds of other bits of wonderful nonsense. 214 limericks, 3 sets of Nonsense Botany, 5 Nonsense Alphabets. 546 drawings by Lear himself, and much more. 320pp. 5⅜ x 8.
T167 Paperbound **$1.00**

**SINGULAR TRAVELS, CAMPAIGNS, AND ADVENTURES OF BARON MUNCHAUSEN, R. E. Raspe, with 90 illustrations by Gustave Doré.** The first edition in over 150 years to reestablish the deeds of the Prince of Liars exactly as Raspe first recorded them in 1785—the genuine Baron Munchausen, one of the most popular personalities in English literature. Included also are the best of the many sequels, written by other hands. Introduction on Raspe by J. Carswell. Bibliography of early editions. xliv + 192pp. 5⅜ x 8.  T698 Paperbound **$1.00**

**HOW TO TELL THE BIRDS FROM THE FLOWERS, R. W. Wood.** How not to confuse a carrot with a parrot, a grape with an ape, a puffin with nuffin. Delightful drawings, clever puns, absurd little poems point out farfetched resemblances in nature. The author was a leading physicist. Introduction by Margaret Wood White. 106 illus. 60pp. 5⅜ x 8.
T523 Paperbound **75¢**

**JOE MILLER'S JESTS OR, THE WITS VADE-MECUM.** The original Joe Miller jest book. Gives a keen and pungent impression of life in 18th-century England. Many are somewhat on the bawdy side and they are still capable of provoking amusement and good fun. This volume is a facsimile of the original "Joe Miller" first published in 1739. It remains the most popular and influential humor book of all time. New introduction by Robert Hutchinson. xxi + 70pp. 5⅜ x 8½.
T423 Paperbound **$1.00**

*Prices subject to change without notice.*

*Dover publishes books on art, music, philosophy, literature, languages, history, social sciences, psychology, handcrafts, orientalia, puzzles and entertainments, chess, pets and gardens, books explaining science, intermediate and higher mathematics, mathematical physics, engineering, biological sciences, earth sciences, classics of science, etc. Write to:*

*Dept. catrr.*
*Dover Publications, Inc.*
*180 Varick Street, N.Y. 14, N.Y.*